W9-CSL-899

ADDISON-WESLEY   WESTERN CANADIAN EDITION

Applied Mathematics 11

SOURCE BOOK

Robert Alexander
Mathematics Teacher
and Consultant
Richmond Hill, Ontario

Cam Bennet
Dauphin Regional
Comprehensive
Secondary School
Dauphin, Manitoba

Ron Coleborn
Burnaby South
Secondary School
Burnaby, British Columbia

Garry Davis
Saskatoon Public Board
of Education
Saskatoon, Saskatchewan

Florence Glanfield
Professor of Mathematics
Education
University of Saskatchewan
Saskatoon, Saskatchewan

Carol Besteck Hope
Elmwood High School
Winnipeg, Manitoba

Stephen Khan
Mathematics Education
Consultant
Winnipeg, Manitoba

Duncan LeBlanc
Sir Robert L. Borden Business
and Technical Institute
Scarborough, Ontario

Brent Richards
Crocus Plains Regional
Secondary School
Brandon, Manitoba

David Sufrin
Ballenas Secondary School
Parksville, British Columbia

Paul Williams
Red Deer College
Red Deer, Alberta

Elizabeth Wood
Calgary Board of Education
Calgary, Alberta

Rick Wunderlich
Shuswap Junior
Secondary School
Salmon Arm, British Columbia

Leanne Zorn
Mount Boucherie
Secondary School
Kelowna, British Columbia

PEARSON
Addison
Wesley

Toronto

PUBLISHER, SECONDARY MATHEMATICS
Claire Burnett

MANAGING EDITOR, SECONDARY MATHEMATICS
Enid Haley

PRODUCT MANAGER
Reid McAlpine

SENIOR CONSULTING EDITOR
Lesley Haynes

DEVELOPMENTAL EDITOR
Susan Lishman

COORDINATING EDITOR
Mei Lin Cheung

EDITORIAL CONTRIBUTORS

Margaret Bukta
Santo D'Agostino
Virginia Dalziel
Anna-Maria Garnham
Ryan Nickelchok
Alison Reiger

Barbara J. Canton
Rosina Daillie
Annette Darby
Gay McKellar
Eileen Pyne-Rudzik

RESEARCHER
Rosina Daillie

DESIGN/PRODUCTION
Pronk&Associates

ART DIRECTION
Pronk&Associates

ELECTRONIC ASSEMBLY/TECHNICAL ART
Pronk&Associates

ClarisWorks™ is a trademark of Claris Corporation. Claris® is a registered trademark of Claris Corporation. Microsoft® and Windows™ are either registered trademarks or trademarks of Microsoft Corporation. Macintosh® is a registered trademark of Apple Computer Inc. *The Geometer's Sketchpad®* is a registered trademark of Key Curriculum Press Inc.

ISBN 0–201–39591–6

This book contains recycled product and is acid free.

7 8 – FP – 07

Printed in Canada

Pilot Teacher Reviewers

The authors and publishers would like to extend special acknowledgment to the pilot teachers and their students who worked with this resource before it was in final form.

Barry Blair
Alberni District Secondary School
Port Alberni, British Columbia

Lisa C. Douglas
J. H. Bruns Collegiate
Winnipeg, Manitoba

Eva Goldfeld
Daniel McIntyre Collegiate
Winnipeg, Manitoba

Janine Klevgaard
William E. Hay Composite High School
Stettler, Alberta

**Ron McAndrew,
Ed Klettke**
Chilliwack Senior Secondary School
Chilliwack, British Columbia

Gail Poshtar
Father Lacombe High School
Calgary, Alberta

Ken Petkau
Morden Collegiate
Morden, Manitoba

Kevin Weimer
Lester B. Pearson High School
Calgary, Alberta

Reviewers

Addison-Wesley Applied Mathematics 11 Source Book

Welcome

CONTENTS

CONTENTS

Welcome to Addison-Wesley Applied Mathematics 11

Western Canadian Edition

Addison-Wesley Applied Mathematics presents mathematics as an essential tool in everyday life and in many careers. In this course, you will apply mathematics in many different contexts. You will develop new mathematical concepts and skills by examining authentic situations and investigating solutions.

To meet the requirements of the Applied Mathematics course, you need to work from both the Project Book, and the Source Book. These introductory pages illustrate how your student books work.

Source Book

The Source Book has 7 chapters and 3 reference sections. Like the Project Book, it is designed for regular use during the course, with time taken out to work on projects.

Each chapter starts with an Overview. This table tells you what mathematics you will learn.

Each chapter presents a Chapter Project, and a series of Tutorials.

Chapter Project

The Chapter Projects in the Source Book are more structured than the projects in the Project Book. They will help you develop the study skills and work habits you need to complete more open-ended projects.

You will find an introduction to the Chapter Project at the start of the chapter. You revisit the Chapter Project at later points in the chapter, to complete portions of the required project work.

Each time you see the Chapter Project, you will find a Project Link. This short section tells you what mathematical concepts and skills you need for the project, and the tutorials you might complete to develop those concepts and skills.

FYI Visit refers you to our web site, where you can connect to other sites to research the Chapter Project.

You return to the Chapter Project after completing relevant Tutorials.

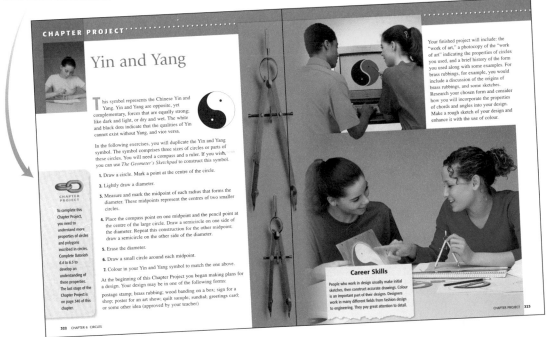

Tutorials

Each Tutorial develops a specific mathematical concept or result. Often you will reach that outcome by conducting an **Investigation**. Sometimes, you will follow **Examples** and their completed Solutions.

Here is how a typical Tutorial works.

- **Practise Your Prior Skills** provides exercises on relevant topics learned in earlier grades.

- An **Investigation**, or a series of Investigations, leads you to explore mathematical concepts.

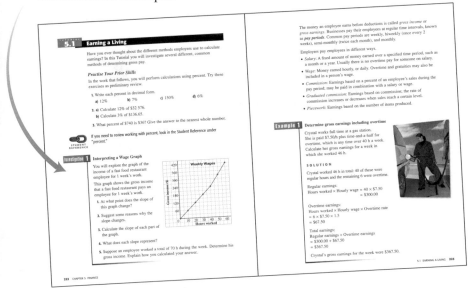

- **Examples** illustrate how to use new mathematical methods.

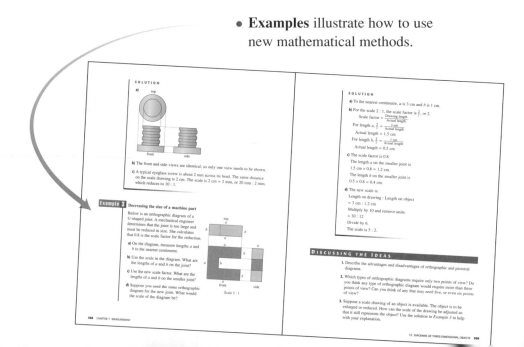

- **Discussing the Ideas** provides suggestions for classroom discussion of concepts you worked with in Investigations or Examples.

- **Exercises** give you opportunities to work with the same mathematical concepts and skills in different contexts.

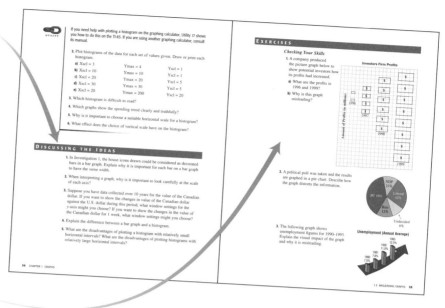

- **Project Link** emphasizes the focus of the Tutorial, and highlights the projects that involve the same concepts and skills.

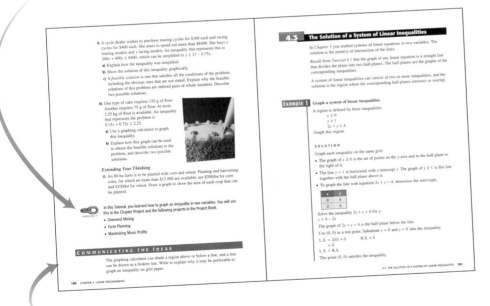

- **Communicating the Ideas** suggests a writing activity in which you summarize the key learning for the Tutorial.

Consolidating Your Skills

Each chapter ends with a **Consolidating Your Skills** section.
This starts with a table that summarizes the work of the chapter.

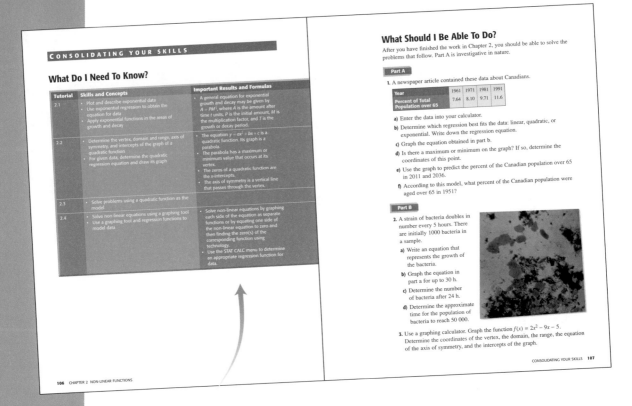

Review this column to identify important results and formulas.

The remainder of the section gives a 3-part review of the chapter.

Part A involves an activity, just like the Investigations in the chapter.

Part B has some review problems, similar to the Examples and Exercises you did in the Tutorials.

These photographs show you some actual student work.

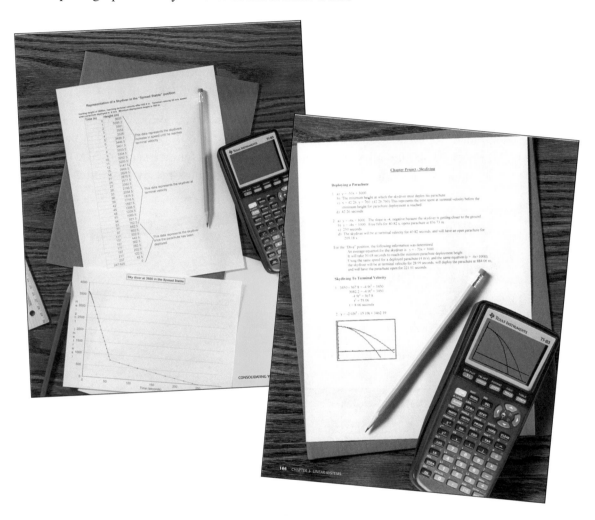

Follow-up questions develop your skills at assessing project work.

Use Part C for inspiration with your own project, and to learn how to examine your own work critically.

Reference Sections

People at work use many different references. For example, an editor refers to a dictionary regularly. A contractor needs to look up building codes. A bank worker refers to daily postings of approved interest rates.

Your Source Book has been constructed to develop your skills in using reference materials as the need arises. In addition to research you will do outside the text, you will be able to use three important reference sections within the Source Book: Utilities, Student Reference, and Answers.

In a Tutorial, you may see a comment that directs you to the Utilities or the Student Reference section at the back of the Source Book. Projects in the Project Book may also refer you to the Student Reference section. You decide whether you need to follow the references for a quick review or a mini-lesson.

Utilities

A link symbol indicates the Utilities section, highlighted by the blue colour across the top of each page.

Utilities 17–23 teach you how to use specific tools for this course.

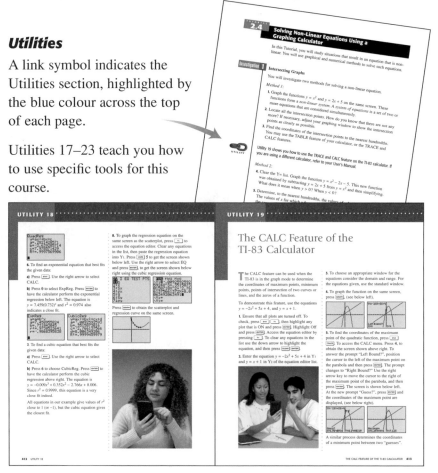

Read the Utility while you work with the tool you are learning. If you are reading a Utility about the graphing calculator, key in the instructions as you read. Check that your results match the results shown in the Utility. Check with another student if you have a problem.

The Utilities 1–16 from *Applied Mathematics 10* are available from your teacher, should you need them.

Student Reference

The link symbol indicates the Student Reference section with pages that have the red colour across the top.

This section of the Source Book is organized alphabetically, like a glossary. It does more than a glossary, though, because it gives a quick review for many prerequisite skills.

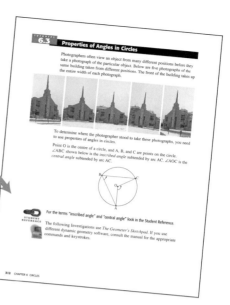

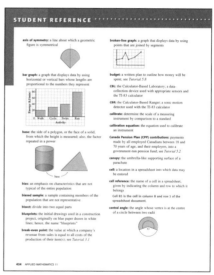

The Student Reference provides:

- definitions for key terms
- general results, such as the Pythagorean Theorem
- brief review of concepts from previous grades
- examples when relevant
- references to Source Book tutorials when relevant

Answers

Check your answers after completing a set of Investigations or Exercises to see how well you understood the material.

By using the Answers responsibly, you can improve your mathematical learning and develop good study habits.

Project Book

The Project Book is designed for regular use during the course. The Project Book provides 24 ideas for open-ended projects. Each project relates to a specific career area, and ties to one or more chapters from the Source Book.

You do not have to complete all the projects, but you may be interested in pursuing several of them. To cover all of the grade 11 Applied Mathematics curriculum, you will need to complete projects in three compulsory areas. Within these areas, you will have some choice of project topics.

Here is how a typical project works.

- **The Task** explains the purpose of the project and describes a specific application you will investigate.

- **Materials** describes the supplies you need to complete the project.

- **Background** provides some interesting facts about the topic or sets up a possible scenario for your project.

- **Source Link** points you to required skills in the Source Book, if you need them.

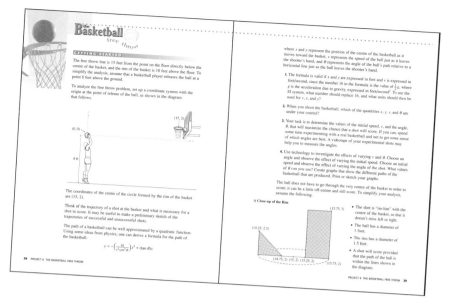

- **Getting Started** leads you to explore some of the basic mathematical concepts underlying the application.

- **Project Presentation** lets you pursue a variety of extensions of the work done in Getting Started, and suggests ways to present your project report.

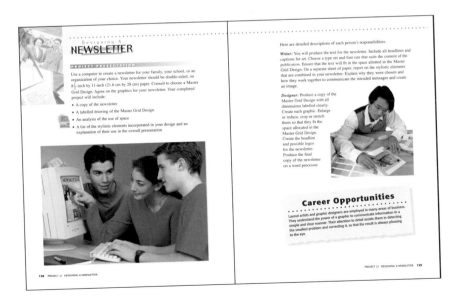

- **Career Opportunities** describes how the mathematical skills needed in the project relate to careers.

1

GRAPHS

PROJECT

You should do at least one project that uses the skills you learn in this chapter. **To cover the curriculum, you should complete Glyphs in the Project Book.** Other recommended projects in the Project Book are:

- An Outdoor Recreational Resort

- Oil Exploration

Overview

Examining Data

In today's information society, data are all around us. Data can be presented in different forms and may serve many different purposes. Numerical data and graphs are often used to support inferences, claims, or arguments being made by companies or groups. These groups may include governments, pollsters, political parties, labour unions, lobbyists, as well as advertisers and other special interest groups. Often, contradictory claims or inferences may be made using similar data or even the same set of data. As citizens and consumers, it is important that we develop the ability to interpret and critically analyze data. This will allow us to judge inferences and arguments.

In this project, you will examine and analyze numerical data and graphs presented in newspapers and magazines. As you work through this chapter, check newspapers and magazines for articles or advertisements that present data in either a graphical or numerical format. Collect as many advertisements and articles as you can during the next two weeks. You will need this material to complete the Chapter Project.

Here are some questions regarding the use and presentation of data. Consider these questions as you collect articles and advertisements.

- What occupations involve an extensive use of data?
- How might numbers and graphs be used in these occupations?
- What is the advantage of presenting data graphically as opposed to numerically?
- How does the presentation of data within an article assist the reader?
- Is it possible to misuse data?

If you do not have access to newspapers or magazines at home, visit your library to begin your collection. The articles that you use do not have to be current.

CHAPTER PROJECT

To complete this Chapter Project, you will need to interpret and analyze different types of graphs. Complete *Tutorials 1.1* to *1.5* to develop an understanding of the necessary concepts. You will return to this Chapter Project on page 52.

FYI Visit: www.awl.com/canada/school/connections

You can start your research from our Internet site: Click on <u>MATHLINKS</u> followed by the *Applied Mathematics 11* logo. Then select a topic under Examining Data.

Interpreting Graphs and Tables of Data

In this chapter you will collect, display, and analyze data. In previous grades you studied different ways to represent data graphically: circle graphs, histograms, bar graphs, and line graphs. In this Tutorial you will learn how to adapt histograms, bar graphs, and line graphs to compare and contrast sets of data.

Practise Your Prior Skills

In this Tutorial you will read tables and interpret graphs. Try these exercises for preliminary review.

1. The following histogram shows the weekly earnings of a group of students between the ages of 16 and 18.

Weekly Earnings

Number of Students vs. *Earnings ($)*

a) What is the most frequent range of earnings for this sample?

b) How many students were sampled in this survey?

2. The heights, in centimetres, of students in a grade 11 class are given below.

165, 183, 196, 163, 176, 156, 178, 180, 158, 184, 203,
159, 168, 171, 185, 186, 162, 167, 173, 192, 188, 182,
174, 161, 166, 189, 182, 183, 200, 181

a) Copy and complete this table.

Height (cm)	Tally	Frequency
155–159		
160–164		
165–169		
170–174		
175–179		
180–184		
185–189		
190–194		
195–199		
200–204		

b) Use the table to draw a histogram.

c) What is the most frequent range of heights in this class?

3. Study the following line graph.

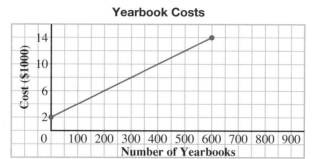

a) What is the cost of producing 500 yearbooks?

b) Suppose 500 yearbooks are produced. What is the cost per yearbook? What is the cost per yearbook if 1000 yearbooks are produced? Explain why the costs are not the same.

c) A total of $14 000 is available. How many yearbooks could be produced?

d) Use the graph to find the cost when zero yearbooks are produced. Explain this cost.

4. The following bar graph shows the number of computers per 100 people for various countries.

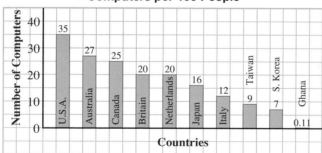

a) How many more computers per 100 people are there in the U.S. than in South Korea?

b) Which two countries have the same number of computers per 100 people?

We are living in the "Information Age." Information is everywhere: in newspapers, books, magazines, and on the Internet. Often numerical information is presented in a table or graph. The ability to read and interpret data presented in these forms is an important skill.

Example 1 Interpreting Tabular Data

This table gives estimates of the population, in thousands, for males and females in Canada for the year 1996.

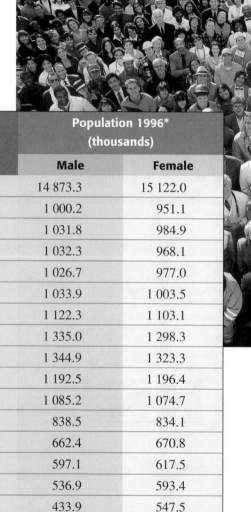

	Population 1996* (thousands)	
	Male	**Female**
All ages	14 873.3	15 122.0
0–4	1 000.2	951.1
5–9	1 031.8	984.9
10–14	1 032.3	968.1
15–19	1 026.7	977.0
20–24	1 033.9	1 003.5
25–29	1 122.3	1 103.1
30–34	1 335.0	1 298.3
35–39	1 344.9	1 323.3
40–44	1 192.5	1 196.4
45–49	1 085.2	1 074.7
50–54	838.5	834.1
55–59	662.4	670.8
60–64	597.1	617.5
65–69	536.9	593.4
70–74	433.9	547.5
75–79	289.3	415.6
80–84	174.8	292.8
85–89	77.6	161.8
90 and over	31.9	88.1

*Post-censal estimate of 1996 population
Source: Statistics Canada,
CANSIM, Matrices 6367 (estimates).

Study the table, then answer the following questions.

a) Which age group has the greatest population of females? of males? What is the size of each population?

b) During the "baby boom" there was a greater number of births than in the years before or after. What evidence is there for a baby boom? When did the "baby boom" occur?

c) Which group appears to live longer, females or males? What is the evidence for this answer?

d) Describe any other trends in this table.

SOLUTION

a) By comparing the populations for each age group we can see that the 35–39 age group has the largest population of both males and females. There are about 1.3233 million females and 1.3449 million males in this age group.

b) There is a bulge in the population that begins with the age range 45–49 and has maximum effect in the age range 30–39. This means that the baby boom began in 1947 and had its greatest effect from 1957 to 1966.

c) Females appear to live longer. The number of females is less than the number of males in nearly all age ranges up to the age of 54. From age 55, the number of females in each range exceeds the number of males. Also, the ratio of females to males in each range increases as the age increases. This suggests that females outlive males.

d) The table suggests that there may have been more male births than female births in Canada over the past few decades. It is difficult to see other trends in this table.

Governments and other agencies use population distributions to predict future social and economic needs. Aging populations foretell large groups of people who will require social security pensions and increased medical care. Increased birth rates suggest a larger working population in the future.

A **population pyramid** is a graphical representation of the number of people in various age groups living in a country. It consists of two histograms with horizontal bars back-to-back, and a common vertical axis. Older age groups stack on top of younger ones, so the pyramids have pointed tops. The shape of a pyramid gives information about trends in the population. The pyramid at the top of the next page indicates a population with a high rate of population growth but also high child mortality. The pyramid at the bottom of the next page is typical of a population in which there are fewer births than deaths in a given year.

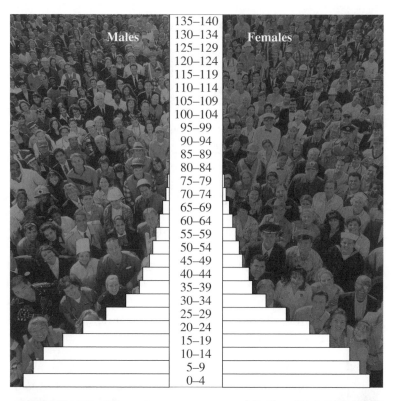

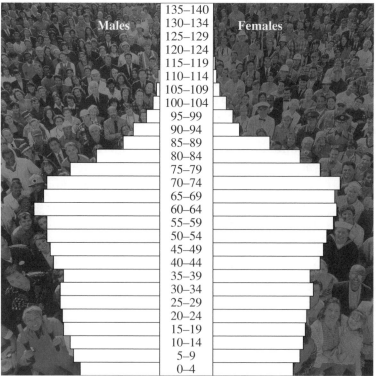

Example 2 Interpret a Population Pyramid

The following population pyramid shows the predicted population of Canadian males and females by age, for the year 2001, based on the 1993 population estimates.

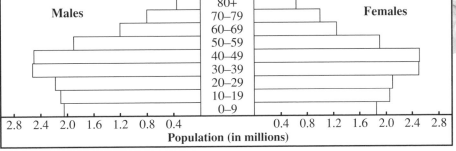

Source: U.S. Census Bureau, International Data Base.

a) What is the approximate ratio of female births to male births?

b) Which age group has the largest population of females? of males?

c) At what age do the numbers of females start to decrease? the numbers of males?

d) The birth rate was low during World War II (1939–1945). What is the evidence for this statement?

e) Describe any other trends you observe from the population pyramid.

f) Estimate the total population in Canada for the year 2001.

SOLUTION

a) The number of female births for the 0–9 age range is approximately 1 900 000.

The number of male births for the 0–9 age range is approximately 2 100 000.

The ratio of female births to male births is approximately $\frac{1\ 900\ 000}{2\ 100\ 000} = \frac{19}{21}$.

b) The largest population is indicated by the longest bar. For females, this is the 40–49 age group, and for males it is the 30–39 age group.

c) For females, the bars begin to shorten after the 40–49 age range. The number of females decreases from 50 years of age onward. Similarly, the number of males decreases from 40 years of age onward.

d) World War II took place during the years 1939–1945. Babies born during this time will be between 56 and 62 years of age in 2001. The population pyramid shows large decreases in the numbers in the 50–59 and 60–69 age groups. These decreases are larger than those for the 70–79 and 80–89 age groups.

e) There are significantly greater numbers of both females and males between the ages of 30 and 50. This may be due to the baby boom population born in the 1950s and 1960s.

f) Add the populations indicated by the length of each bar. There are approximately 16.0 million males and 15.7 million females. The total population is approximately 31.7 million.

A population pyramid is one way to present data. It is particularly useful when the data are gender specific. If totals in each category and overall totals are important, a stacked bar graph may be a better way to represent the data. Stacked bar graphs can also be used to represent sales information.

Example 3 **Stacked Bar Graph**

The following stacked bar graph shows the number of new passenger cars sold in Canada for the years 1990 to 1998.

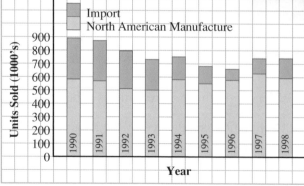

Passenger Cars Sold in Canada

Legend:
- Import
- North American Manufacture

Units Sold (1000's): 0, 100, 200, 300, 400, 500, 600, 700, 800, 900

Years: 1990, 1991, 1992, 1993, 1994, 1995, 1996, 1997, 1998

Year

Source: *Canadian Almanac*, 1999.

a) In what year was the sale of passenger cars in Canada the greatest?

b) In what year was the sale of North American cars the greatest?

c) During what year was the sale of imported cars the greatest?

d) Describe the trend for the total number of cars sold over this period.

e) Describe the trend for the sales of imported cars.

S O L U T I O N

a) Look at the total lengths of the bars. The year 1990 shows the greatest number of sales.

b) Look at the lengths of the bottom portions of the bars. The year 1997 shows the greatest number of sales of North American cars.

c) Look at the lengths of the top portions of the bars. The year 1990 shows the greatest number of sales of imported cars.

d) To see the trend of the total sales, consider the total length of each bar. The total sales of passenger cars dropped from just under 900 000 in 1990 to about 650 000 in 1996. Sales then started to increase to about 750 000 in each of 1997 and 1998.

e) Sales of imported cars decreased from approximately 300 000 in 1990 to approximately 70 000 in 1996. In 1998 sales increased to approximately 100 000.

Suppose we have information about two quantities, measured in the same units, both of which depend on the same quantity. Another way to compare data is to draw two line graphs on the same grid.

Example 4 **Multiple-line Graph**

A small business makes shirts and sells them to retail stores. Each shirt costs $6 to make. This cost is called the *variable cost* because it depends on the total number of shirts made, and so varies with the number of shirts produced. The business sells the shirts to stores for $16 per shirt. This is termed the *revenue* of the business. The *fixed* monthly costs of the business, such as rent, salaries, and insurance, are $5000. The total monthly costs of the business are 5000 plus 6 times the number of shirts produced: $y = 6x + 5000$. The graph on the next page can be used to predict expected profits or losses.

Break-Even Analysis

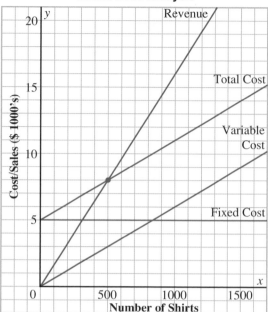

a) How many shirts must be sold for the business to break even? What is the sales revenue at this point?

b) What is the net profit for sales of 1000 shirts?

c) What is the gross profit for sales of 1200 shirts?

d) Suppose only 200 shirts are sold. What is the net loss?

SOLUTION

a) The business *breaks even* when sales revenue equals total costs. This occurs where the line representing total cost intersects the line representing sales revenue. The point of intersection is (500, 8000). For the business to break even, 500 shirts must be sold. The sales revenue is $8000.

b) The *net profit* is the difference between the sales revenue and total costs. To calculate the net profit on the sale of 1000 shirts, draw a vertical line through 1000 on the horizontal axis, as shown on the graph on the following page. For 1000 shirts, the revenue is $16 000 and the total cost is $11 000, so the net profit for sales of 1000 shirts is $5000.

c) The *gross profit* is the difference between the sales revenue and the variable cost. For 1200 shirts, the revenue is approximately $19 200 and the variable cost is approximately $7200, so the gross profit is about $12 000.

d) The sales revenue from 200 shirts is approximately $3200 and the total cost is approximately $6200. The *net loss* is the difference between these values, indicated on the graph below. The net loss on the sale of 200 shirts is $3000.

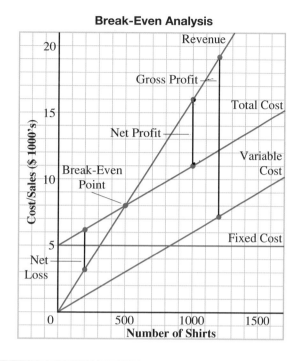

Break-Even Analysis

DISCUSSING THE IDEAS

1. Consider Examples 1 and 2. Is it easier to see overall trends by looking at a table or a graph? Is it easier to obtain exact figures by looking at a table or a graph?

2. Use the information in the bar graph in Example 3. Predict the total sales for passenger vehicles for 1999. How precise and how reliable would your prediction be?

3. Another way to represent the data of Example 3 would be to draw a double-bar graph, with the bars side by side. What are the advantages and disadvantages of a stacked bar graph compared to a double-bar graph?

4. Sometimes other types of compound graphs are drawn to illustrate comparisons. A tourism magazine wishes to draw a compound graph showing the average precipitation and the mean temperature each month of the year for a particular city. These quantities are measured in different units, so a common vertical scale is impossible. Suggest ways this graph could be drawn. Would you use the same type of graph for each set of data, or would different types of graphs be easier to read? How can two different vertical scales be shown?

EXERCISES

Checking Your Skills

1. The population pyramid below shows the estimates of the ages of the male and female population in Egypt for 1998.

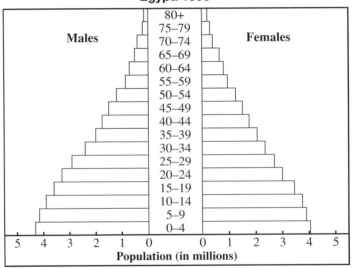

Egypt: 1998

Source: U.S. Census Bureau, International Data Base
http://www.census.gov/cgi-bin/ipc/idbpyry.pl

a) Estimate the number of male births and female births during the years 1994–1998. What is the ratio of male births to female births?

b) What evidence, if any, is there that male births have always outnumbered female births?

c) Is there any evidence of a baby boom in Egypt? Explain why or why not.

d) Explain why the bars of the pyramid decrease in length as the age ranges increase.

e) Estimate the total population of Egypt in 1998.

2. The table to the right compares the total population of Canada and the total population of Ethiopia for the year 1998.

Age Group	Canada (thousands)	Ethiopia (thousands)
0–9	4 027	19 424
10–19	4 081	13 875
20–29	4 213	9 321
30–39	5 242	6 172
40–49	4 742	4 208
50–59	3 337	2 807
60–69	2 357	1 680
70–79	1 769	741
80+	907	164

Source: U.S. Bureau of the Census, International Data Base.

a) Describe the trend for the population of Canada for the first three age ranges: 0–9, 10–19, and 20–29.

Describe the trend for the population of Ethiopia for the same three age ranges. How are the trends different for each country? What information might you conclude about these two countries based on the entries in the table?

b) Compare the overall trends for Canada and Ethiopia. Did Ethiopia experience a baby boom similar to Canada's? Justify your answer.

c) Describe the relative life spans of Canadians and Ethiopians. Explain how the table justifies your conclusions.

d) Which country had the greater population in 1998?

3. The following graph was obtained from Statistics Canada. It consists of two population pyramids, one superimposed upon the other. The population pyramids are for Canada for 1961 and 1991. Separate data are shown for males and females.

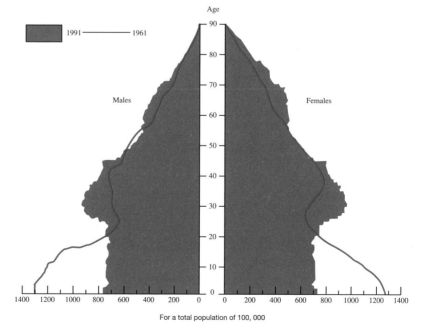

For a total population of 100, 000

Source: Statistics Canada, *Canadian Social Trends*, Catalogue 11-008E, Number 29, Summer 1993, page 6.

a) What is the approximate ratio of male to female births? Has this ratio changed from 1961 to 1991?

b) What evidence is there for a baby boom? What were the years of the baby boom?

c) The birth rate was low during the years of the Great Depression (1929–1939). What is the evidence for this?

d) The birth rate was low during the years of World War II (1939–1945). What is the evidence for this?

4. The stacked bar graph shows the sales of ice cream from The Ice Cream Factory during one year. The bottom sections indicate the number of litres of ice cream sold in 3-L cartons, and the top sections indicate the number of litres of ice cream sold in cones.

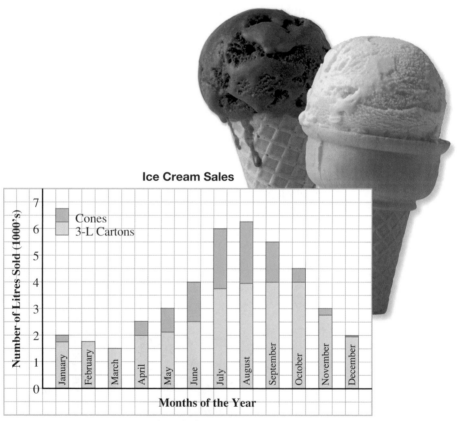

a) Which month had the greatest total sales?

b) Which month(s) had the greatest sales of cartons of ice cream? Explain.

c) During which month(s) was the sale of cones the greatest? Explain.

d) Describe the sales trend for cartons over the year.

e) Describe the sales trend for cones over the year.

f) What happened to the sales of cones during February and March? Explain.

5. The bar graph below shows the projected Canadian population, by age group, for the period from 1992 to 2036.

Projected population, by age group, 1992 to 2036

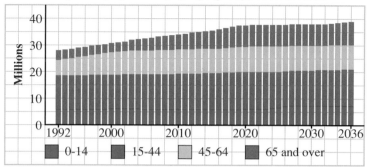

a) In which year is Canada's population expected to reach 30 million?

b) Describe the rate of increase of Canada's population, both overall and by age group.

c) Estimate the median age of the Canadian population in 1992 and in 2036.

d) Estimate when Canada's population will reach 40 million.

6. A small store in a shopping mall sells neckties for $50 each. The ties cost the merchant $25 each. Fixed yearly operating expenses, such as salaries, rent, utilities, and insurance, are $125 000. The store sells 9500 ties in a year. Its break-even analysis graph is shown.

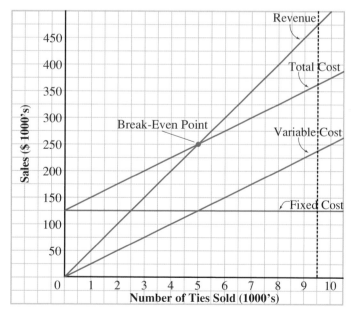

a) What is the net profit?

b) What is the gross profit?

c) What is the fixed cost?

d) Estimate the net loss if only 2000 ties are sold.

7. Oren Promotions is planning an outdoor concert. A ticket will cost $25. Fixed costs for the concert total $20 000. The musicians will receive $5 for every ticket sold. The graph below illustrates the break-even analysis for this concert.

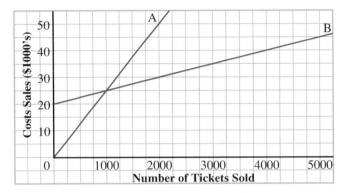

a) The lines are labelled A and B. Which line represents the total costs and which line represents the revenue?

b) How many tickets must be sold for Oren Promotions to break even on the concert?

c) What is the net profit when 2000 tickets are sold?

d) What would be the net loss if only 500 tickets were sold?

8. The following graph shows the number of cases of influenza A and influenza B by type and week of onset for Canada during fall and spring, 1995–96.

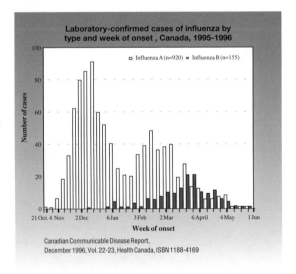

a) When was the outbreak of influenza A at its peak? When was influenza B at its peak?

b) Approximately when did influenza A start spreading?

c) When was the first case of influenza B recorded?

d) Describe the trend for influenza A for the given time period.

e) Which of the two strains of influenza do you think is the most contagious?

f) Do you see any relationship between the two strains of influenza? Explain.

Extending Your Thinking

9. Use the following population pyramids for the years 2000, 2020, and 2040. Write a paragraph to describe future trends in the population of Canada. Discuss which age groups will be prevalent during each 20-year period. How might these trends affect health care, day-care requirements, long-term care for the aged, and the building of new schools? Describe other social and economic changes that you foresee.

Canada 2000

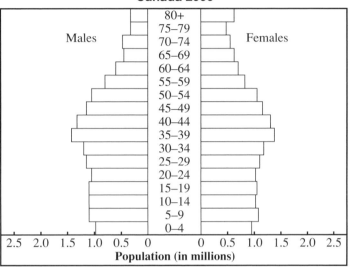

Source: U.S. Census Bureau, International Data Base.
http://www.census.gov/cgi-bin/ipc/idbpyry.pl

Canada 2020

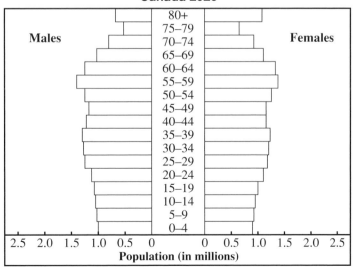

Source: U.S. Census Bureau, International Data Base.
http://www.census.gov/cgi-bin/ipc/idbpyry.pl

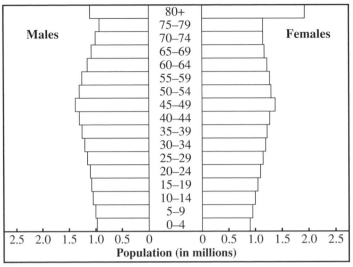

Canada 2040

Males | Females

80+
75–79
70–74
65–69
60–64
55–59
50–54
45–49
40–44
35–39
30–34
25–29
20–24
15–19
10–14
5–9
0–4

2.5 2.0 1.5 1.0 0.5 0   0 0.5 1.0 1.5 2.0 2.5
Population (in millions)

Source: U.S. Census Bureau, International Data Base.
http://www.census.gov/cgi-bin/ipc/idbpyry.pl

PROJECT

In this Tutorial you analyzed data presented in tables and graphs. The skills and concepts you used relate to the Chapter Project, and to the following project in the Project Book:

- Oil Exploration

COMMUNICATING THE IDEAS

What are the advantages and disadvantages of representing data in graphs compared to tables? Find other examples of tables and graphs in the media. Explain the significance of the data and the suitability of the presentation.

Time Graphs

In this Tutorial, you will study graphs where one quantity depends on time.

When you draw the graph of a relation, you must decide whether the points should be joined. The table below shows the cost of movie tickets on half-price night.

Number of Tickets	1	2	3	4	5
Cost ($)	4	8	12	16	20

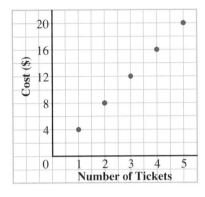

In this relation, intermediate points are meaningless. For example, we cannot buy a quarter of a ticket. This situation produces a graph where the points are not joined. Such data are *discrete*.

Compare the example above with the motion of a car travelling at an average speed of 90 km/h for 2 h.

Time (h)	0	1	2
Distance Travelled ($)	0	90	130

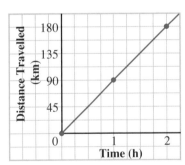

In this relation, intermediate points are meaningful. For example, the point (0.5, 45) tells us that after $\frac{1}{2}$ h the car has travelled 45 km. It is appropriate to join the points of this graph. Such data are *continuous*. The variables can take on any value. The graph is a line or a curve.

Practise Your Prior Skills

You will use a graphing calculator to plot points and interpret graphs. Try the exercises below as preliminary review. Refer to the Utilities from *Applied Mathematics 10*, or your graphing calculator handbook, for a review of graphing.

1. Use the graphing calculator to graph the equation $2y + 5x = 12$. You may need to rearrange the equation. Choose a suitable window for the calculator and determine the intercepts of the graph.

2. Use a graphing calculator to graph the data in each table. Enter the data in lists. To join the points, select the appropriate graph type on the STAT PLOT menu. Choose a suitable window for your graph.

a)

x	y
0	12.5
100	6.8
200	4.2
300	1.6

b)

x	y
0	1
5	51
10	151
15	301

Time is continuous. Therefore, should the points on a graph of data collected over time always be connected by a smooth curve? You will consider this question in the following Investigations.

Investigation 1 **Olympic Records**

You will investigate the graph of discrete data gathered over time.

The following graph shows the winning distances for women's Olympic discus from 1928 onward.

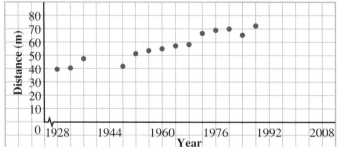

1. What was the winning distance in 1980? What was the winning distance in 1984?

2. Why is there no Olympic discus result in 1982? Why is there no result for 1940 or 1944?

3. Use your answers to exercises 1 and 2 to explain why these data are discrete.

4. Consider all the data from 1928 onward. What conclusion might you draw?

5. The winning distances in 1948 and 1984 do not fit the trend. Give possible explanations for each of these anomalies.

Joining adjacent points with line segments to produce a line graph is not valid for discrete data. Drawing a line or curve of best fit is a way to indicate the trend for discrete data.

Investigation 2   **Wasted Water**

You will investigate how much water is wasted each year by a dripping tap. There is a world shortage of drinkable water; in the late 1990s, 1.3 billion people did not have access to safe drinking water. However, in Canada we take the availability of clean water for granted.

Work with a partner. You will need a plastic pop bottle with a capacity of at least 1 L, a pin or thumbtack, one or two graduated cylinders, and a stopwatch (or timepiece with a second hand).

1. Use the pin or thumbtack to make a small hole in the lid of an empty plastic pop bottle. This hole should be very small so that the water drips out slowly. A hot (but not red hot) pin works best. Take care doing this, so that no one is hurt.

2. One partner should fill the bottle with water and place it so that the water drips into a graduated cylinder. The other partner should start timing as soon as the bottle is in place. Record the volume in the cylinder every 30 s for 5 min. (You may need to use an additional measuring cylinder.)

3. Record the data in a table. You may use the LIST feature of a graphing calculator.

4. Graph the data.

5. Estimate the volume of water collected after 2.25 min.

Time (minutes)	Volume (litres)
0	
0.5	

6. Are the data discrete or continuous? Show the trend of the data.

7. Extend the graph to predict the volume of water that would be collected in 10 min. This assumes that the supply in the bottle could be replenished.

8. Use your result from exercise 6 to estimate the volume of water that would be collected in 1 h, then 1 d.

The manager of a business may draw a time graph to record data collected month-by-month. This shows an overall trend of the operation of the business. During any year, a business may experience peaks and troughs in its revenue due to seasonal variations. If there is an overall net profit for the year, the business is solvent. If there is an overall net loss, the business may need to reconsider its operation, obtain further funding, or close down.

Example 1 **A Profit and Loss Cycle**

A small local store collected these monthly totals of costs and sales on the last day of every month during a year. Here are the corresponding graphs.

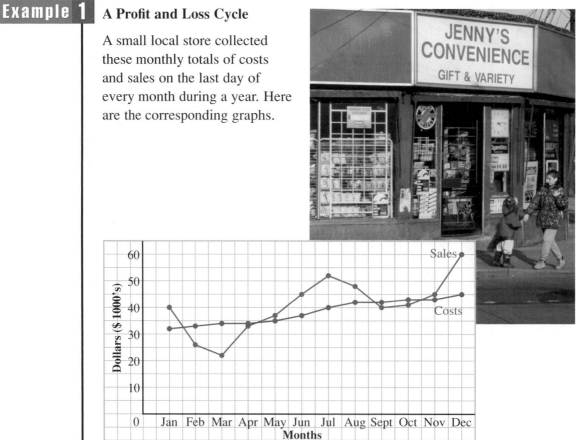

a) Are these data discrete or continuous? Explain.

b) Estimate the sales and costs for July. Was there a profit or a loss for July?

c) Did the business make a profit or a loss in March? Justify your answer.

d) For which months was a net profit recorded? For which month(s) was a net loss recorded?

e) Did this business have a successful year? Is it solvent? Justify your answer.

SOLUTION

a) Points between the plotted points have no meaning because the totals are recorded at the end of each month. The data are discrete.

b) July sales are about $52 000, and costs approximately $40 000. Since sales were greater than costs, there was a profit in July of approximately $12 000.

c) March sales are approximately $22 000, and costs are approximately $33 000. Since costs are greater than sales, there was a loss in March of approximately $11 000.

d) There is a profit when the sales point is above the cost point for that month. The months of January, May, June, July, August, November, and December record profits. The months of February, March, April, September, and October record losses.

e) Calculate the total sales revenue by adding the sales made each month. This is approximately $483 000. Calculate the total cost by adding the values of the costs for each month. This is approximately $460 000. The business made an overall profit of approximately $23 000 this year. It is solvent.

For a continuous time graph, joining the points with a line or smooth curve is valid. With experimental data, it may be appropriate to draw a line or curve of best fit. Estimation of a value between two data points of a graph is called *interpolation*. Estimation of a value that lies beyond the plotted data points of a graph is *extrapolation*.

DISCUSSING THE IDEAS

1. In *Investigation 1*, which method better indicates the trend of the data: joining adjacent dots with a line segment, or drawing a line of best fit?

2. In *Investigation 1*, is it likely that the winning throw in the 2008 Olympic Games will be under 70 m?

3. Why can you not interpolate values in *Investigation 1*?

4. In *Investigation 2*, you plotted a volume-time graph. Suggest another situation with a quantity that would result in a continuous time graph.

5. In *Investigation 2*, is exercise 5 an example of interpolation or extrapolation? Which is exercise 8? Explain.

6. In *Example 1*, why were adjacent points joined with line segments?

E X E R C I S E S

Checking Your Skills

1. Suppose a time graph was drawn to illustrate the following data. Which data are discrete, and which are continuous?

a) Age vs weight of a child

b) Month vs month-end sales

c) Time of day vs number of people in school

d) Year vs Indy 500 winning time

e) Year vs world population

f) Time of day vs temperature in Yellowknife

2. The following table shows the population of British Columbia.

Year	Population (millions)
1992	3.514
1994	3.681
1996	3.882
1998	4.009

a) Graph the data.

b) Are these data discrete or continuous? Explain.

c) Use the graph to estimate the population for 1997. Is this interpolation or extrapolation?

d) Assuming the trend has been the same during the 1990s, estimate the expected population of British Columbia in 1999. Is this interpolation or extrapolation?

3. The following table shows the amount, in billions of dollars, spent by Canadians on food for the years 1994 to 1998.

Year	Amount ($ billions)
1994	52.6
1995	53.5
1997	55.9
1998	57.9

a) Plot the data on a graph.

b) Are these data continuous or discrete?

c) The amount for 1996 is missing. Estimate what it might be.

d) Use your graph to predict the spending by Canadians for 2000.

4. The graph below shows a typical profit/loss cycle for a department store.

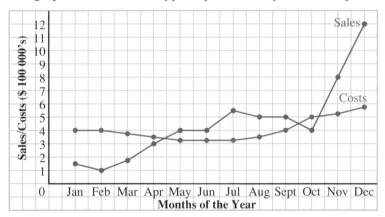

a) During which months did the department store make a profit?

b) During which months did the department store experience a loss?

c) During periods of net loss, what might the business do to continue operations?

d) Over which two quantities, sales or costs, does the business have the most managerial control?

5. The following graph shows the populations of snowshoe hare and lynx over a period of 5 years. The data were collected every 3 months.

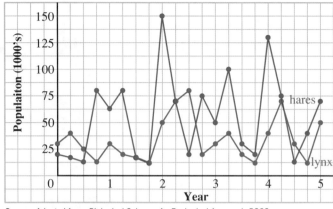

Source: Adapted from *Biological Science, An Ecological Approach*, BSCS Publications Rand McNally, 1973, page 73.

a) Approximately when is the lynx population greater than that of the snowshoe hare?

b) When are the populations the same?

c) Generally, when the hare population drops, what happens to the lynx population?

d) Generally, when the lynx population drops, what happens to the hare population?

e) Why were the two graphs plotted on the same grid?

6. The following graph shows the amount of fuel in pounds in a helicopter's fuel tank. Initially, the tank is full.

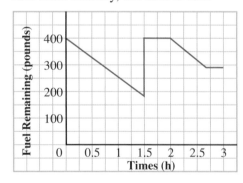

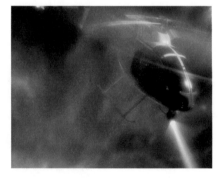

a) The points on this graph have been joined. Is this because the data are continuous, or is it to show a trend?

b) What is the fuel capacity of this helicopter?

c) There are five line segments. Describe what each segment represents.

7. The graph below shows the death rate for the United States from 1900 onward.

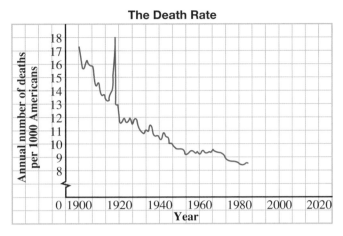

The Death Rate

a) What was the death rate in 1900? in 1940? in 1980?

b) What is the trend? How might you illustrate this trend on the graph?

c) In 1910, suppose you had used the data available at that time. What might you have predicted for the death rate between 1917 and 1919? Why would you have been incorrect? What caused this result?

d) Given the overall trend of the graph, what do you predict the death rate will be in the year 2020? Describe possible scenarios that might prove you wrong.

8. Money invested in Guaranteed Investment Certificates (GICs) earns compound interest. The table shows the amounts to which a principal of $1250 grows, at an annual interest rate of 3.75% compounded annually.

Year	Amount ($)
0	1250.00
1	1296.88
2	1345.51
3	1395.96
4	1448.31
5	1502.62

a) Graph the data. Should the points be joined? Explain.

b) Suppose the amount after 5 years was reinvested at the same rate. Estimate the amount after 7 years.

Extending Your Thinking

9. The graph below shows the median age of the Canadian population from 1920 to 2020. Below the graph is a time line describing major events from 1920 until 1960. The median age can be used as an indicator of the aging of our society.

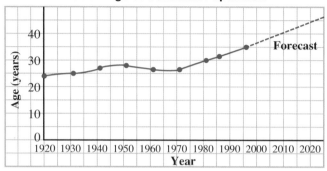

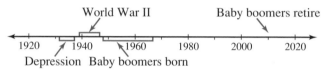

a) Explain why the median age rose in the 1930s and 1940s.

b) Explain why the median age dropped, starting in the 1950s.

c) Explain why the median age has increased steadily since the 1970s.

PROJECT

In this Tutorial you graphed data gathered over time. The skills and concepts you used relate to the Chapter Project, and to the following project in the Project Book:

• Oil Exploration

COMMUNICATING THE IDEAS

Explain the difference between discrete and continuous data. Use examples to illustrate your ideas.

Misleading Graphs

Benjamin Disraeli, a 19th-century British prime minister, is frequently quoted. Two of his sayings are:

"This shows how much easier it is to be critical than to be correct."

"There are three kinds of lies: lies, damn lies, and statistics."

Source: *http://www.cp-tel.net/miller/billee/quotes/Disraeli.html*

In this Tutorial, you will investigate how different displays of data can lead to different interpretations.

A graph gives a visual representation of data. It should display data as truthfully and clearly as possible. Sometimes, a graph is designed to promote a particular point of view. It is important to look critically at the data in this type of graph. Interpreting graphs presented in advertising material or in the media is an important life skill. In the following Investigation, you will explore two different presentations of the same data and evaluate their truthfulness.

Investigation 1   **An Advertisement**

A construction company built twice as many houses in 1990 as it did in the 1980. An employee drew two different picture graphs to represent these data.

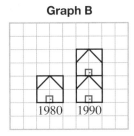

1. In graph A, what is the height of each house icon? What are their widths? What are their areas?

2. What is the relationship between the areas of the house icons in graph A?

3. In graph B, what is the height of each house icon? What is the width? What is the area?

4. What is the relationship between the areas of the house icons in graph B?

5. Which graph fairly represents the data? Explain.

6. Explain why you think the other graph is misleading.

In Tutorial 1.2, you discovered that data gathered over time may be discrete or continuous. Adjacent points of a discrete data set are often joined by line segments to show the trend. This can lead to possible distortion in the presentation. In Investigation 2, you will determine the effect on the appearance of a graph when the scales are changed.

Investigation 2

The Canadian Dollar

The value of the Canadian dollar in U.S. dollars has changed radically in recent years. Its value may rise and fall during one day as dealers trade the currency on the money market. The table below shows the value of the Canadian dollar, expressed in U.S. dollars (to two decimal places), at the close of trading on the second day of each month.

	Value (US ¢)
1998 Jan.	70.14
Feb.	68.82
Mar.	70.09
April	70.04
May	69.87
June	68.80
July	68.18
Aug.	66.34
Sept.	64.66
Oct.	64.46
Nov.	64.96
Dec.	65.09
1999 Jan.	65.10

1. Enter the data for the Canadian dollar into your calculator. Put the months into list L1 using the code January 1998 = 1, February 1998 = 2, and so on. Set the window as Xmin = 1, Xmax = 14, Xscl = 1. Keep these settings throughout the investigation. Graph the data for each of the following Y settings of the window. Set the plot type on the STAT PLOT menu to joined points. Sketch or print each graph as it is displayed on the screen.

   a) Ymin = 0, Ymax = 80, Yscl = 5

   b) Ymin = 62, Ymax = 71, Yscl = 2

2. Which graph appeared to change little over the time period? Which graph appeared to change more over the time period?

3. How can changing the window create different impressions of the same data? How would you produce a graph that appeared to show greater change over the same time period? To check your prediction, make the changes, draw the graph, then print or sketch it.

4. A graphing calculator shows only the graph and axes with tick marks. What other information must be given when presenting these graphs?

5. Even when all the information necessary for a truthful display is given, one graph in exercise 1 has more impact than the other. Why do you think this is?

In the following Investigation, you will explore the effect of changing scales on a histogram.

Investigation 3

A Class Survey

The following list gives the number of dollars spent on clothes during January by 31 students in a grade 11 class.

0, 10, 15, 25, 35, 38,
35, 54, 58, 52, 42, 45,
40, 48, 44, 68, 0, 18,
30, 35, 30, 50, 55, 55,
59, 45, 40, 45, 43, 65, 96

1. Enter the data into a list in your calculator. Set the window to Xmin = 0, Xmax = 100, Ymin = 0. Changing the value of Xscl changes the width of each rectangle of a histogram drawn on the graphing calculator.

If you need help with plotting a histogram on the graphing calculator, Utility 17 shows you how to do this on the TI-83. If you are using another graphing calculator, consult its manual.

2. Plot histograms of the data for each set of values given. Draw or print each histogram.

a) Xscl = 3	Ymax = 4	Yscl = 1
b) Xscl = 10	Ymax = 10	Yscl = 1
c) Xscl = 20	Ymax = 20	Yscl = 5
d) Xscl = 30	Ymax = 30	Yscl = 5
e) Xscl = 20	Ymax = 200	Yscl = 20

3. Which histogram is difficult to read?

4. Which graphs show the spending trend clearly and truthfully?

5. Why is it important to choose a suitable horizontal scale for a histogram?

6. What effect does the choice of vertical scale have on the histogram?

DISCUSSING THE IDEAS

1. In Investigation 1, the house icons drawn could be considered as decorated bars in a bar graph. Explain why it is important for each bar on a bar graph to have the same width.

2. When interpreting a graph, why is it important to look carefully at the scale of each axis?

3. Suppose you have data collected over 10 years for the value of the Canadian dollar. If you want to show the changes in value of the Canadian dollar against the U.S. dollar during this period, what window settings for the y-axis might you choose? If you want to show the changes in the value of the Canadian dollar for 1 week, what window settings might you choose?

4. Explain the difference between a bar graph and a histogram.

5. What are the disadvantages of plotting a histogram with relatively small horizontal intervals? What are the disadvantages of plotting histograms with relatively large horizontal intervals?

Checking Your Skills

1. A company produced the picture graph below to show potential investors how its profits had increased.

   a) What are the profits in 1996 and 1999?

   b) Why is this graph misleading?

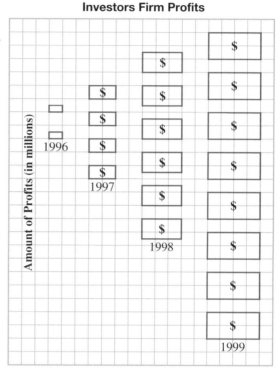

Investors Firm Profits

2. A political poll was taken and the results are graphed in a pie chart. Describe how the graph distorts the information.

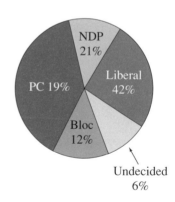

3. The following graph shows unemployment figures for 1990–1993. Explain the visual impact of the graph and why it is misleading.

Unemployment (Annual Average)

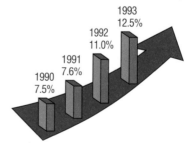

4. The graph to the right illustrates the profits of a computer manufacturing company for consecutive years. Why is this graph misleading?

5. Recall that to indicate a scale has been shortened we use a small zigzag mark, as if the scale were crumpled. This is called a *scale break*. The graph below has the caption "Have you plotted your future? If not, you will be interested in the graphic presentation of our salary structure, based on reward for enthusiasm and hard work."

a) What information can you get from this graph?

b) Why may the graph be misleading?

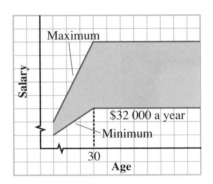

Extending Your Thinking

6. Obtain the game result records of a team of your choice. Create a display of the data that is truthful. Create another display that distorts the data but has more visual impact.

PROJECT

In this Tutorial, you analyzed graphs for truth and clarity of presentation. The skills and concepts you used relate to the Chapter Project, and to the following project in the Project Book:

• Oil Exploration

COMMUNICATING THE IDEAS

From a newspaper or magazine, collect an example of a graph that is misleading. Explain briefly how the graph is deceptive, and then show how the data might be presented more fairly or in a less distorted fashion. Include the graph with your work, and cite its source.

In the preceding Tutorial, you learned to recognize a misleading graph. It is important to produce clear and accurate graphs from which correct inferences can be drawn. In this Tutorial, you will construct different graphs, focusing on the clarity and truthfulness of presentation. You will draw graphs that you analyzed in earlier Tutorials: population pyramids, stacked bar graphs, and line graphs.

A bar graph is easy to draw, and colour or shading can be added to increase the visual impact. By stacking or compounding the bars, different sets of data can be compared.

Example 1   **Multiple-Bar Graph**

The table gives data on telecommunications use for different regions of the world based on income.

Design a graph to display these data.

Income Range	Phone Lines (per 100 people)	Personal Computers (per 100 people)
Low	1.5	0.14
Lower Middle	8.4	0.72
Upper Middle	14.4	2.68
High	51.4	18.26

Source: *New Internationalist*, December 1996.

SOLUTION

These data give two sets of information about four different regions. The data may be represented by a *multiple-bar graph*. Each income range has two bars, one representing phone lines and the other personal computers. A key to identify the bars is required. The bars can be placed vertically, as shown here, or horizontally to save space. A horizontal scale must be chosen to fit the data. The scale is from 0 to 60.

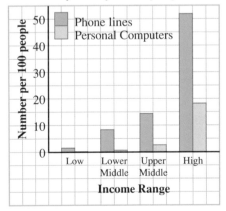

When data have been gathered over time, a line graph shows the trend. Best fit lines or curves then allow predictions to be made from the data.

Example 2 **Line Graphs**

The following data, from Statistics Canada, give figures on home appliances owned by Canadians for various years from 1965. The numbers represent the percent of households with the item.

	1965	1970	1975	1980	1985	1990	1996	1997
Telephones	89.4	93.9	96.4	97.6	98.2	98.5	98.7	98.6
Radios	96.1	97.2	98.3	98.7	98.7	99.1	98.6	98.7
Televisions	92.6	96.0	96.8	97.7	98.3	99.0	99.1	99.1

Design a graph that clearly shows the trends in the percent of households with telephones since 1965.

SOLUTION

Draw a broken-line graph of the data for households with telephones. The horizontal axis represents the years, and the vertical axis represents the percent of households with a telephone. To show the changes in percents clearly, the vertical scale is labelled from 89% to 99%. The zigzag mark above zero indicates a scale break in the vertical axis. Adjacent points are joined to highlight the trend.

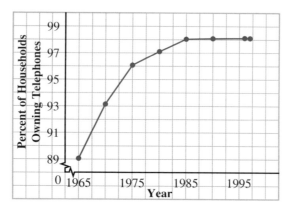

Example 3 **Graph with Two Vertical Scales**

The following data, from Statistics Canada, indicate the numbers and sizes of families in Canada for various years since 1961.

	1961	1971	1981	1991
Number of families (millions)	4.15	5.07	6.33	7.36
Average size (people)	3.90	3.70	3.30	3.10

a) Graph the data to show the trends for the number of families and the size of the family unit.

b) What conclusions, if any, can you draw from the graph?

SOLUTION

The number of families is in the millions. The average size of family unit is less than 4, so two different vertical scales are needed.

To distinguish between the two sets of data, use two different types of graph and two different colours. Use a bar graph for the number of families and a line graph for the average size of the family unit. The horizontal axis will represent the year.

a)

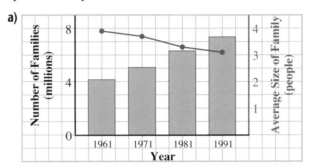

b) The number of families in Canada is rising while the average size of a family is dropping.

DISCUSSING THE IDEAS

1. In Example 1, why is a stacked bar graph not suitable to represent the data?

2. Sometimes numerical data are listed on a bar graph. In Example 1, do you think the actual figures should be included on the bar graph? Explain.

3. In Example 1, the graph has no title. Suggest a possible title.

4. In Example 2, why did the vertical scale not start at zero?

5. What other type of graph, if any, would be suitable to display the data in Example 2?

6. Why do you think a broken-line graph and a bar graph were chosen to the display the data in Example 3? Discuss the possible use of two bar graphs, or two line graphs.

7. Why are two scales necessary in Example 3?

Checking Your Skills

1. The table below gives the percent of Canadians who smoke cigarettes regularly, by age, for the years 1989 and 1995.

   a) Represent the data as a multiple-bar graph.

Age Range	15–19	20–44	45–64	Over 65
1989	22	34	32	17
1995	23	29	25	11

   Source: Statistics Canada, Catalogue 82F007XCB.

   b) Describe any trends.

2. Use the data in Example 2. Construct a multiple-bar graph showing the percent of households with radios and the percent with televisions. You could use the graphing capabilities of a spreadsheet program.

   a) Describe any trends.

   b) Explain which graph shows the trends more clearly: the graph in Example 2 or the one you drew in part a.

3. The Consumer Price Index is a record of the relative costs of selected items over a period of years. The table below is a section of a Consumer Price Index table in which the price of a bundle of goods that cost $100 in 1992 is given for the years 1986 to 1997.

Year	Food	Shelter
1986	82.8	84.4
1987	86.4	87.3
1988	88.7	90.6
1989	92.0	93.8
1990	95.8	95.8
1991	100.4	99.5
1992	**100.0**	**100.0**
1993	101.6	101.0
1994	102.1	101.2
1995	104.5	103.1
1996	105.9	105.3
1997	107.5	106.6

   Source: *Canadian Almanac Directory*, 1999

   Design a graph that shows the change in the Consumer Price Index for food and for shelter for the given years. You could use the graphing capabilities of a spreadsheet program.

4. The following data show the average value, in dollars, of Canadian houses. Data for the territories were not available.

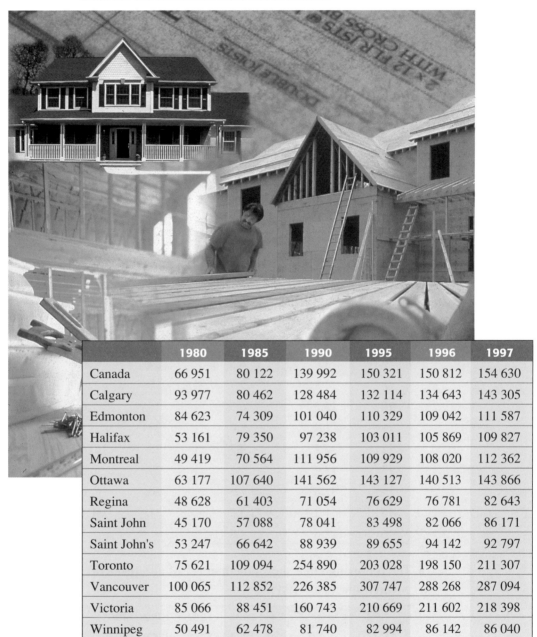

	1980	1985	1990	1995	1996	1997
Canada	66 951	80 122	139 992	150 321	150 812	154 630
Calgary	93 977	80 462	128 484	132 114	134 643	143 305
Edmonton	84 623	74 309	101 040	110 329	109 042	111 587
Halifax	53 161	79 350	97 238	103 011	105 869	109 827
Montreal	49 419	70 564	111 956	109 929	108 020	112 362
Ottawa	63 177	107 640	141 562	143 127	140 513	143 866
Regina	48 628	61 403	71 054	76 629	76 781	82 643
Saint John	45 170	57 088	78 041	83 498	82 066	86 171
Saint John's	53 247	66 642	88 939	89 655	94 142	92 797
Toronto	75 621	109 094	254 890	203 028	198 150	211 307
Vancouver	100 065	112 852	226 385	307 747	288 268	287 094
Victoria	85 066	88 451	160 743	210 669	211 602	218 398
Winnipeg	50 491	62 478	81 740	82 994	86 142	86 040

Source: The Canadian Real Estate Association.

a) Construct a multiple-line graph that compares the average house value in Canada with the average house value in a city of your choice.

b) Describe any trends.

c) What factors do you think might lead to a substantial increase in average house prices? What might cause average prices to fall?

5. The following table shows the mean temperature and precipitation for January 1999 in Vancouver. Illustrate the data on a graph with two different vertical scales.

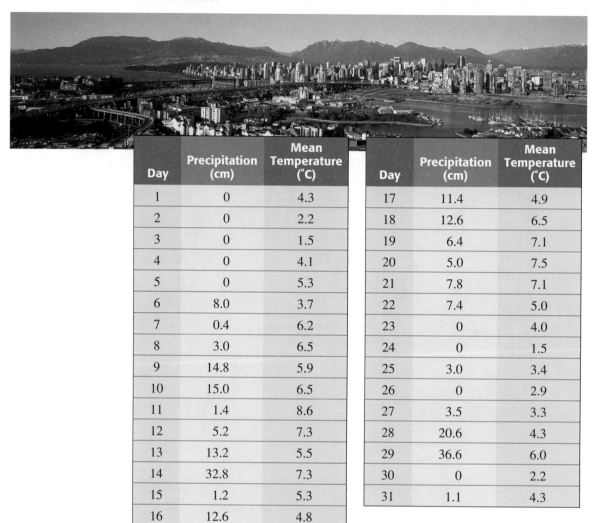

Day	Precipitation (cm)	Mean Temperature (°C)	Day	Precipitation (cm)	Mean Temperature (°C)
1	0	4.3	17	11.4	4.9
2	0	2.2	18	12.6	6.5
3	0	1.5	19	6.4	7.1
4	0	4.1	20	5.0	7.5
5	0	5.3	21	7.8	7.1
6	8.0	3.7	22	7.4	5.0
7	0.4	6.2	23	0	4.0
8	3.0	6.5	24	0	1.5
9	14.8	5.9	25	3.0	3.4
10	15.0	6.5	26	0	2.9
11	1.4	8.6	27	3.5	3.3
12	5.2	7.3	28	20.6	4.3
13	13.2	5.5	29	36.6	6.0
14	32.8	7.3	30	0	2.2
15	1.2	5.3	31	1.1	4.3
16	12.6	4.8			

6. The following table shows the number of city residents living below the poverty line, since 1985.

Year	1985	1987	1989	1991	1993	1995	1996
Total	3831	3768	3785	4067	4277	4408	5294
Children under 18	1175	1125	1083	1250	1330	1358	1498
Adults 18 to 65	2211	2173	2123	2400	2538	2713	3074
Seniors 65 and over	445	470	579	417	409	337	722

a) Construct a stacked bar graph that represents the data.

b) Describe any trends.

7. Construct a population pyramid for the following data for Sweden in 1998. The numbers are in thousands.

Age	Male	Female
0–9	576	547
10–19	535	507
20–29	579	556
30–39	643	611
40–49	608	589
50–59	594	579
60–69	387	416
70–79	319	405
80+	152	284

Source: Figures taken from data from U.S. Census Bureau.

Extending Your Thinking

8. The following tables list the number of homicides and the population by province and territory for various years.

Province	Number of Homicides					
	1967	1972	1977	1982	1987	1992
Alberta	33	37	70	70	73	92
British Columbia	47	87	90	110	76	122
Manitoba	15	36	44	35	44	52
New Brunswick	5	11	38	13	20	11
Newfoundland	1	3	8	6	5	2
Northwest Territories	2	3	4	7	2	13
Nova Scotia	10	14	14	12	14	21
Ontario	114	141	192	184	204	242
Prince Edward Island	0	2	1	0	–	0
Quebec	75	155	194	192	174	166
Saskatchewan	29	28	46	39	30	32
Yukon	6	2	6	2	–	2

	Population (thousands)					
Province	1967	1972	1977	1982	1987	1992
Alberta	1490	1657	1912.7	2314.5	2377.7	2 562.7
British Columbia	1945	2241	2499.4	2787.7	2925	3 297.6
Manitoba	963	991	1027.4	1033.3	1079	1 096.8
New Brunswick	620	640	684.1	696.6	712.3	729.3
Newfoundland	499	530	559.8	566.2	568.1	577.5
Northwest Territories	29	37	42.8	47.4	52	56.5
Nova Scotia	760	795	833.4	849.5	878	906.3
Ontario	7127	7810	8353.1	8702.5	9265	10 098.6
Prince Edward Island	109	113	119.3	122.4	127.3	130.5
Quebec	5864	6054	6284	6462.2	6592.6	6 925.2
Saskatchewan	957	914	934.9	977	1015.8	993.2
Yukon	15	20	21.8	23.9	24.5	27.9

a) Choose one province or territory. Design a graph to represent the number of homicides and the population for the years 1967 to 1992. You may wish to use a spreadsheet program.

b) Calculate the number of homicides per 1000 people for each year for your chosen region. Graph these data.

c) Write a report on the homicide rate of your chosen region. Support your report with a suitable graph (or graphs).

PROJECTS

In this Tutorial you graphed data. The skills and concepts you used relate to the Chapter Project, and to the following project in the Project Book:

• Oil Exploration

COMMUNICATING THE IDEAS

Make a chart that illustrates the different types of graphs you have investigated. Include a rough sketch for each type.

1.5 Contour and Weather Maps

In the previous Tutorials, a variety of information was presented in graphs and tables. Two other types of pictorial representation of data are contour maps and weather maps. A contour map conveys information about the height above sea level of land formations. Similarly, a weather map conveys information about the barometric pressure exerted on a region. In this Tutorial, you will explore how to interpret these graphs.

A contour map uses contour lines to show the outlines of hills and valleys at regular intervals above or below sea level. Each contour line shows the outline, from above, of a section of Earth's surface at a particular height. The closeness of the contour lines gives an indication of the slope of the land. If the contour lines are close together, the hill is steep; if they are far apart, the land is fairly flat. Depending on the map system used, the contour lines are drawn at intervals of 10, 50, 100, or 1000 m. Read the map carefully to find the contour interval. A contour map, like all maps, has a horizontal scale that allows us to estimate horizontal distances.

Investigation 1 Interpreting Contour Maps

In this *Investigation*, you will explore the information conveyed in a contour map.

The following diagram shows part of a contour map of a river valley. Use this map to complete the exercises.

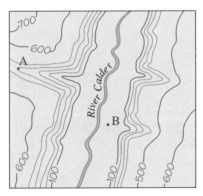

Scale 1 cm = 200 m

1. What contour interval is used in this diagram?

2. What is the height of the land at point A? at point B?

3. What is the horizontal distance between points A and B?

4. What height is the highest point on this map? How precise can you be in your answer?

5. Rivers flow downhill. Can you tell the direction that the river flows from this map? Explain.

6. Do you expect the river to be fast flowing? Explain.

7. The 100 m to 400 m contour lines are very close. Describe the land formation represented by these contour lines.

8. What letter of the alphabet would best describe the shape of this river valley?

9. There are 3 dry valleys leading to the river valley shown in the diagram. What letter would best describe the shape of each of these?

To better visualize the topography of a region in a contour map, a *profile* may help. This is a side view of a land surface, showing the slope of the land along a given straight line. *Vertical exaggeration* is an increase in the vertical scale compared to the horizontal scale for the sake of clarity. A true profile would have the same scale both vertically and horizontally. However, this often results in a profile that is too low to clearly see the land features. You will draw a profile from a contour map in the following *Investigation*.

Investigation 2   **Constructing a Profile from a Contour Map**

This contour map has a horizontal scale of 1 cm = 1 km. Complete the steps to construct a profile from A to B on grid paper. Use a vertical exaggeration with a scale of 1 cm = 100 m.

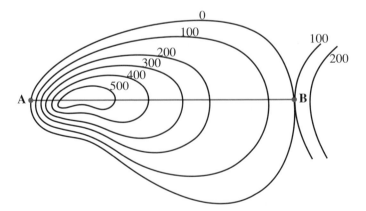

1. Measure the distance between points A and B on the map. Draw a horizontal line with this length on grid paper and mark the points A and B. This is the base line for the profile.

2. Draw the vertical axis at each end of the base line, using the scale 1 cm = 100 m.

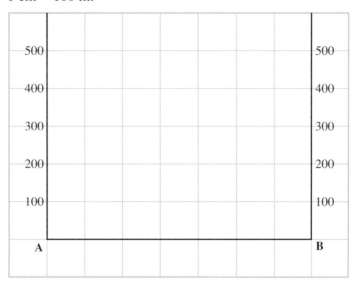

3. Take a blank piece of paper and place it with one straight edge along the path from A to B. Mark and label A and B on the blank paper. Make small tick marks on the blank paper at the points where the contour lines cross the edge of the paper. Label these marks with the appropriate heights shown from the map.

4. Place the marked paper along the base line, and mark a point on the grid at each appropriate height.

5. Connect all the points on the grid with a smooth curve to produce the profile.

Weather maps are similar to contour maps. Instead of contour lines, a weather map has *isobars* that connect places with the same barometric pressure. *Isotherms* connect places of equal temperature. Meteorologists use these maps to help predict weather. Generally, wind moves from high pressure areas to low pressure areas (like water flowing downhill). This often results in bad weather in the region with low pressure. On Environment Canada weather forecast maps, the letters H and L label regions of high and low pressure, respectively.

The prevailing wind direction in Canada is from the west. On the weather maps published daily, a *warm front* is indicated by a red line with semicircles, and a *cold front* by a blue line with triangles. These lines show the leading edges of warm and cold air masses as they move eastward. Areas where warm and cold fronts meet are associated with storms. A weather map often contains information about temperatures and precipitation. These are shown with different colours and different shadings.

Weather Maps

Study the weather map. It shows the atmospheric pressure, measured in hectopascals (hPa), forecast at various weather stations for May 08, 1999.

a) What is the lowest pressure in Canada predicted by this map?

b) What is the highest pressure in Canada predicted by this map?

c) What are the atmospheric pressures at points X and Y marked on the map?

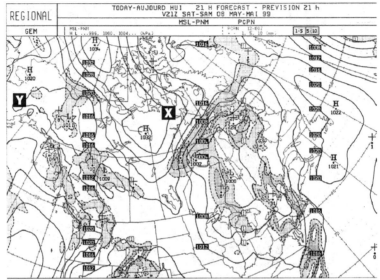

Source: Environment Canada.

S O L U T I O N

a) The lowest pressure recorded was 1000 hPa at the southern end of Hudson Bay.

b) The highest pressure recorded was 1034 hPa in the western Arctic.

c) Follow the isobars around from X and Y to get the pressures at X of 1028 hPa and at Y of 1016 hPa.

D I S C U S S I N G   T H E   I D E A S

1. For a contour map, describe the region where contour lines are very close to each other. Describe the region where the contour lines are far apart.

2. How can you tell which way a river is flowing by inspecting a contour map?

3. Explain why it is common practice to use different vertical and horizontal scales when drawing a profile. Why is it important to know these scales?

4. How are contour maps and weather maps similar?

5. Explain why the weather map in the Example has two kinds of lines similar to contour lines. How can you tell which is which?

EXERCISES

Checking Your Skills

1. Match each block model of a basic landform with its associated contour map.

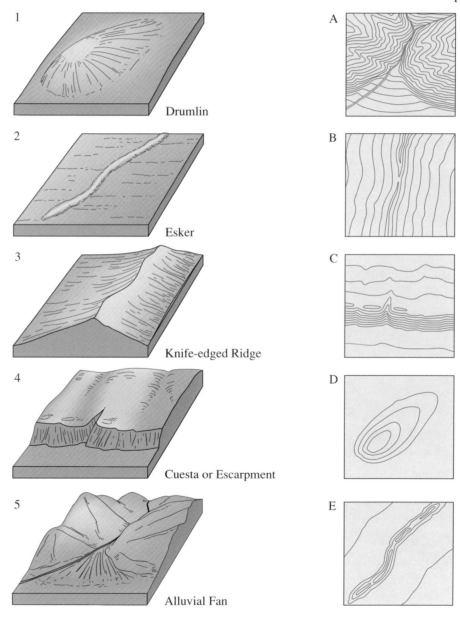

1   Drumlin

2   Esker

3   Knife-edged Ridge

4   Cuesta or Escarpment

5   Alluvial Fan

A

B

C

D

E

2. The diagrams below show a sketch of a block model and its associated contour map.

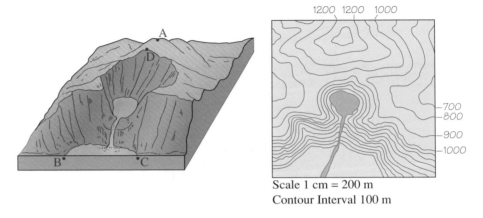

Scale 1 cm = 200 m
Contour Interval 100 m

a) What is the altitude at point A?

b) At what altitude is the lake?

c) What is the horizontal distance between points B and C?

d) How much higher is point D than the lake?

3. Draw a profile from A to B for the following map. Choose your own vertical scale.

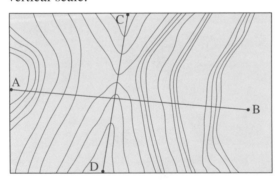

Scale 1 cm = 1 km

4. Draw a profile from C to D, using the map in exercise 3 and the same vertical scale.

5. The weather forecast map (page 51, left) was published in The Vancouver Sun on April 10, 1999. Each colour indicates an area with a specific temperature range.

a) Write the temperature range for each city: Vancouver, Edmonton, Calgary, Winnipeg, Ottawa, New York, and Dallas.

b) In which cities in part a is rain predicted?

c) Describe areas on the map where there is the potential for storms to form.

Rain Freezing Snow Lightning High Low TROWAL Warm Cold
Rain Pressure Pressure (Trough of Warm Air Aloft) Front Front

6. Repeat exercise 5 parts b and c, using the weather map given on the right above.

Extending Your Thinking

7. Obtain a current Environment Canada weather map. You may need to search the Internet.

a) Estimate the atmospheric pressure forecast at your location.

b) What is the lowest pressure predicted for the date on your map?

c) What is the highest pressure predicted for the date on your map?

d) Give a brief forecast for the atmospheric pressure and precipitation in Vancouver, Edmonton, Saskatoon, and Winnipeg.

PROJECT

In this Tutorial you worked with contour and weather maps. The skills and concepts you used relate to the following projects in the Project Book:

• An Outdoor Recreational Resort

• Oil Exploration

COMMUNICATING THE IDEAS

"Never go hiking in the wilderness without a map and compass." Explain how a contour map and a compass could help you estimate your location on a wilderness hike.

Analyzing Data from Graphs

You should now have a number of articles or advertisements that have graphs or numerical data within them.

Part A: Analyzing Graphs

Choose one article or advertisement that includes at least one graph to complete the following exercises.

1. In a paragraph, briefly describe the inferences or claims being made within the article or advertisement. Explain how the data are being used to support these claims.

2. Do the data presented support the inference or claim being made? Explain your response.

3. What questions do you have regarding the data presented?

Part B: Creating Graphs

Choose one article or advertisement that includes numerical data but no graphs to complete the following exercises.

4. In a paragraph, briefly describe the inferences or claims being made within the article or advertisement. Explain how the data are being used to support these claims.

5. Do the data presented support the inferences or claims being made? Explain your response.

6. Create an appropriate graph or set of graphs for the given numerical data.

7. Explain your choice of graphs to present the given information.

8. What advantage is there to presenting data in numerical as well as graphical form?

Part C: Misleading Data

Choose one article or advertisement that includes a graph that could be considered misleading. Complete the following exercises.

9. In a paragraph, briefly describe the inference or claim being made based on the misleading graph.

10. Explain why the graph that is presented could be considered misleading. What should be done to the graph to make it more truthful.

11. Use the data presented to create a graph that is truthful.

12. Why do you think the author or company presented the graph they used, as opposed to the one you created?

13. Suppose the company used your graph. Could the claim or inference that was made still be considered valid? Explain.

Your finished project will include:

- the three articles you chose to use

- a write-up for each of the articles that includes the answers to exercises in parts A, B, or C

- a graph or set of graphs for part B

- a graph for part C

Career Skills

The ability to create and interpret data is a relevant skill in today's workplace, marketplace, and society. Most companies use data and graphs of some kind to guide business decisions. As a consumer, you must be able to critically analyze the claims that are being made by advertisers. As a citizen, it is important that you are able to analyze the data used to support arguments that are often contradictory.

CONSOLIDATING YOUR SKILLS

What Do I Need To Know?

Tutorial	Skills and Concepts	Important Results and Formulas
1.1	• Interpret a variety of statistical graphs, including population pyramids, stacked and compound bar graphs, multiple-line graphs, and combinations of graphs	
1.2	• Distinguish between discrete and continuous time graphs • Extract information from time graphs, including interpolations and extrapolations	• Interpolation is the estimation of the values of a relation between known values • Extrapolation is the estimation of values of a relation beyond the known values
1.3	• Analyze how given graphs may be misleading or ambiguous • Understand that plotting the same data on axes with different scales can produce graphs that appear to have different interpretations	
1.4	• Design different ways of presenting data, focusing on truthful display and clarity of presentation	
1.5	• Interpret contour maps and weather maps • Draw profiles from the contour maps	

What Should I Be Able To Do?

After you have finished the work in Chapter 1, you should be able to solve the problems that follow. Part A is investigative in nature.

Part A

1. A company sells sporting equipment. The table shows the annual sales for the years 1990 to 1994.

Year	New Sales ($)
1990	105 923
1991	98 263
1992	143 829
1993	149 066
1994	177 062

a) Enter these data into LIST on your calculator. Enter the years in list L1 and sales in list L2. Set the window as Xmin = 1990, Xmax = 1994, Xscl = 1.

b) Are these data discrete or continuous? Choose an appropriate plot type on the STAT PLOT menu.

c) Draw a graph of these data using the following Y settings for the window:

   i) Ymin = 0,   Ymax = 180000,   Yscl = 5000
   ii) Ymin = 90000,   Ymax = 180000,   Yscl = 1000
   iii) Ymin = 0,   Ymax = 300000,   Yscl = 10000

d) Which graph represents the increase in sales most truthfully? Explain.

Part B

2. A survey on the month of birth for grade 11 students at Ballenas High School on Vancouver Island, B.C., produced the following results.

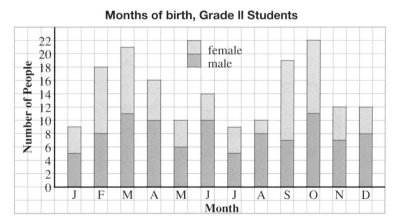

Months of birth, Grade II Students

a) During which month(s) are there the most birthdays?

b) During which month(s) were the most males born?

c) During which month(s) were the most females born?

d) During which month were the same number of females and males born?

e) How many females are in grade 11 at Ballenas School?

f) How many males are in grade 11 at Ballenas School?

g) How many students are in grade 11 at Ballenas School?

3. The table below shows the average total precipitation, in millimetres, for each month of 1998 at Vancouver International Airport and at Edmonton International Airport. Display this information as a multiple-line graph. Are these data continuous or discrete?

Month	Jan	Feb	Mar	Apr	May	Jun	July	Aug	Sep	Oct	Nov	Dec
Vancouver	154	115	101	60	52	45	32	41	67	114	150	182
Edmonton	24	18	16	20	42	77	92	78	46	15	17	22

4. The development of a fetus is measured using ultrasound technology. The table below shows a portion of a doctor's chart for the average sizes of head and abdomen for particular stages of development.

Age (week)	Head Circumference (cm)	Abdominal Circumference (cm)
12	7.1	5.6
16	12.4	10.5
20	17.5	15.2
24	22.1	19.7
28	26.2	24.0
32	29.7	28.0
36	32.5	31.8
40	34.5	35.4

a) Graph the head circumference against age and the abdominal circumference against age on the same grid.

b) Are these data discrete or continuous?

c) Estimate the head circumference at 30 weeks.

d) Estimate the abdominal circumference at 25 weeks.

e) A fetus has a head circumference of 25.6 cm. Estimate the age of the fetus in weeks.

5. The following contour graph represents a river valley.

a) Which side of the river valley is the steepest, the western side or the eastern side?

b) What is the altitude at point A? What is the altitude at point B?

c) What geographical feature is at X? Which way does the river flow, north or south?

d) What is the approximate horizontal distance between A and B?

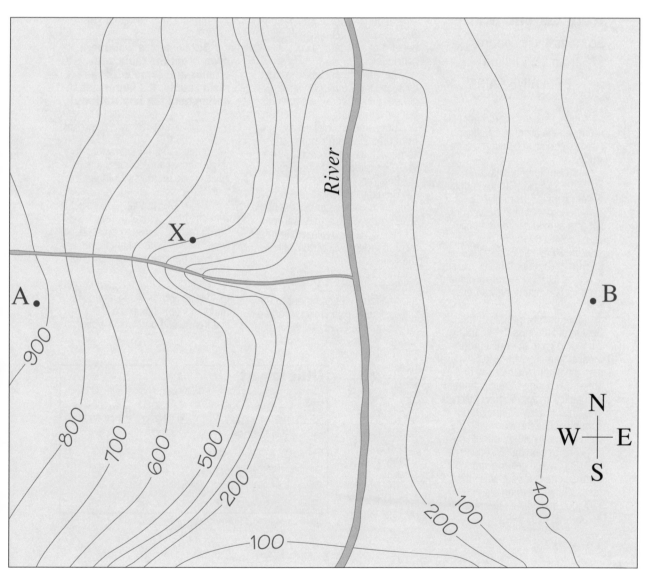

Scale 1 cm = 108 m

The Chapter Project combines many skills and concepts covered in this Chapter. Here is a sampling of student work from different stages of the project. Review these samples to gain insights into your own project work.

6. Here is one of the articles the student chose to study. This article was used for Part B.

Rich would benefit from tax cut: Study

Economist says poorest get $26 from $6.5 billion

BY ELAINE CAREY
DEMOGRAPHICS REPORTER

General tax cuts would put little money in the average Canadian family's pocket, according to a new study.

A $6.5 billion tax reduction — twice the $3 billion cut the federal government is reportedly considering — would deliver only $466 to a middle income family earning $40,000 to $65,000 a year, says the study released yesterday.

The one in four families earning less than $20,000 a year would fare even worse, netting only an extra $26.

More than two-thirds of the benefit of an across-the-board tax cut would go to the one in four families earning over $65,000 a year, says the study by University of Toronto economist Ernie Lightman and policy analyst Andrew Mitchell. The Child Poverty Action Group commissioned the study with the child Care Education Foundation.

Families earning $65,000 to $100,000 would get an extra $910 from a general tax cut while the most affluent, earning over $100,000, would gain the most — an average of $2,099.

Families with children, who are supposed to be the focus of the federal budget which is expected Feb. 29, would get only half the benefits of a general tax cut, it concludes.

The government assumes that everyone will be happy with a general tax cut because everyone will get something, said Lightman.

"But some are walking away from the table with crumbs and some with the main course," he said. "It's important to understand the implications."

Middle income Canadians have been hit hard in recent years, he said, "and with this, they will wind up getting nailed again, while upper income groups will once again reap the gains."

The debate over tax cuts is so politically charged that "good information isn't getting out to the public," said Crista Freiler, program director of the Child Poverty Action Group.

"Tax cuts aren't free, they're potentially very costly," she said. "A $6.5 billion tax cut doesn't translate into a lot of money in family pockets."

The study found the average family's

tax rate would fall by less than one per cent — a net gain of only $476 — under a $6.5 billion tax cut.

'But some are walking away from the table with crumbs and some with the main course. It's important to understand the implications.'
— ERNIE LIGHTMAN
UNIVERSITY OF TORONTO ECONOMIST

Nearly half the gains would go to single people and childless families while single mothers would get less than 2 per cent.

"As a measure to assist families with children, general tax relief is a highly inefficient way to proceed," it says. "It represents highly regressive — even perverse — tax policy for Canada."

It concludes that targeted tax cuts to specific groups like low and middle income families with children would be a better policy.

Little impact

A federal tax cut of $6.5 billion will have little effect on middle and lower income families:

Income type	% of families in category	Avg. income change due to cut
Low income: Under $20,000	25.8	$26
Modest income: $20,000 to $40,000	27.7	145
Middle income: $40,000 to $65,000	22.0	466
Advantaged: $65,000 to $100,000	15.8	910
Affluent: $100,000 plus	8.7	2,099

SOURCE: General Tax Relief: Impact on Canadian Families

- Is the student's description of the inferences or claims being made complete?

- Do you agree that the data support the claim?

Part B: Creating Graphical Data

4. The Article I used for this part of the project is attached as Appendix B at the end. This article is about how general tax cut would not really help the average family. The data supports these claims as it shows data shows that a middle income family would save $466, modest income families $145 and low income families only $26. This represents 75.5% of the families. The article states that the budget was supposed to help families with children, but instead it makes the rich richer by helping the most affluent save $2099 in taxes.

5. The data supports the claims. As an example Advantaged families earn on average $82,500, which is less than twice what Middle income families earn which is $52,500. The tax savings for advantaged income families are more than twice that of middle income families. This trend is seen with all the data so it shows that the budget is really helping the rich get richer.

6. See Graph on the next page.

7. I chose to use pie charts because people will be able to quickly compare the two charts and notice the differences in the size of the slice for each category.

8. Having both the graph and the numbers is very important. The graph let's one quickly see what is going on, and the numbers allows the person to look at the data more carefully if this is what was wanted.

7. Here is the set of graphs the student created.

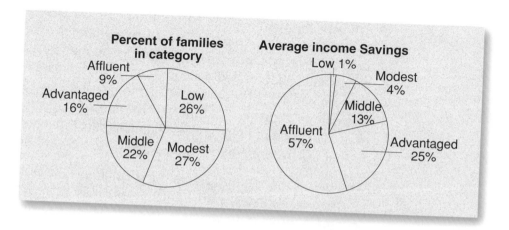

- Are the graphs appropriate to these data? Are they clear and easy to read?

- If you do not agree with the student's analysis explain.

- Suggest another type of graph you could use to present these data.

2

Non-Linear Functions

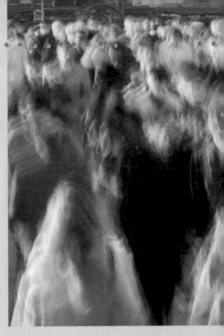

Overview

PROJECT

You should do at least one project that uses the skills you learn in this chapter. Recommended projects in the Project Book are:

- Video Game Design
- Hypothermia
- The Basketball Free Throw
- Radiometric Dating

The World's Population

The world's population has been increasing steadily for centuries, but it has never grown as rapidly as it has during the last 50 years. Many scientists are asking how many people Earth can support. Concern about world population is not new. In 1798 the economist Thomas Malthus published his *Essay on the Principle of Population as It Affects the Future Improvement of Society*. Malthus reasoned that the world population was doubling every 25 years, and the world's food supply would not be able to keep up with the demand.

You have probably heard the phrase "population explosion." The current population density, starving children, and inadequate supplies of clean water and suitable housing in many areas of the world make the study of the world's population growth crucial.

In this Project you will explore some of the mathematics of population growth. You will study different mathematical models that describe the growth of the world's population, write a short report on the subject, and create a poster display. Here are some initial questions to consider.

- Do you think the world's population will continue to grow indefinitely?

- Can the food supply grow at the same rate as the population?

- How is the huge growth in human population affecting Earth?

- What factors might slow down the growth of population?

Research world population. Sources of information include the Internet and the library. Books on biology and ecology might also be useful.

CHAPTER PROJECT

To complete this Chapter Project, you must be able to understand exponential and quadratic functions. Complete *Tutorials 2.1* and *2.2* to develop your skills. You will return to this Chapter Project on page 82 of this chapter.

FYI Visit: www.awl.com/canada/school/connections

You can start your research from our Internet site: Click on <u>MATHLINKS</u> followed by the *Applied Mathematics 11* logo. Then select a topic under World Population.

Exponential Graphs

You may recall from your work in grade 10 that in a *recursive table*, each row, after the first row, is defined in terms of preceding rows. In this Tutorial, you will study a special type of function that is used to represent growth or decay situations. The amount of growth or decay at a particular period is a fixed multiple of the preceding value.

For example, suppose a piece of paper is cut and the resulting pieces are stacked again. The number of layers of paper after any number of cuts is twice the number of layers before the last cut was made. The function that represents the number of layers of paper in the stack after n cuts is $f(n) = 2^n$.

Since the variable occurs in the exponent, this function is called an *exponential function*. Such functions are used to model growth and decay patterns in many fields, such as biology, chemistry, finance, and economics.

Practise Your Prior Skills

You will work with exponents and functions in this Tutorial. Try these exercises as preliminary review.

1. Use the laws of exponents to simplify each expression. Do not use a calculator.

a) $(x^3)^4$ **b)** $3y^0$ **c)** $\dfrac{(2x^5)(x^3)}{(6x^4)(x^7)}$ **d)** $3y^{-4}$

2. What are the domain and range of the following functions?

a) $f(x) = 2x + 4$ **b)** $g(x) = \sqrt{x - 1}$ **c)** $h(x) = x^2 + 2$

STUDENT REFERENCE

If you would like to review the "laws of exponents" or the "domain and range of a function," look in the Student Reference section of this book.

You will explore an application of exponential growth in the following Investigation.

Investigation 1 Insect Colonies

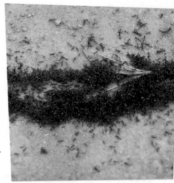

A colony of insects has a population of 500. The number of insects of this species doubles every 30 d.

1. Create a table in lists L1 and L2 of your calculator to show the numbers of insects in the colony after 0, 30, 60, 90, 120, and 150 d. Assume that no insect dies during this time. Enter time in days in L1 and number of insects in L2.

2. Create a scatterplot of the data. Set the window with $Ymin = 0$ and appropriate values for the remaining settings. Sketch or print your graph. Label the axes and show the scales.

3. The points on the scatterplot do not lie in a straight line. One method to determine the equation of the curve that passes through the points is to look at patterns in the data, then use algebraic reasoning.

The initial population (0 d) is 500.

After 30 d, the population is $500 \, (2) = 500 \times 2^1$.

After $2 \times 30 \, \text{d} \, (60 \, \text{d})$, the population is $(500 \times 2^1)(2) = 500 \times 2^2$.

After $3 \times 30 \, \text{d} \, (90 \, \text{d})$, the population is $(500 \times 2^2)(2) = 500 \times 2^3$.

After $n \times 30$ d, the population is $(500 \times 2^{n-1})(2) = 500 \times 2^n$.

Let $x = n \times 30$, so $n = \frac{x}{30}$.

After x days, the population is $500 \times 2^{\frac{x}{30}}$.

Graph the equation $y = 500 \times 2^{\frac{x}{30}}$. Verify that the curve passes through the points of the scatterplot from exercise 2.

Write this equation on your graph.

The equation is called an exponential growth equation. In this example, the *initial value* was 500, the *multiplication factor* is 2, and the *growth period* is 30 d. Note where these numbers appear in the equation.

4. If the colony had started with 600 insects, what equation would model the growth?

5. Your calculator will provide an equation for a curve that fits the data, using the regression feature. Use the exponential regression choice to determine the equation of best fit for the data. This equation will be different from the one derived in exercise 3.

UTILITY

If you have never used the exponential regression feature of a graphing calculator to determine an equation of best fit, Utility 18 shows you how to do this on the TI-83 calculator.

6. The calculated equation will give the same predicted value as the algebraic equation from exercise 3. Verify this by using each equation to predict the number of insects after 100 d.

The data you generated in *Investigation 1* were discrete. Next you will collect continuous data, then graph and describe them.

Cooling Temperatures

You will explore the relationship between temperature and time as an object cools. You will need:

- a CBL unit with a temperature probe. If this technology is unavailable, use a Celsius thermometer with a range that includes 0–100°C, and a stopwatch or clock that shows seconds

- hot water

- crushed ice

- a Thermos or insulated mug

- a container to hold hot water

Work in groups of 3.

Alert: You will use hot water: take care that no one is burned.

1. Fill a Thermos jug or insulated mug with crushed ice. Put the temperature probe of the CBL unit or the thermometer into the hot water (be careful not to burn anyone or to let the thermometer touch the bottom of the container). Keep the probe or thermometer in the water for approximately 30 s.

If you are using a thermometer, do exercises 2 and 3. If you are using a temperature probe with a CBL, continue with exercise 4.

2. One person will be the timer, calling out "now" every 10 s. One person will monitor the thermometer, calling out the temperatures. One person will be the recorder, writing down the readings. When the thermometer has risen to its maximum value, record this temperature, start the clock, and quickly transfer the thermometer into the crushed ice. Take readings every 10 s for 1 min as accurately as possible. Use a table similar to the one started below, and enter the data directly into the lists L1 and L2 of your calculator.

Time (s)	Temperature (°C)
0	
10	
20	
30	

3. Use the regression feature of the graphing calculator to determine the equation of the cooling curve you produced.

4. **With a CBL and temperature probe:** Make sure that your calculator contains the HEAT program available on the disk included with the CBL unit. Turn on the CBL and start the HEAT program. Enter 5 at the "HOW MUCH TIME" prompt to collect data every 5 s for 3 min. Start the CBL and immediately transfer the probe into the crushed ice. When the CBL has finished taking readings remove the probe from the ice. The program stores the data in your calculator. Sketch the graph you obtained in your notebook.

5. Use the regression feature of the calculator to determine the equation of the curve you produced. Graph the equation.

You should obtain an exponential decay graph similar to this one.

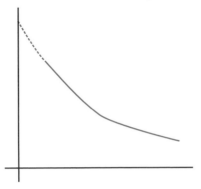

Once the equation of the exponential growth or decay is determined, it can be used to solve problems and make predictions.

The growth rate of a population is often expressed as a percent per year. Consequently the growth period is 1 year.

Example 1 Population Growth

The population of a city was growing at a rate of 5% annually. In 1990, the population was 500 000.

a) Create a table for the annual population of the city during the years 1990–1996.

b) Determine an exponential growth equation for this situation.

c) Select an appropriate window and graph the equation for years up to 2010.

d) Estimate the year when the population exceeds 1 000 000.

SOLUTION

a) The entries in the population column are related recursively. The population in any year is equal to the population from the preceding year plus 5% of the preceding year's population. That is, the population is 105% of the preceding year's population. So, multiply the preceding year's population by 1.05.

Year	Population
1990	500 000
1991	525 000
1992	551 250
1993	578 813
1994	607 754
1995	638 142
1996	670 049

b) The growth equation can be obtained by using either the regression feature of the calculator or algebraic reasoning.

Method 1: Use the regression feature.
Enter the data into the lists of the calculator and use the regression menu to choose ExpReg.
The equation is $y = 3.403\ 607 \times 10^{-37} \times 1.05^x$ ①

Method 2: Use algebraic reasoning.
The initial population is 500 000, the multiplication factor is 1.05, and the growth period is 1 year. The population, y, multiplies by 1.05 each year.

In 1990, the population is $y = 500\ 000$
In 1991, the population is $y = 500\ 000 \times 1.05$
In 1992, the population is $y = (500\ 000 \times 1.05) \times 1.05$
$$= 500\ 000 \times 1.05^2$$
In general, t years after 1990, $y = 500\ 000 \times 1.05^t$
Year x is $x - 1990$ years after 1990, so set $t = x - 1990$.
In year x, the population is $y = 500\ 000 \times 1.05^{x-1990}$ ②
Equations ① and ② are different. Both are correct and give equivalent predictions.

c) Choose a window. Set Xmin = 1990, Xmax = 2010, Xscl = 1, Ymin = 0, Ymax = 1 500 000, and Yscl = 100 000. Graph the equation.

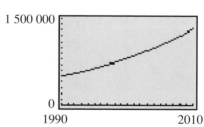

If you used *method 1* in part b, turn off the plot. Use the graph and TRACE to determine the approximate population in 2010. This is 1 326 649, or about 1 300 000. If a regression equation is used, substitute $x = 2010$ into the equation and use a calculator to obtain a population of approximately 1 300 000.

d) To estimate the year when the population exceeds 1 000 000 use the TRACE feature. Move the cursor until you see the Y-coordinate, displayed at the bottom of the screen, just exceed 1 000 000. This occurs when X = 2004.25. The year will be 2004. If a regression equation is used, substitute different values for x into the regression equation. Use trial and error to obtain the value $x = 2004$.

As a radioactive isotope emits radiation, its quantity decreases. The isotope decays into other isotopes. The *half-life* of an isotope is the time taken (on average) for one-half of the isotope to decay. Different isotopes may have radically different half-lives. For example, sodium-24 has a half-life of 15 h, whereas uranium-235 has a half-life of 713 million *years*. The reduction of an isotope over time is called *radioactive decay* and is modelled by an exponential decay curve.

Example 2   Radioactive Decay

The half-life of sodium-24 is approximately 15 h.

a) Determine an exponential decay equation for sodium-24 that models the percent of sodium-24 remaining.

b) Determine the percent of a sample of sodium-24 that remains after 24 h.

SOLUTION

a) *Method 1: Use the calculator.*
Create a table of values. Because we are working with percents, assume there is 100 g of sodium-24 initially.

Time (h)	Mass Remaining (g)
0	100.0
15	50.0
30	25.0
45	12.5
60	6.25

Enter these numbers in the lists L1 and L2 of a graphing calculator. Graph the points.

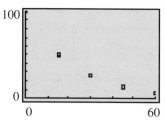

Use the exponential regression feature to obtain the equation of an exponential curve of best fit for the data. This is $y = 100(0.954\ 841\ 603\ 9)^x$, where x is the time in hours, and y is the portion of sodium-24 remaining.

Method 2: *Use reasoning*.
The initial quantity of sodium-24 is 100 g.
The isotope is reduced by one-half each period, so the *multiplying factor* is 0.5.
The *period* (in this case the *decay period*) is the half-life of the isotope, 15 h.
The decay equation is: $A = 100(0.5)^{\frac{t}{15}}$, where A is the amount remaining after t hours.

b) To obtain the amount remaining after 24 h, use the graph of the exponential function and the TRACE feature, or substitute $t = 24$ in either regression equation. The mass remaining after 24 h is about 33 g. Since we began with 100 g, the percent remaining is about 33%.

A general equation for exponential growth and decay may be given by $A = PM^{\frac{t}{T}}$, where A is the amount after time t units, P is the initial amount, M is the multiplication factor, and T is the growth or decay period.

DISCUSSING THE IDEAS

1. Compare the two equations in *Example 1*. Describe how they differ. Explain how you manipulate one equation to get the other.

2. In *Investigation 2*, the graphs display a series of points. Why is it appropriate to join these points?

3. In *Example 1*, explain why the exponent was changed from "t" to "$x - 1990$."

4. Consider the equations you obtained using the calculator and ExpReg in *Example 1* and *Example 2*. What distinguishes a growth equation from a decay equation?

5. Consider the equations obtained using algebraic reasoning in *Example 1* and *Example 2*. What distinguishes a growth equation from a decay equation?

6. When you input an exponential equation from algebraic reasoning in *Example 2* into the calculator, the exponent must be in brackets. Why?

7. Exponential growth and decay depend upon the growth or decay rates remaining constant. Discuss the limitations of an exponential model for population growth.

EXERCISES

Checking Your Skills

1. A certain strain of bacteria doubles every 5 h. An initial count showed 2000 bacteria.

   a) Create a table to show the population size every 5 h for a total of 25 h.

   b) Determine an exponential equation to represent this situation.

   c) Graph the growth curve up to 25 h. Sketch or print the graph. Indicate the window settings you used.

   d) Determine the number of bacteria after 12 h and after 24 h.

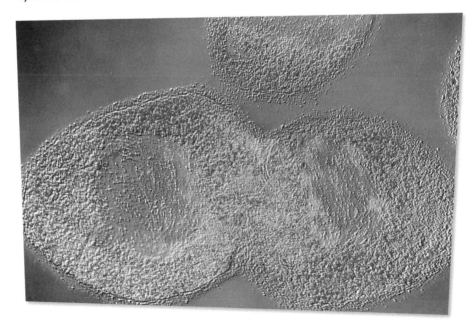

2. This table contains estimates of the world's population from the year 1650 to 1988.

Date	Population
1650	500 000 000
1850	1 100 000 000
1930	2 000 000 000
1950	2 500 000 000
1970	3 600 000 000
1988	5 100 000 000

a) Graph the data.

b) Determine an exponential equation that best describes the population growth.

c) Estimate when the population reached 4 billion.

d) Predict the present world population. Explain why the exponential equation gives a poor prediction.

e) Repeat parts b and d using data from 1930 onward.

3. The population of a particular city grows 3.5% per year. In 1995, the population was 2.3 million.

a) Create a table to show the population every year from 1995 to 2010.

b) Determine the growth equation for this population.

c) Graph the growth curve up to the year 2010. Sketch or print the graph. Indicate the window settings you chose.

d) Predict the population in the year 2015 if the growth rate remains unchanged.

e) Estimate the year when the population first exceeded 5 million.

4. Carbon-14 is a radioactive form of carbon. It is used by scientists to determine the age of organic objects. The half-life of carbon-14 is 5700 years.

a) Determine an equation that represents the percent of carbon-14 remaining in a given sample of material after t years.

b) Graph the equation in part a for up to 30 000 years.

c) Determine the percent of carbon-14 remaining in a sample of material after 20 000 years.

d) Estimate the age of an object that shows 40% of carbon-14 remaining in a sample.

5. The following graph shows the decay of strontium-90.

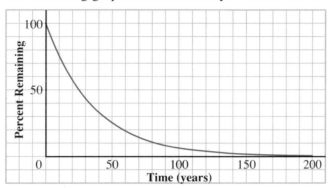

a) Estimate the half-life of strontium-90.

b) Estimate the percent of strontium-90 remaining after 100 years.

c) Estimate how long it takes for strontium-90 to decay to 10% of its original mass.

6. The growth of a $7000 investment is shown in the table.

Time (years)	Value ($)
0	7 000
1	7 630
2	8 317
3	9 065
4	9 881
5	10 770

a) Plot the data and determine the equation that represents the growth of the investment.

b) Estimate the time needed for the investment to double.

c) Determine the value of the investment after 12 years.

7. A herd of caribou, known as the Kaminuriak, ranges in the Northwest Territories, west of Hudson Bay. After decades of decline, a census in 1980 indicated a population of 39 000 animals. In the next five years, the population increased dramatically, as indicated in the table below.

Years since 1980	0	1	2	3	4	5
Population (thousands)	39	60	91	138	210	320

a) Plot the data and determine an exponential equation that represents the population growth.

b) Use the graph of the growth equation to estimate the size of the herd in 1990.

Extending Your Thinking

$$T = A(B^t) + C$$

8. Newton's Law of Cooling may be expressed as
$$T = A(B^t) + C,$$
where T is the temperature in degrees Celsius, A is the difference between the environmental temperature and the original temperature of the cooling object, B is a constant that depends upon the material being cooled and its container, C is the environmental temperature, and t is the time in seconds.

a) Water cooling in a glass beaker has a cooling constant of 0.992. Water was heated to the boiling point of 100°C. It was then taken off the heat and allowed to sit in a room at 24°C. Write an equation for the cooling curve. Graph this equation on a calculator. Use the graph to determine how long it would take the water to cool to body temperature (37°C).

b) In *Investigation 2*, a thermometer with a temperature reading of 100°C was cooled in an environment of 0°C. The cooling constant in this environment is 0.9943. Write the cooling equation.

PROJECT

In this Tutorial you worked with exponential data. The skills and concepts you used relate to the Chapter Project, and to the following projects in the Project Book:

• Hypothermia

• Radiometric Dating

COMMUNICATING THE IDEAS

Describe the similarities and differences between exponential growth equations and exponential decay equations. Use examples to illustrate your ideas.

Quadratic Graphs

What do the path of a baseball, the revenue from tickets to a hockey game, the height of a springboard diver above the water, and business profits have in common? All of them produce the same type of graph. In this Tutorial, you will investigate the characteristics of these graphs.

Investigation 1 **What Goes Up**

An object is thrown vertically upward, then allowed to fall. You will investigate the relationship between the object's height above the ground and its time in the air.

If you have access to either a CBR or CBL unit with a motion sensor, complete Part A; otherwise, complete Part B.

Part A Using a CBR or CBL
You will need a CBL or CBR unit, the program BALLDROP in a graphing calculator, a small soft pillow, and a stopwatch or a clock that displays seconds. Work in pairs.

1. One person operates the motion detector, the other throws up the soft pillow. Place the motion detector on the floor.

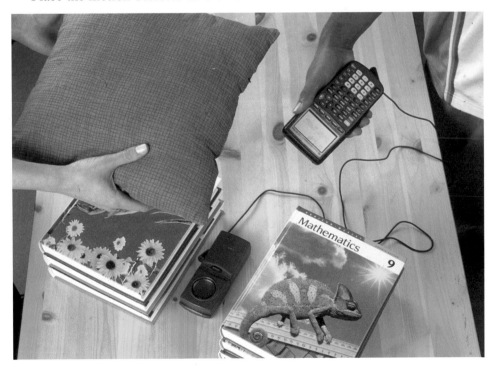

2. Start the BALLDROP program on the calculator; (data collection begins when you press [TRIGGER] on the CBL or CBR). As [TRIGGER] is pressed, the person with the pillow should hold it steady for a moment, then throw it straight up, directly above the motion detector. Allow it to drop onto the unit (a soft pillow will not damage the detector). Estimate the maximum height, in metres, that the pillow reaches, and how long the pillow was in the air.

3. Experiment a few times until you have obtained a good set of data. The calculator will plot a series of dots. Sketch the graph.

4. Use the TRACE feature of the calculator and move the cursor to the highest point on your graph. Record the coordinates. Compare the y-coordinate at the bottom of your screen to the estimated maximum height reached by the cushion.

5. Use the TRACE feature to move the cursor to the x-intercept on the right of the graph. Compare the x-coordinate of this point to the time the cushion was in the air.

Part B Without a CBR or CBL

In a science experiment, a ball was thrown vertically upward. Stroboscopic camera equipment recorded its height every 0.2 s. The table below gives these heights.

1. Graph the data on a graphing calculator. Sketch or print out the graph. The points appear to lie on a smooth curve. Sketch a curve through the points.

Time (s)	Height Above the Ground (m)
0.0	0.0
0.2	1.8
0.4	3.2
0.6	4.2
0.8	4.8
1.0	5.0
1.2	4.8
1.4	4.2
1.6	3.2
1.8	1.8
2.0	0.0

2. What are the coordinates of the maximum point of the graph? How does this point relate to the maximum height reached by the ball?

3. Estimate how long it took the ball to reach one-half its maximum height.

4. Determine the coordinates of the *x*-intercept. Relate it to the time the ball was in the air.

5. What is the relation between the *x*-coordinate of the maximum point of the graph and the total time the ball was in the air?

Investigation 1 produced a curve called a *parabola*. The function that produces this graph, a quadratic function, increases to a maximum, then decreases. Other quadratic functions produce parabolas that decrease to a minimum point, then increase.

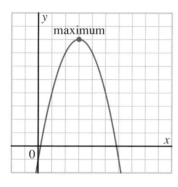
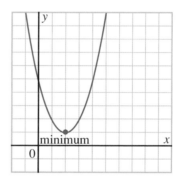

> The equation of a **quadratic function** is $y = ax^2 + bx + c$, where a, b, and c are constants, and $a \neq 0$.
>
> The graph of every quadratic function is a curve called a *parabola*.

Next you will explore the graphs of quadratic functions.

Investigation 2 **The Characteristics of Quadratic Graphs**

Set the window on your calculator to Xmin = −9.4, Xmax = 9.4, Xscl = 1, Ymin = −6, Ymax = 6, and Yscl = 1.

1. Use the [Y=] key to graph the function $y = x^2 - 4x + 3$.

    a) What is the shape of the graph? Does it have a maximum or a minimum point?

b) Locate the two points where the graph intersects the x-axis. Record the coordinates of these points from the display at the bottom of the screen. What is the y-value for each of these points? The x-coordinates of these points are the *zeros* of the function. You can determine the zeros using the CALC menu and a method similar to that used in *Investigation 1*.

UTILITY

If you need help using the CALC feature of your calculator, refer to Utility 19 for the TI-83. If you are using another calculator, consult your handbook.

c) Locate the point where the graph meets the y-axis. Record its coordinates. What is the x-coordinate of this point? What is the value of the constant term in the given equation? Explain the relationship between these two values.

d) Use TRACE and CALC to find the coordinates of the minimum point on this graph. Record these coordinates (m, n).

e) The DRAW feature of the calculator enables you to graph horizontal and vertical lines. To draw a horizontal line press 2nd DRAW **3**. Enter a number, for example 5, and the calculator draws the horizontal line $y = 5$. To draw a vertical line, choose **4** from the DRAW menu. Enter a number, for example -6, and the calculator draws the vertical line $x = -6$. Clear the lines by selecting **1**: ClrDraw from the DRAW menu. Refer to part d. Draw:

  i) the horizontal line $y = m$ **ii)** the horizontal line $y = n$
  iii) the vertical line $x = m$ **iv)** the vertical line $x = n$

Which of the above lines is a line of symmetry for the parabola? Write the equation of this line.

f) The domain of this graph is all the real numbers. What is the range?

2. Repeat exercise 1 for each equation. You may wish to record your answers in a table.

  i) $y = -x^2 - 2x + 3$ **ii)** $y = x^2 - 4x + 7$
  iii) $y = 5x^2 - 10x + 5$ **iv)** $y = -2x^2$
  v) $y = -0.5x^2 - 1$ **vi)** $y = -3x^2 - 2x + 1$

The *zeros* of a quadratic function are the x-coordinates of the points where the function intersects the x-axis. They are the x-intercepts of the graph, and may be found by equating y to 0. The maximum or minimum point on a parabola is the *vertex*. The *axis of symmetry* is a vertical line through the vertex of the parabola. If the vertex is located at a point (m, n), the equation of the axis of symmetry is $x = m$.

DISCUSSING THE IDEAS

1. In *Investigation 1*, how would you label the x- and y-axes to represent the real quantities measured? What does the x-coordinate of the maximum point represent? What does the y-coordinate of the maximum point represent?

2. In *Investigation 1*, Part B, why was Xmin chosen to be zero?

3. Consider *Investigation 2*. Does a quadratic function always have two zeros? Explain your answer using examples.

4. Look at the equation in *Investigation 2*. How can you tell whether the graph of the function has a maximum or a minimum?

5. By looking at the equation, how can you tell what the y-intercept is?

6. Will the graph of a quadratic function always have exactly one y-intercept? Explain.

7. Why is the domain of a quadratic function always all the real numbers?

8. Suppose a parabola has a minimum point at (3, –4). What is the range of the function the parabola represents?

EXERCISES

Checking Your Skills

1. **a)** Is each function quadratic? Explain.

   i) $y = 3x^2 + 2x + 5$ **ii)** $y = 25 - x^2$

   iii) $y = 2x^3 - 1$ **iv)** $y = \sqrt{x^3 + 1}$

   v) $y = x^2 + \sqrt{x}$ **vi)** $y = \frac{1}{x}$

   b) From part a, choose one quadratic function and one function that is not quadratic. Explain how you identified each function.

2. Identify each of the following for each graph below:

   i) the coordinates of the vertex

   ii) the equation of the axis of symmetry

   iii) the intercepts

   iv) the domain and range

a)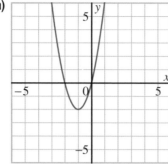

b)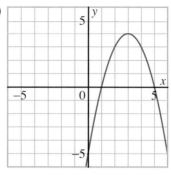

c)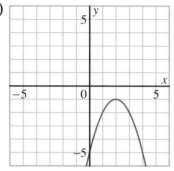

d)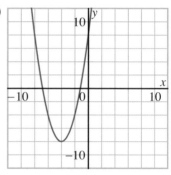

3. Graph the following functions using a graphing calculator. Choose window settings that display the vertex and the x- and y-intercepts. Sketch or print the graphs. Identify the equation of the axis of symmetry, the coordinates of the vertex, the intercepts, the domain, and the range for each graph.

a) $y = 2x^2 + 5x - 3$

b) $y = -5x^2 - 10x + 30$

c) $y = x^2 - 7x + 10$

d) $y = 8 - 31x - 4x^2$

e) $y = 3 + 2x - 0.5x^2$

f) $f(x) = 6 + 3x - 3x^2$

4. Determine the zeros of each function.

a) $f(x) = x^2 + 4x - 12$

b) $y = 8 - 31x - 4x^2$

c) $g(x) = 5 - 11x + 2x^2$

d) $y = 6x^2 - 6x - 12$

5. A rock is dropped from a bridge into a river. Its height, h metres, above the river t seconds after it is released is modelled by the quadratic function $h(t) = 82 - 4.9t^2$.

a) Graph the function for reasonable values of t.

b) State the domain and the range of the function.

c) How high is the rock after 2.5 s?

6. When a flare is fired vertically upward, its height, h metres, after t seconds is modelled by the function $h(t) = -4.9t^2 + 153.2t$.

a) Graph the function. Adjust the window settings, if necessary, to show the vertex and zeros of the function.

b) What are the coordinates of the vertex?

c) For how many seconds is the flare higher than 1 km?

d) Estimate the domain and range of the function.

Extending Your Thinking

7. Graph the function $y = (x - 1)(x - 5)$.

a) What kind of function is it?

b) What are the zeros of this function?

c) What is the equation of the axis of symmetry for this function?

d) Without graphing, determine the zero and the equation of the axis of symmetry for the following functions.

    i) $y = (x - 3)(x - 7)$ **ii)** $y = (x + 2)(x - 6)$

PROJECT

In this Tutorial, you analyzed the characteristics of a quadratic graph. The skills and concepts you used relate to the following projects in the Project Book:

- Video Game Design
- The Basketball Free Throw

COMMUNICATING THE IDEAS

Explain the meaning of each term: quadratic function; maximum; minimum; vertex; zeros of a quadratic function; parabola; axis of symmetry; y-intercept.

Modelling the Growth of the World's Population

At this stage of the Project you will study and interpret graphs that describe various aspects of the growth of the world's population.

CHAPTER PROJECT

In the next stage of this Chapter Project you will investigate a mathematical model for world population growth that accounts for a maximum population being reached. *Tutorials 2.3* and *2.4* will help you develop an understanding of the related skills. You will return to this Chapter Project on page 104.

1. The table below shows life expectancy and infant mortality for various regions of the world.

Life Expectancy at Birth in 1998

	Infant Mortality (deaths per 100 live births)	Life Expectancy (years)
Western Europe	6	78
North America	6	76
Latin America and Caribbean	33	69
Near East and North Africa	51	68
Asia	59	65
Sub-Saharan Africa	92	49

Represent these data in a graph.

2. According to United Nations predictions, Earth can be expected to support up to 20 billion people. The graph on page 85 describes the world's population in billions as a curve, and the population increase (from the preceding decade), in millions, as a bar graph.

   a) What time period does each bar represent?

   b) Estimate the world's population in the year 2000.

   c) During which decade did the world's population reach approximately 5 billion people?

   d) Estimate when the world's population is predicted to reach 8 billion people?

e) When was the greatest increase in population? What was that increase?

f) Suppose the trend for the increase of population continues past 2050. Describe how this will affect the shape of the population curve.

g) Suppose the line graph became horizontal. What would this represent? What would the bar graph look like in this instance?

h) Use the graph to describe any trends in the world's population.

3. The curve in exercise 2 resembles an exponential curve. Exponential equations are often used to model world population. In 1950, the world's population was approximately 2.56 billion and was growing at a rate of about 1.47% per year.

a) Assume this growth rate continues. Write an exponential equation that models the world's population, P, for n years after 1950.

b) Use a calculator to graph the equation in part a for the years 1950 to 2050. Print or sketch the graph.

c) Use this model to predict the world's population in 2000, 2010, 2020, and 2100.

d) Use TRACE on the calculator to predict the year when the population of the world will exceed 8 billion.

4. The table below is from the U.S. Census Bureau. It shows the world's population and growth rate from 1950, and includes the projected figures up to 2020.

Year	Population (billions)	Growth Rate (%)
1950	2.56	1.47
1960	3.04	1.33
1970	3.71	2.07
1980	4.45	1.69
1990	5.28	1.55
2000	6.07	1.25
2010	6.83	1.11
2020	7.56	0.90

Investigate how the predictions in exercise 3 may change when different data are used. Use the data for 1960, and repeat for at least one other year. You will use this table again when you return to the project on page 104.

5. Predictions of the world's population depend upon the growth rate. The U.S. Census Bureau table in exercise 4 indicates that this rate is expected to drop. Briefly describe factors that might cause significant changes in the world's growth rate and the limitations of using exponential models for the world's population growth. Save your graphs and writing to use as part of your final project presentation.

Career Skills

When modelling a situation using mathematics, investigators graph results and use the regression capabilities of a calculator or software to obtain an equation.

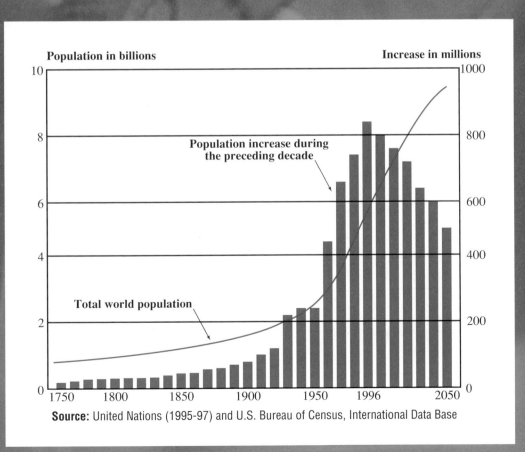

Population in billions

Increase in millions

Population increase during
the preceding decade

Total world population

Source: United Nations (1995-97) and U.S. Bureau of Census, International Data Base

In this Tutorial you will use quadratic functions to solve problems in business, science, and sports.

Have you ever wanted to attend a concert or game but found that the tickets were too expensive? The arena or concert hall manager tries to determine the ticket price that will maximize revenue. If she sets the price too low, revenue will be low even if all the tickets are sold. If she sets the price too high, people will not buy the tickets and, again, revenue will be low.

Example 1 Ticket prices

A hockey arena has 1600 seats. When the price of a ticket is $10, all seats are sold for every game. The manager needs to increase the revenue from the sale of tickets, so she commissions a survey to predict ticket sales for different ticket prices. The results are shown in the table below.

Ticket Price ($)	Expected Sales
10	1600
15	1300
20	1015
25	590

a) Draw a graph to illustrate the expected revenue for the different ticket prices.

b) Use the graph to determine the ticket price that will produce the maximum revenue.

SOLUTION

a) The graph illustrates the expected revenue against the ticket price. Create a table of values in lists L1 and L2 of your calculator. The ticket prices are in list L1. The revenue (price of a ticket × number of tickets sold) is in list L2.

L1	L2
10	16000
15	19500
20	20300
25	14750

Graph these data. A suitable window has settings Xmin = 0, Xmax = 30, Xscl = 2, Ymin = 0, Ymax = 22000, Yscl = 2000.

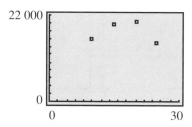

b) To predict the maximum revenue, we need the best-fit graph for the data. The points appear to lie on a parabola, so try a quadratic regression. Press [STAT] [▶] 5 [ENTER] to obtain the screen below.

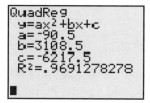

Graph the equation using the Y= list.
Press [Y=] [CLEAR] [VARS] 5 [▶] [▶] [1]

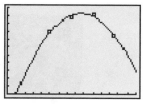

Turn off STAT PLOT. Press [GRAPH].
Determine the maximum using the TRACE and CALC features. The maximum occurs when $x = 17.17$ and $y = 20\ 475$.
The manager should charge about $17 to produce a maximum revenue of about $20 475.

In *Tutorial 2.2* you saw that a quadratic function models the height of an object above the ground at specified times, if the object is thrown vertically upward. The graph of the function is a parabola that relates the height, h, above the ground to the elapsed time, t. This parabola is *not* a graph of the path of the object in the air. The graph of the path of the object is shown at the top of the next page. Note the different horizontal scales of the two graphs.

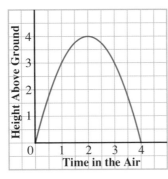

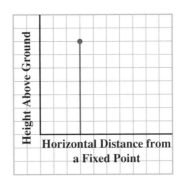

In *Example 2*, you will use a formula from physics that relates the height of an object thrown upward to the time.

The height of a projectile, h metres above the ground, at time t seconds, is given by the equation

$$h = -\frac{1}{2}gt^2 + vt + s$$

where g is the acceleration due to gravity (9.8 m/s^2 on Earth); v is the initial vertical velocity in metres per second; and s is the initial height above the ground in metres.

Example 2 The height of a projectile

Annie Pelletier won a bronze medal in the women's springboard competition at the 1996 Summer Olympics in Atlanta. Pelletier somersaults from a 3-m springboard, with an initial upward velocity of 8.8 m/s.

a) Use the general formula given to determine the equation that models the height above the water, h metres, at time t seconds after she leaves the diving board.

b) Graph this equation on a calculator.

c) Use the graph to determine Annie's maximum height, and the time taken to reach this height.

d) Use the graph to determine the time Annie is in the air.

SOLUTION

a) Use the equation $h = -\frac{1}{2}gt^2 + vt + s$ for height. Acceleration due to gravity, g, is 9.8 m/s². The initial velocity, v, is 8.8 m/s, and the initial height, s is 3 m. The equation is: $h = -4.9t^2 + 8.8t + 3$.

b) Choose a window for the graph. Since we record time from 0, choose Xmin = 0, Xmax = 3.5, Xscl = 0.5. Set Ymin = 0 to represent the water level. The initial height is 3 m. This example considers a diver jumping upward, use Ymax = 7, Yscl = 1. Enter the equation from part a in the Y= list. The graph is shown.

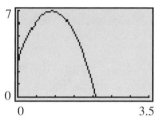

In parts c and d, when you press TRACE for this graph the bottom right of the graph is covered with the display for Y= . Also, the top of the graph is covered by the equation. Adjust the window by choosing a greater value for Ymax and a negative value for Ymin. Try Ymin = −2 and Ymax = 8. (Remember when you choose a window, you may need to adjust your settings by trial and error until you obtain a good result such as the one below.)

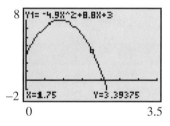

c) To find the maximum height and the time to reach this height, use the TRACE or CALC feature of the calculator. The maximum height is given by the y-coordinate of the vertex and the time to reach this height is given by the x-coordinate of the vertex. The maximum height, 6.95 m above the water, is reached 0.9 s after takeoff.

d) The time in the air is given by the x-coordinate of the point that represents the diver hitting the water. This is the value of x for which $y = 0$: the *zero* of the function. Use either the TRACE or the CALC feature of the calculator. The time in the air is 2.09 s.

1. In *Example 1*, why was quadratic regression chosen?

2. In *Example 2*, how would the equation change if Annie Pelletier had dived off a 5-m board with an initial speed of 7.2 m/s?

3. In *Example 2*, what do negative values of y represent? Would the equation still be correct for negative values of y? Explain.

E X E R C I S E S

Checking Your Skills

1. Use the formula $h = -\frac{1}{2}gt^2 + vt + s$. Determine the equation for the height, h metres, of a projectile after time t seconds, for each set of conditions.

   a) Initial height 50 m, initial vertical velocity 20 m/s upward, on Earth ($g = 9.8$ m/s^2).

   b) Initial height ground level, initial vertical velocity 10 m/s upward, on Earth.

   c) Initial height 3000 m, the projectile drops directly downward, on Earth.

   d) Initial height ground level, initial speed 50 m/s upward, on the Moon ($g = 1.63$ m/s^2).

2. Determine the quadratic regression equation that represents the data in each table. Does each function have a maximum or a minimum?

a)

x	y
0	1
0.5	−1
1	−2
2	−1

b)

x	y
0	0
5	75
12	96
10	100

c)

x	y
−1	18
2	0
4	−2
7	10

d)

x	y
2	180
5	375
10	500
20	0

3. A company sells canoes for $500 each At this price it can sell 60 canoes in a season, generating revenue of $30 000. To increase revenue, management is planning to increase the selling price. It estimates that for every $50 increase in price, the number of canoes sold will drop by 4.

   a) Copy and complete this table.

Price per Canoe ($)	500	550	600	650
Canoes Sold	60	56	52	48
Total Revenue ($)	60 × 500 = 30 000			

b) Determine the quadratic regression equation for the total revenue as a function of the selling price.

c) Graph the quadratic regression equation.

d) Calculate the selling price that will give the maximum revenue. What is this revenue?

4. A company that charters a boat for tours around the Gulf Islands can sell 200 tickets at $50 each. For every $10 increase in the ticket price, 5 fewer tickets will be sold.

a) Copy and complete this table. Find the quadratic regression equation for the total revenue as a function of the ticket price.

Price per Ticket ($)	50	60	70	80	90
Number of Tickets Sold	200	195	190	185	180
Total Revenue ($)	10 000				

b) Graph the quadratic regression equation.

c) Calculate the selling price that will give maximum revenue. What is this revenue?

5. "The Rock" is an indoor climbing wall that has been operating for one year. The following table shows the monthly profits, as well as the accumulated profit each month. A negative value indicates a loss.

Month	Monthly Profit ($)	Net Profit ($)
1	−2 500	−2 500
2	−2 200	−4 700
3	−1 900	−6 600
4	−1 600	−8 200
5	−1 300	−9 500
6	−1 000	−10 500
7	−700	−11 200
8	−400	−11 600
9	−100	−11 700
10	200	−11 500
11	500	−11 000
12	800	−10 200

a) Enter the data in a graphing calculator, with months in list L1 and net profit in list L2.

b) Determine the quadratic regression equation for the data, then graph the data.

c) Suppose this trend continues. Estimate how long it will take this business to make a net profit.

d) Suppose this trend continues. Estimate the profit at the end of 20 months.

6. In the case of a forced landing, private and military aircraft often carry a flare pistol that can be fired to attract the attention of rescuers. The height of the flare above the ground is a function of the elapsed time since firing. A typical flare is projected with an initial speed of 100 m/s.

a) Use the formula $h = -\frac{1}{2}gt^2 + vt + s$ to determine the equation of a flare that is shot upward from sea level.

b) This function models how the height of the flare varies with time, from the time it is fired until it hits the ground. Graph this function, then sketch the graph.

c) Determine the maximum height of the flare.

d) Determine how long the flare is in the air.

e) How much higher will a flare rise if its initial speed is 153 m/s?

7. A diver dives into the sea at Alcapulco from a height of 35 m. His initial speed is 1 m/s upward.

a) Use the formula $h = -\frac{1}{2}gt^2 + vt + s$ to determine the equation of the height of the diver.

b) Graph the equation in part a.

c) Determine the maximum height of the diver above sea level.

d) Determine how long the diver is in the air.

In your work so far, you have graphed parabolas that related height above the ground to time. These parabolas are not trajectories. A *trajectory* is the actual path of the object moving through the air. It relates the height above the ground to the horizontal distance travelled, and it *does* illustrate the path of a moving object.

8. A long jumper reaches a maximum height of 0.73 m before landing 6.8 m from where she started her jump. Assume that her trajectory is a parabola.

a) List three points on her trajectory that can be plotted on the calculator.

b) Use the quadratic regression feature of the calculator to determine the equation of the parabola that models the trajectory.

c) Graph the trajectory on your calculator, then sketch the graph.

9. A high school football player made a 45-yard kickoff. The football reached a maximum height of 4.2 yards. Assume that its trajectory is a parabola.

a) List three points on its trajectory and plot them on the calculator.

b) Determine the equation of the parabola that models the trajectory.

c) Graph the trajectory.

10. The trajectory of a snow boarder who jumps from a 2.5-m jump is given by the equation $h = -0.11d^2 + 0.56d + 2.5$, where h is the height in metres and d is the horizontal distance in metres.

   a) Graph the trajectory.

   b) What is the maximum height reached?

   c) How far is the jump?

11. The trajectory of a certain basketball shot can be represented by the equation $h = -0.088d^2 + 0.92d + 2.5$, where h is the height in metres, and d is the horizontal distance in metres of the ball from the player.

   a) Graph the trajectory.

   b) What is the maximum height reached by the ball?

   c) How far had the ball travelled horizontally when it reached its maximum height?

   d) What was the initial height of the ball?

Extending Your Thinking

12. A stone is dropped down a well that is 10-m deep. How much time elapses until the stone hits the water?

PROJECT

In this Tutorial you solved problems using a quadratic function. The skills and concepts you used relate to the following projects in the Project Book:

• Video Game Design

• The Basketball Free Throw

COMMUNICATING THE IDEAS

The vertex of a parabola is an important point. Write a paragraph to explain its importance. Use examples to illustrate your explanation.

Solving Non-Linear Equations Using a Graphing Calculator

In this Tutorial, you will study situations that result in an equation that is non-linear. You will use graphical and numerical methods to solve such equations.

Investigation 1 **Intersecting Graphs**

You will investigate two methods for solving a non-linear equation.

Method 1:

1. Graph the functions $y = x^2$ and $y = 2x + 5$ on the same screen. These functions form a *non-linear system*. A *system of equations* is a set of two or more equations that are considered simultaneously.

2. Locate all the intersection points. How do you know that there are not any more? If necessary, adjust your graphing window to show the intersection points as clearly as possible.

3. Find the coordinates of the intersection points to the nearest hundredths. You may use the TABLE feature of your calculator, or the TRACE and CALC features.

UTILITY

Utility 19 shows you how to use the TRACE and CALC feature on the TI-83 calculator. If you are using a different calculator, refer to your User's Manual.

Method 2:

4. Clear the Y= list. Graph the function $y = x^2 - 2x - 5$. This new function was obtained by subtracting $y = 2x + 5$ from $y = x^2$ and then simplifying. What does it mean when $y > 0$? When $y < 0$?

5. Determine, to the nearest hundredths, the values of x for which $y = 0$. The values of x for which a function $y = f(x)$ has a value of 0 are called the *zeros* of the function. How do the zeros relate to the x-intercepts of the graph?

6. How do the values you found in exercise 5 relate to those in exercise 2?

7. Describe two methods of solving the equation $x^2 = 5x - 4$.

8. Test the methods you described in exercise 7 by solving the following equations.

a) $3x^2 + 2 = -7x$

b) $4x + 5 = 2^x$

In real situations, data are often presented in tabular form. It may be difficult to model a problem algebraically, especially if the data are non-linear. The graphing calculator has several regression functions that can be used to develop a suitable model. In an earlier grade, you used the linear regression technique to determine the equation of a line of best fit for data.

Investigation 2 — Modelling Real Situations Using Regression Techniques

You will use the regression functions of the graphing calculator to derive an algebraic model for data. Work in groups of three. Each of you should complete one of these activities.

UTILITY

If you have never used the regression functions to determine a possible algebraic representation of data, Utility 18 shows you how to do this on a TI-83 calculator. If you are using a different calculator, consult the User's Manual.

A. A certain telecommunications system requires subscribers to be linked to every other subscriber in the community. This can be represented pictorially as shown below for communities of 2, 3, 4, and 5 subscribers.

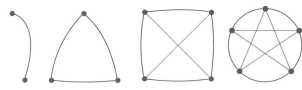

a) Create a table listing the number of subscribers for up to 7 subscribers and the corresponding number of links. Enter the data in lists L1 and L2 of the graphing calculator.

b) Graph the data using the STAT PLOT menu.

c) Use the STAT CALC menu to determine a possible algebraic representation for the data. Experiment by graphing the various regression curves to investigate how well each fits the data.

d) When you obtain a regression curve that you think best fits the data, record the equation and the graph in your notebook.

B. A packaging company has large quantities of cardboard measuring 28 cm long and 21 cm wide. Each piece is used to make a box with no top. Equal squares are cut from the corners and the sides are folded up. When 5-cm squares are removed, the box measures 18 cm by 11 cm by 5 cm and has a volume of 990 cm^3.

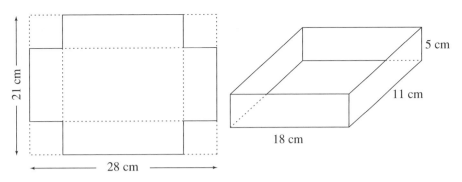

a) Visualize how the shape and volume of the box changes when squares of other sizes are removed.

b) Create a table listing the side length of the square removed and the corresponding volume, for squares from 1 cm to 10 cm. Enter the data in lists L1 and L2 of the graphing calculator.

c) Graph the data using the STAT PLOT menu.

d) Use the STAT CALC menu to determine a possible algebraic representation for the data. Experiment by graphing the various regression curves to investigate how well each fits the data.

e) When you have determined a regression curve that you think best fits the data, record the equation and graph in your notebook.

C. Streptococci bacteria cause many infections, such as "strep throat." After a person has been infected, the bacteria can double in number every 20 min. Consider the initial number of bacteria to be 100.

a) Create a table listing the time in 20-min intervals for 2 h and the corresponding number of bacteria present. Enter the data in lists L1 and L2 of a graphing calculator.

b) Graph the data using the STAT PLOT menu.

c) Use the STAT CALC menu to determine a possible algebraic representation of these data. Experiment by graphing the regression equations to investigate how well the regression curve fits the data.

d) When you have determined a regression curve that you think best fits the data, record the equation and graph in your notebook.

1. Share your results with the other members of your group.

2. The telecommunications company has material for 200 links. Use the results of activity A to write an equation to represent this situation. What is the largest community that can be served by the company so that all subscribers are linked to one another?

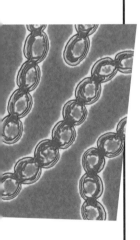

3. The packaging company has an order for open rectangular boxes with a volume of 750 cm^3. Use the results of activity B to write an equation to represent the situation. Determine the dimensions of the boxes that have a volume of 750 cm^3.

4. A medical researcher needs to determine when a streptococcal infection has 10 000 bacteria. Use the results of activity C to write an equation to represent the situation. Determine the number of minutes from the time when 100 bacteria are present until there are 10 000.

5. Choose one of activities A, B, or C. Use a different method to solve the equation.

6. Compare your two solutions to the same activity. Which method gives a solution that results in fewer rounding errors and other inaccuracies?

The term with the greatest exponent, or exponent sum, determines the *degree* of the equation. An equation of degree *n* may have up to *n* real solutions. Graphing is a method that can always be used to determine real solutions of an equation.

Example   **Solve a non-linear equation using a graphing calculator**

Solve the equation $x^3 + x = 20$ graphically.

SOLUTION

Method 1

Rearrange the equation to obtain zero on one side: $x^3 + x - 20 = 0$.

Enter $y = x^3 + x - 20$ into the Y= list of the calculator. Adjust the window so that all points where the graph intersects the *x*-axis are visible on the diagram. Use Xmin = −4.7 and Xmax = 4.7 to provide *x*-coordinates increasing by 0.1 when tracing.

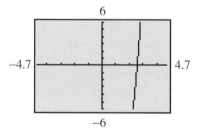

Use TRACE and ZOOM to find the point(s) on the graph whose *y*-coordinates are approximately 0, or use the CALC menu. The *x*-coordinate where $y = 0$ is approximately 2.59. The solution of $x^3 + x = 20$ is $x \doteq 2.59$.

Method 2

Enter the equations $y = x^3 + x$ and $y = 20$ in the Y= list of the graphing
calculator. Adjust the window so that the intersection point is clearly visible. On
the graphs below, use Xmin = –4.7 and Xmax = 4.7 to provide *x*-values that
increase by 0.1 when tracing.

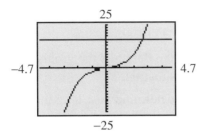

Use TRACE and ZOOM, or use the CALC menu, to find the coordinates of the
intersection point. The intersection point is approximately (2.6, 20). The
x-coordinate is the solution of the equation. The solution of $x^3 + x = 20$ is
$x \doteq 2.6$.

DISCUSSING THE IDEAS

1. Explain why the equations in *Investigation 1*, exercise 1, form a non-linear
system.

2. In *Investigation 1*, you determined the intersection points numerically using
the TABLE feature of your calculator, or graphically using the ZOOM
feature. Discuss the accuracy of the two methods.

3. Suppose you have to solve the equation $x^3 + x - 30 = 0$ graphically.
Describe two different systems of equations you could graph on the same
grid to solve this equation.

4. In *Investigation 2*, exercise 2, what is an appropriate way to round the
answer?

5. In *Investigation 2*, exercise 5, explain how there can be two boxes with
volume 750 cm^3.

6. To solve a non-linear equation, you can determine the zeros of the
appropriate function or the intersection points of an appropriate system of
equations. Explain which method you find easier to use.

7. When you solve a non-linear equation using a graphing calculator, how can
you tell when the roots are exact? Use an example to support your answer.

Checking Your Skills

1. Solve graphically.

    a) $x^3 + 2x = 10$ **b)** $x^4 - 15x^2 = 20$ **c)** $x^3 + x - 15 = 0$

2. The height, h metres, of a rescue flare above the ground t seconds after release is given by $h = -4.9t^2 + 75.0t + 2.3$.

    a) What is the value of h when the flare hits the ground? Write the quadratic equation that represents this situation.

    b) Use a graphing calculator to determine how long the flare is in the air.

    c) Will the flare reach a height of 1000 m? If so, when?

    d) The flare is visible for 8.5 s. At what height does the flare burn out?

3. Annie Pelletier won a bronze medal in the women's springboard competition at the 1996 Olympics in Atlanta. She somersaults from a 3-m board. Her height, h metres, above the water t seconds after she leaves the springboard is given by $h = -4.9t^2 + 8.8t + 3$.

    a) What is the value of h when Pelletier hits the water? What quadratic equation represents this situation?

    b) Use a graphing calculator to solve the equation. Determine the time of flight of Pelletier's dive.

    c) Determine how long she is in the air, to the nearest 0.1 s, before she passes the springboard on her way down by graphing the system $h = -4.9t^2 + 8.8t + 3$ and $h = 3$.

4. A circular washer is cut from a square piece of metal with side lengths 4 cm. The area, A, of the washer material is $A = \pi R^2 - \pi r^2$.

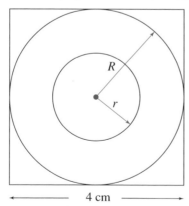

4 cm

    a) What is the outside radius, R, of the washer in the diagram above? Write an expression for the area, A, of this particular washer.

b) What inside radius, r, of a washer cut from the square in the diagram will give a washer with an area of metal 6 cm²? Use a graphing calculator to solve the equation correct to two decimal places.

c) What area of metal is wasted from each square piece when the washer is made?

5. A hockey arena seats 1600 people. The price of a ticket for a hockey game is $10. At this price, every ticket is always sold. To obtain more revenue, the manager plans to increase the price of the tickets. However, the manager is concerned that if the price is increased too much, the attendance will drop and revenue may decrease. The manager conducts a survey to estimate the revenue generated for different ticket prices. The results of the survey are shown in the table.

Ticket Price ($)	Projected Revenue ($)
10	16 000
15	19 500
20	20 300
25	14 750
30	5 000

a) Find the quadratic function that best fits these data.

b) What ticket price(s) will generate revenues of $20 000?

c) Between which two prices will the revenue be greater than $20 000?

d) What ticket price will generate the greatest revenue?

6. The speed of a vehicle, v kilometres per hour, at the moment the brakes were applied can be estimated from the length, d metres, of its skid marks. The equation is $d = \left(\frac{v-8}{12.6}\right)^2$, for $v > 8$. If a skid mark measures 60 m, approximately how fast was the vehicle travelling before the brakes were applied?

7. According to *The Guinness Book of Records*, a square pyramid containing 5525 cans was built in 1995. The number of cans, C, in a square pyramid with n layers is given by $C = \frac{n(n+1)(2n+1)}{6}$. How many layers did the pyramid have?

8. A fuel tank is in the shape of a cylinder with a hemisphere at each side.

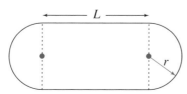

The formula for the volume, V in cubic metres, of such a tank is given by $V = \pi r^2 L + \frac{4}{3}\pi r^3$, where L metres is the length of the cylindrical part of the tank and r metres is the radius of the hemispheres.

a) Suppose the cylindrical section of a tank is 8 m long. Write a formula to represent the volume of this tank with radius r metres.

b) Suppose the fuel tank has a volume of 200 m³. What is its radius?

9. The volume, V in cubic metres, of a spherical segment with base radius r metres, and height h metres, is given by the formula $V = \frac{1}{6}\pi h\,(3r^2 + h^2)$. The roof of a domed stadium is in the shape of a spherical segment with a base radius of 150 m.

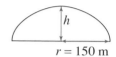

a) Write an equation for the volume of the dome with base radius $r = 150$ m as a function of the height, h metres.

b) Suppose the volume of the stadium is 3 500 000 m³. Determine the height at its centre.

10. Several equations can be used to model the growth of the world's human population since 1995. One such equation is $P = 5.73(1.018)^n$, where P is the population in billions and n is the number of years since 1995. Use this model to predict the year when the world's population will reach 10 billion people.

11. The sum of $1000 was invested 8 years ago. This table shows the value of the investment every 2 years.

Year	Value ($)
0	1000.00
2	1221.02
4	1490.95
6	1820.41
8	2222.73

a) Enter the values in the table on your graphing calculator. Determine which type of function would best describe these data. Give the equation of the function (with numbers correct to 3 decimal places) and plot its graph.

b) The growth continues to follow the same pattern. How many years will it take from the start of the investment for the value to be $3000?

c) What is the annual interest rate?

12. A student bounces a ball and collects the following data.

Bounce Number	0	1	2	3	4	5	6
Height (cm)	100	60	36	21.6	12.96	7.78	4.67

a) Graph the data.

b) Use your graphing calculator to determine the equation that best fits this data.

c) At which bounce is the height below 1 cm?

Extending Your Thinking

13. When a satellite is h kilometres above Earth, the time for one complete orbit, T minutes, is given by the formula $T = 1.66 \times 10^{-4} \times \sqrt{(6370 + h)^3}$. The number 6370 in the formula is the radius of Earth in kilometres. A telecommunications satellite is placed above the equator so that it is always above the same point on Earth's surface. Thus, the satellite will complete one orbit in 24 h.

a) If the time for one orbit is 24 h, what is the value of T?

b) Choose appropriate window settings and graph the function. Sketch the graph.

c) What is the height of the satellite?

d) Use the height you found in part c to determine how far the satellite travels in 24 h.

e) Calculate the satellite's speed, in kilometres per hour.

PROJECT

You learned how to solve a non-linear equation. You will use this skill in the Chapter Project and in the following projects in the Project Book.

- Hypothermia
- Radiometric Dating
- The Basketball Free Throw

COMMUNICATING THE IDEAS

Describe the two methods you can use to solve a non-linear equation graphically. Explain when it might be advantageous to use one method rather than the other.

A Logistic Model for the Growth of the World's Population

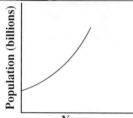

I n your earlier work you used an exponential function to model the world's population. A better model has a graph such as the one below left. This reflects that Earth's population will eventually reach a maximum. In this final section of the project, you will use a logistic model to obtain a graph for the world's population.

According to United Nations projections, the maximum capacity for Earth's population is between 8 billion and 28 billion people. A model for the population growth depends upon the maximum capacity of Earth. It also depends upon the total population and the annual increase for the particular year in which the study is made.

Ask your teacher for the program WORLDPOP. Enter it into your calculator.

UTILITY

The WORLDPOP program is shown in Utility 24.

Run the program. It will prompt you to enter the initial population, P, the maximum sustainable population, M, and the growth rate for that year, R. When the word DONE appears, press STAT ENTER. A screen similar to the one below will appear.

L1	L2	L3	2
0	**5.28**	------	
10	6.1338		
20	7.0604		
30	8.0467		
40	9.0753		
50	10.125		
60	11.173		

L2(1)=5.28

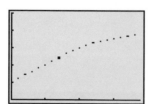

To graph the data, select STAT PLOT and turn the plot on. Select a dot as the plotting mark. Press GRAPH. The graph will look similar to the one to the left.

To obtain an equation of best fit press STAT ►, and select **B: Logistic**. This is the equation for a curve representing population growth that takes into account the maximum population.

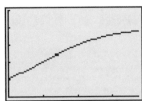 Graph the curve using ⌊ Y= ⌋. Turn off the PLOT to TRACE on the curve. Wait for a screen similar to the one above to appear.

1. Use the WORLDPOP program with the 1990 figures from the table on page 84. Choose a maximum population of 20 billion. Enter $P = 5.28$, $R = 1.55$, and $M = 20$. Graph the data for 200 years using 1990 as the zero year. Use ⌊TRACE⌋ to determine the population in 2000, 2010, and 2100.

2. Use the program for three more values for M, and use data from the U.S. Census table for the year of your choice. Sketch the graphs. Use ⌊TRACE⌋ to predict the population in 2000, 2010, 2020, and 2100.

Write a short report on the world's population growth. Describe factors that influence the growth. Describe possible mathematical models and explain any assumptions made.

Produce a poster featuring your report, illustrated with the graphs from the various models.

Career Skills

People in government and world agencies have a responsibility to plan for the expected population of Canada and other countries. Population projections must be as accurate as possible if future needs are to be met.

What Do I Need To Know?

Tutorial	Skills and Concepts	Important Results and Formulas
2.1	• Plot and describe exponential data • Use exponential regression to obtain the equation for data • Apply exponential functions in the areas of growth and decay	• A general equation for exponential growth and decay may be given by $A = PM^{\frac{t}{T}}$, where A is the amount after time t units, P is the initial amount, M is the multiplication factor, and T is the growth or decay period.
2.2	• Determine the vertex, domain and range, axis of symmetry, and intercepts of the graph of a quadratic function • For given data, determine the quadratic regression equation and draw its graph	• The equation $y = ax^2 + bx + c$ is a quadratic function. Its graph is a parabola. • The parabola has a maximum or minimum value that occurs at its vertex. • The zeros of a quadratic function are the x-intercepts. • The axis of symmetry is a vertical line that passes through the vertex.
2.3	• Solve problems using a quadratic function as the model	
2.4	• Solve non-linear equations using a graphing tool • Use a graphing tool and regression functions to model data	• Solve non-linear equations by graphing each side of the equation as separate functions or by equating one side of the non-linear equation to zero and then finding the zero(s) of the corresponding function using technology. • Use the STAT CALC menu to determine an appropriate regression function for data.

What Should I Be Able To Do?

After you have finished the work in Chapter 2, you should be able to solve the problems that follow. Part A is investigative in nature.

Part A

1. A newspaper article contained these data about Canadians.

Year	1961	1971	1981	1991
Percent of Total Population over 65	7.64	8.10	9.71	11.6

   a) Enter the data into your calculator.

   b) Determine which regression best fits the data: linear, quadratic, or exponential. Write down the regression equation.

   c) Graph the equation obtained in part b.

   d) Is there a maximum or minimum on the graph? If so, determine the coordinates of this point.

   e) Use the graph to predict the percent of the Canadian population over 65 in 2011 and 2036.

   f) According to this model, what percent of the Canadian population were aged over 65 in 1951?

Part B

2. A strain of bacteria doubles in number every 5 hours. There are initially 1000 bacteria in a sample.

   a) Write an equation that represents the growth of the bacteria.

   b) Graph the equation in part a for up to 30 h.

   c) Determine the number of bacteria after 24 h.

   d) Determine the approximate time for the population of bacteria to reach 50 000.

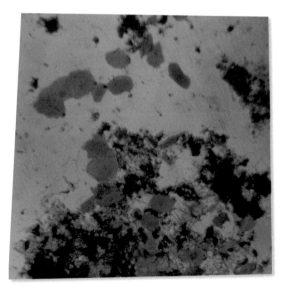

3. Use a graphing calculator. Graph the function $f(x) = 2x^2 - 9x - 5$. Determine the coordinates of the vertex, the domain, the range, the equation of the axis of symmetry, and the intercepts of the graph.

4. Use quadratic regression on a graphing calculator to determine the quadratic function that best fits the following data. What is the maximum value of the function?

x	y
0	0
14.6	10.2
29.2	17.9
43.8	23.2
58.4	26.0
87.6	24.3
102.2	19.8
116.8	12.8
131.4	3.4

5. A rescue flare is projected upward at 60 m/s from an initial height of 20 m.

a) Determine the equation that relates the height of the flare to the length of time it is in the air.

b) Graph the equation in part a.

c) What is the maximum height reached by the flare, and how long did it take to reach this maximum height?

d) How long was the flare in the air?

6. The atmospheric pressure, p, at a given altitude, h, is given in the following table.

h (km)	1	10	20	30	40
p (kPa)	101	25	6.3	2.0	0.53

a) Graph the data.

b) Determine the function that best represents these data and graph this on the same screen as the scatterplot.

c) What is the pressure at a height of 2.5 km?

7. The non-linear equation $V = \frac{2}{3}\pi r^3 + 20\pi r^2$ represents the volume V in cubic centimetres, of a cylindrical container that is hemispherical at one end. The length of the cylinder is 20 cm and the radius is r centimetres.

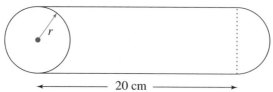

Use a graphing calculator to determine the radius of this container when the volume is 500 cm^3. Express your answer to 1 decimal place.

The Chapter Project combines many skills and concepts covered in this Chapter. Here is a sampling of student work from different stages of the Project. Review these samples to gain insights into your own project work.

8. Here are a student's graphs for a logistic model of population growth. He has used figures from the U.S. Census Bureau for 1960 and for 1990.

- Are the scales correct for each axis?
- Has the correct formula been used?
- Are the graphs clear and easy to read?
- Are the predictions for the years 2000, 2010, and 2020 correct?
- Were reasonable values chosen for *M*?

A Logistics Model for the Growth of the World's Population.

1. Using the WORLDPOP program, the Logistics regression, and the Trace command, we found the following:

In 1990 the population $P = 5.28$ billion, and the rate $R = 1.55$. The chart below illustrates the predictions for a variety of years, and maximum sustainable population.

	Predicted Population (in billions) for the given maximum sustainable			
Year	M=10 billion	M=15 billion	M=20 billion	M=25 billion
2000	6.09	6.12	6.12	6.13
2010	6.84	7.00	7.05	7.08
2100	9.77	13.26	15.69	17.47

2. Using the 1960 data, population 3.04 and $R = 1.33$ gives the following results:

	Predicted Population (in billions) for the given maximum sustainable		
Year	M=10 billion	M=15 billion	M=20 billion
2000	4.84	4.96	5.01
2010	5.32	5.53	5.62
2020	5.79	6.12	6.28
2100	8.64	10.86	12.32

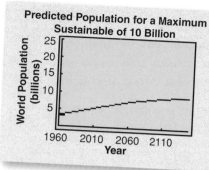

Predicted Population for a Maximum Sustainable of 10 Billion

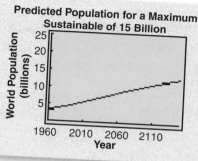

Predicted Population for a Maximum Sustainable of 15 Billion

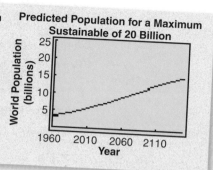

Predicted Population for a Maximum Sustainable of 20 Billion

9. Below is a portion of the same student's final report on World's Population.

- Read the report. Are the statements clear? Is there a logical flow to the ideas?
- Has the student clearly conveyed the mathematical principles underlying modelling of world population growth?
- How do the student's graphs support the written work?

Write a summary of your assessment of this student's work.

No one really knows what the maximum population of the earth can be. If you simply looked at land area, all the people in the world could easily stand in Canada. The problem we face is not just where the people are, but also the food required, the pollution, where they live. As more people populate the earth, more food is required to feed them. To grow the food, more land is needed. We already have famine problems in the world, and as the population increases, this will only get worse. More people will produce more garbage, sewage, pollution, and require somewhere to live. This again requires more space. We are depleting rainforests, and creating holes in the ozone layer, which will get worse.

The various models about future trends give us some hope. The first graph, which was an exponential model, should be discounted. This model assumes that the rate of growth will always be increasing, but we have recently seen a decline. The other two graphs use a logistics model, which shows the trends the best. On each graph, there are projections for different maximum populations. These show how the population would grow depending on the maximum sustainable population. There are different models because we do not really know what the earth can hold. These models are more accurate as they include the recent decline in the growth rate. The United Nations population division predicts that the growth rate will continue to decline in the next century.

With this declining trend, we are starting to see an older overall population. Although there are still 3 times as many children under 15 as there are seniors over 60, this will change towards an older population. This will help reduce the growth rate. At some point there should be a balance where the fertility rate equals the mortality rate, and no growth exists. This could be at the maximum, but when?

3

Linear Systems

Overview

You should do at least one project that uses the skills you learn in this chapter. The recommended project in the Project Book is:

- Balancing Dietary Protein in Livestock Feeds

Skydiving

Parachuting and skydiving have been around since the 1100s, when the Chinese jumped from high places with umbrella-like structures. Today, skydiving attracts thousands of newcomers each year and teams compete internationally. Modern equipment and safety procedures make skydiving a safe and exciting pastime.

When a skydiver jumps from an airplane, the force of gravity causes him to accelerate until *terminal velocity* is reached. At this point the air resistance balances the skydiver's mass, so the net force is zero and no further acceleration occurs. Air resistance is determined by altitude and atmospheric density, by the skydiver's mass and position in the free fall, and by the type of suit worn. After reaching terminal velocity, a skydiver *free falls* at a constant speed until he deploys his parachute, or *canopy*, which slows his descent for a safe landing.

In this Project, you will explore some of the mathematics involved in skydiving. You will research skydiving and design a skydiving information poster. Sources of information include the Internet and the library. Here are some initial questions to consider:

- How long does it take to reach terminal velocity?
- How does opening the parachute affect terminal velocity
- What is air resistance?
- How does the skydiver's body position while free falling affect terminal velocity?
- What is the minimum height above which the skydiver must deploy the parachute?
- How fast does the skydiver fall with an open parachute?

CHAPTER PROJECT

To complete this Chapter Project, you must solve linear systems by graphing and by substitution. Complete *Tutorials* 2.1 to 2.3 to develop your skills. You will return to this Chapter Project on page 140.

FYI Visit: www.awl.com/canada/school/connections

You can start your research from our Internet site: Click on <u>MATHLINKS</u>
followed by the *Applied Mathematics 11* logo. Then select a topic under
Skydiving.

Solving Linear Systems by Graphing

You may recall that the graph of a linear function is a straight line. Many situations produce data that can be represented by two or more linear functions. One example from the business world is the determination of the break-even point of a newly opened business.

A set of two linear equations in two variables is called a *linear system*. The solution to a linear system is the set of all ordered pairs (x, y) that satisfy *both* equations. In this Tutorial you will use graphs to solve linear systems.

Practise Your Prior Skills

You will work with linear equations and their graphs. Try the exercises below as preliminary review.

1. Graph the equation $y = 0.5x + 4$. Use your graph to determine the x- and y-intercepts.

2. Rearrange each equation so it can be graphed using the Y= feature of a graphing calculator.

   a) $2x + 3y - 6 = 0$ **b)** $5x - 2y + 1 = 0$

3. What is the slope and y-intercept of each line?

   a) $y = 2x - 3$ **b)** $y = 6 - 4x$ **c)** $x + 3y + 15 = 0$

4. What is an equation of the line with y-intercept -2 and slope $\frac{3}{4}$?

5. Determine an equation of the line joining the points $(2, 1)$ and $(-3, 11)$.

STUDENT REFERENCE

If you need to review the "linear equation and its graph" refer to the Student Reference.

In *Investigation 1*, you will collect data and plot graphs. You will determine when two people walking toward each other at a constant speed will meet and pass each other.

Meeting and Greeting

Work in groups of four. You will need a measuring tape, masking tape, and either a CBR, or a CBL with motion detector, or 2 stopwatches. You need approximately 5 m of clear floor space in front of a wall.

1. Place masking tape on the floor in a line perpendicular to the wall. Measure and mark a scale on the tape. Start your scale at 0 at the wall, then mark every 0.5 m to 5 m.

If you are using a CBR or CBL, do exercise 2, omit exercise 3, then continue from exercise 4. If you are not using technology, omit exercise 2 and continue from exercise 3.

2. Work in pairs.

a) In your notebook create a table similar to the one below.

	Start		Finish	
	Time (s)	Distance from Wall (m)	Time (s)	Distance from Wall (m)
Student A				
Student B				

b) Run the RANGER program on a graphing calculator.
Enter the set-up instructions:
Select **1:SETUP/SAMPLE** to access the set-up menu.
Press ENTER ◄ until the settings are as shown in this screen.

Main Menu	Start Now
Real Time	No
Time(s)	10
Display	Dist
Begin on	[Trigger]
Smoothing	Light
Units	Meters

Move the cursor to the START NOW command and press ENTER. Follow the instructions on the screen. Detach the CBR when instructed.

c) Student A: Stand close to the wall, but facing away from it, holding and pointing the CBR unit backward toward the wall. Shuffle away from the wall at a constant speed, not lifting your feet from the ground. When you are about 0.5 m from the wall, press ⌜TRIGGER⌝ on the CBR unit and continue walking to the 5-m mark. Reconnect the CBR and follow the instructions on the screen. The graph on the calculator screen should be a straight line with positive slope. If you are not satisfied with your results, repeat the exercise by selecting **5:REPEAT SAMPLE**.

d) The distance–time graph on your calculator relates the distance from the wall to the time. Use the TRACE feature of the calculator to determine the coordinates of the endpoints of the graph. Record these points in the row labelled Student A in your table. Share your results with your group.

e) Student B: Prepare the CBR unit as in part b. Stand 5 m from the wall, facing the wall, holding and pointing the CBR toward the wall. Press ⌜TRIGGER⌝ and shuffle at a constant speed toward the wall, stopping 0.5 m from the wall. Reconnect the CBR unit and follow the instructions on the screen. The graph on the calculator screen should be a straight line with negative slope. If you are not satisfied with your results, repeat the exercise by selecting **5:REPEAT SAMPLE**.

f) Use the TRACE feature of the calculator to determine the endpoints of the graph. Record your results in the row labelled Student B in your table. Share your results with your group.

3. a) In your notebook, create a table similar to the one in exercise 2a.

b) Student A: Stand 0.5 m from the wall, on one side of the line on the floor, facing away from the wall.
Student B: Stand 5 m away from the wall, on the other side of the line on the floor, facing toward the wall.
On a verbal signal you will shuffle at a constant speed to the other end of the marked line, keeping your feet in contact with the floor.

c) The other students act as timekeepers, one for each walker.
One timekeeper gives the verbal signal for walking and timing to begin. Start timing as both students shuffle forward. Stop timing when your student, A or B, reaches the other end of the marked scale. Share your results. For each student, record the times and distances in your table.

4. In your notebook, draw a distance–time graph for each of students A and B on the same grid. Use the coordinates of the points you have recorded.

5. Calculate the slope of each line segment. What are the units for slope? What does the slope represent?

6. Write the equation of each line.

7. Estimate the coordinates of the point of intersection of the lines.

8. Suppose the students started at the same time and the same positions as in exercise 2 or 3, but student A walked much slower than student B. How would this affect your results?

9. Test your prediction in exercise 8 by repeating the walks as described.

In a linear system, the values of *x* and *y* that satisfy both equations can be found by graphing the equations on the same grid and determining their point of intersection. The coordinates of the point of intersection are the solution of the linear system.

In business, the *break-even* point is the point where the revenue from sales equals the production costs. In *Example 1*, you will graph equations to determine the break-even point of a business.

Example 1 **Determine the break-even point of a business**

A lunchtime pizza business has start-up costs of $200. The cost of producing a slice of pizza is $1.50. A slice of pizza sells for $2.00. Determine the number of slices that must be sold for the business to break even.

SOLUTION

Create a table of values.

Number of Slices Sold, *n*	Production Cost, *C* ($)	Sales Revenue, *S* ($)
0	200	0
100	350	200
200	500	400
300	650	600

On grid paper, draw the graph of the number of slices sold against the production cost. On the same grid, draw the graph of the number of slices sold against the sales revenue.

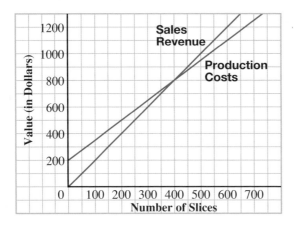

Extend the lines so they intersect.

At the point of intersection, the production cost, C dollars, and the sales revenue, S dollars, are the same. This point represents the break-even point of the business.

From the graph, the point of intersection is (400, 800).

When 400 slices of pizza are made and sold, the production cost and sales revenue are both $800. Thus, the business will break even when it makes and sells 400 slices of pizza.

A point at the intersection of two grid lines is called a *lattice point*. In *Example 1*, the lines intersected at a lattice point, making it easy to determine the coordinates of the point of intersection. When solving a linear system by graphing, it may not be possible to obtain the exact solution. When the lines do not intersect at a lattice point, the solution must be estimated.

Example 2 **Determine the solution of a linear system graphically using technology**

Sales clerks at a computer store have a choice of two methods of remuneration.
Plan A: a straight 5% commission on all sales.
Plan B: a weekly salary of $200 plus a 2% commission on all sales.

Explain which plan is better and why.

SOLUTION

Suppose a sales clerk sells computers valued at x dollars in one month.

Plan A: The weekly pay, y dollars, is 5% of x, so $y = 0.05x$.

Plan B: The weekly pay, y dollars, is the salary plus the commission that is 2% of x, so $y = 200 + 0.02x$.

Each equation represents a linear function. Together, the equations form a linear system. Use a graphing calculator. Graph the equations on the same screen using the Y= feature. Use the graph icons at the left of the Y= screen to select a heavy line for the second equation. This helps to distinguish the graphs on the screen. A suitable window that will lead to simple results when you trace is shown below left.

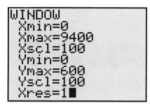
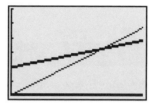

The point of intersection of the graphs represents the point where the weekly sales and the weekly pay are the same for the two plans. The x-coordinate represents the weekly sales and the y-coordinate represents the weekly pay. Use the CALC feature to determine the coordinates of the point of intersection.

If you have never used a graphing calculator to determine the point of intersection of two graphs, Utility 19 shows you how to use the CALC feature of the TI-83 calculator. If you are using a different graphing calculator, consult the User's Manual.

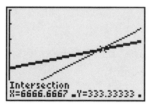

The coordinates of the point of intersection are approximately (6666.67, 333.33). An important step in solving linear systems is checking the answer. The coordinates of the point of intersection should satisfy both equations because the point lies on both lines. Substitute $x = 6666.67$ and $y = 333.33$ into both equations.

$y = 0.05x$	$y = 200 + 0.02x$
L.S. = 333.33 R.S. = 0.05×6666.67 = 333.3335	L.S. = 333.33 R.S. = $200 + 0.02 \times 6666.67$ = 333.3334

The answers are not exactly the same due to rounding. It is sometimes difficult to get exact answers when solving linear systems by graphing.

The solution means that when the weekly sales of computers are $6666.67, both plans pay $333.33. To the left of the point of intersection weekly sales are less than $6666.67. In this region, the graph corresponding to plan B is uppermost, indicating that plan B pays more and, therefore, is the better plan. If the value of sales is greater than $6666.67, plan A is better.

DISCUSSING THE IDEAS

1. In the *Investigation*, the slope of the graph for one student walker is positive and the slope of the graph for the other is negative. Explain why.

2. What is the significance of the point of intersection of the graphs you drew in the *Investigation*?

3. In the *Investigation* and the *Examples*, you solved linear systems graphically. Suggest a situation where this may not be possible.

4. In *Example 1*, for what values of *n* is the business losing money? For what values of *n* does the business make a profit?

5. Examine *Example 1*. Another way to solve this problem would be to graph two different lines. Describe these lines.

6. In *Example 2*, what does the *x*-coordinate of the intersection point represent? What does the *y*-coordinate represent?

7. In *Example 2*, explain the choice of window settings.

8. You could use the TABLE feature of a graphing calculator to determine a solution to a system numerically without using the CALC feature. Explain the advantages and disadvantages of each method.

9. Suppose you found that the intersection point of two lines was (p, q). How might you use the equations of the lines to check your answer?

Checking Your Skills

1. For which of these systems is $(-1, 1)$ a solution?

a) $5x + 6y = 1$
  $6x + 2y = -3$

b) $3x + 4y = 1$
  $5x - 3y = -8$

c) $7x - 3y = 10$
  $6x + 5y = -1$

2. Solve by graphing, then check.

a) $y = 3x$
  $y = 0.5x - 5$

b) $y = x - 7$
  $y = -2x - 10$

c) $y = 1 - x$
  $y = 3x - 11$

3. Solve by graphing, then check.

a) $x + y = 5$
  $3x + y = 3$

b) $x - y = 2$
  $3x + y = -14$

c) $2x + 8y = 8$
  $-2x + y = 10$

4. A crate of 36 apples has a total mass of 4 kg. When 12 apples are removed, the total mass is 3 kg. Equations that represent the situation are $4 = b + 36a$ and $3 = b + 24a$, where b is the mass of the crate in kilograms and a is the mass of one apple in kilograms.

a) Graph the system.

b) Determine the mass of the crate and the mass of one apple.

5. Mollie and Tony go skydiving together. Tony jumps from the airplane, reaching a terminal velocity of 55 m/s at an altitude of 3000 m. Mollie jumps from the airplane, reaching her terminal velocity of 40 m/s at an altitude of 2400 m. They reach their terminal velocity at the same time. At a time, t seconds, after they reach their terminal velocity, their height above the ground, d metres, is $d = -55t + 3000$ for Tony and $d = -40t + 2400$ for Mollie.

a) Graph the equations.

b) Determine the coordinates of the point of intersection of the graphs.

c) How long will it take Tony to overtake Mollie (to the nearest 0.1 s)?

d) At what altitude, to the nearest metre, does Tony overtake Mollie?

6. When Lucy reaches the halfway mark of a 42-km marathon, Julie is 40 m ahead of her. Julie runs at a steady speed of 3 m/s. Lucy increases her speed to a steady 3.5 m/s. The equations for the distance run from the halfway point are $d = 3t + 40$ for Julie and $d = 3.5t$ for Lucy, where d is the distance in metres from the halfway mark after t seconds.

a) Graph these equations on the same grid.

b) Determine the coordinates of the point of intersection of the graphs.

c) From the halfway mark, how long does it take Lucy to overtake Julie?

d) How far from the halfway mark does Lucy overtake Julie?

7. Henry is considering joining The Fitness Zone, a local fitness club. Two payment plans are available:

Plan A: a monthly fee of $30, plus a user fee of $1 per visit.

Plan B: a drop-in charge of $5 per visit.

a) Create a table of values for each payment plan for one month for up to 12 visits.

Plan A

Number of Visits	0	2	4	6	8	10	12
Cost ($)							

Plan B

Number of Visits	1	2	4	6	8	10	12
Cost ($)							

b) Draw the graphs of the two payment plans on the same grid.

c) Use your graphs. What is the minimum number of visits Henry must make per month for Plan A to be worthwhile?

8. While shopping for light bulbs, your mother notices that a regular bulb costs $0.55 and uses electricity costing $6 for 1000 h ($0.006/h). An energy-saver light bulb costs $1.15 and uses $4 worth of electricity for every 1000 h ($0.004/h). The cost, C dollars, of using a regular bulb for h hours is $C = 0.006h + 0.55$. The cost for the energy-saver bulb is $C = 0.004h + 1.15$.

a) Solve the linear system graphically.

b) After how many hours is it cheaper to use the energy-saver bulb? What is the cost of using the energy-saver bulb at this point?

c) Suppose you use the energy-saver bulb. How much do you save after 1000 h of use?

9. A manufacturer of weight-training machines must choose a printing company to print a promotional brochure. Quick and Clear charges $900 for set up and $0.50 per copy. Miles Ahead charges a flat fee of $1500 and $0.38 per copy. Suppose C is the cost in dollars to print n copies of the brochure. Equations that represent the cost for each company are: $C = 0.50n + 900$ and $C = 0.38n + 1500$.

a) Use a graphing calculator to graph the system.

b) Determine the coordinates of the point of intersection of the graphs.

c) How many brochures must be printed for the cost to be the same for both companies? What is the cost?

d) The company wants to print 3000 brochures for a trade show. Which company has the better price? Suppose the company wants to print 5500 brochures for a mail-out campaign. Which company should they choose?

e) Calculate the cost per brochure for the trade show and for the mail-out campaign.

10. An industrial incinerator converts non-recyclable material into ash. Two models are available. Each model produces A tonnes of ash for every w tonnes of waste material burned. Each model requires at least 20 000 t of waste material to operate.

The equation for Model 1 is $A = 1.4w + 20\ 000$.
The equation for Model 2 is $A = 1.0w + 50\ 000$.
For both equations, values of w must be greater than or equal to 20 000.

a) Graph the two linear equations and solve the system. A suitable window setting for your graphing calculator is shown below.

```
WINDOW
 Xmin=20000
 Xmax=100000
 Xscl=1000
 Ymin=0
 Ymax=200000
 Yscl=1000
 Xres=1█
```

b) How much waste must be burned for both incinerators to produce the same amount of ash? What is the total amount of ash produced by each incinerator?

c) A town produces no more than 50 000 t of waste. Which of the two models will produce the least amount of ash? Justify your answer.

d) Another town produces at least 100 000 t of waste. Which of the two models will produce the least amount of ash? Justify your answer.

11. A cellular phone company offers two different plans.

Plan A charges a monthly fee of $28 and allows 30 min of free calling time. For calling time over 30 min, it charges $0.55/min.

Plan B charges a monthly fee of $40 and $0.25/min, with no free calling time.

The equations that represent the monthly cost, C dollars, for t minutes of calling time for each plan are given below.

Plan A: $C = 0.55(t - 30) + 28$

Plan B: $C = 0.25t + 40$

a) Use a graphing calculator. Choose appropriate window settings and graph the equations on the same screen.

b) How many minutes of calling time result in the same monthly fees for both plans?

c) Suppose you use the cellular phone for more than 100 min each month. Which is the better plan for you? Justify your answer.

d) Suppose you use the phone for no more than 50 min each month. Which is the better plan for you? Justify your answer.

e) Explain when it is more economical to use plan A instead of plan B.

Extending Your Thinking

12. The range of visibility of a lighthouse beam on a clear night is 30 km. This range of visibility forms a circle with the lighthouse at the centre. Any vessel on or inside this circle can see the light beam. A coordinate grid is set up with the lighthouse at $(0, 0)$. A circle with centre $(0, 0)$ and radius 30 represents the range of the beam. The course of a ship travelling on a straight line is given by $x + 2y = 40$. The equation of the circle is $x^2 + y^2 = 900$.

a) Graph the system on grid paper.

b) Give the approximate coordinate(s) of the point(s) of intersection of the ship's course and the extremes in the range of the beam.

c) Calculate the approximate distance travelled by the ship while it is within the range of the beam.

d) Is this a linear system? Explain.

PROJECT

In this Tutorial, you have solved a linear system by graphing. You will use this skill when you return to the Chapter Project, and in the following project in the Project Book.

• Balancing Dietary Protein in Livestock Feeds

COMMUNICATING THE IDEAS

What are the advantages and disadvantages of using a graphing calculator to solve a system of equations?

You can solve a problem in many different ways. Some problems can be solved using equations. In this Tutorial you will learn how to translate a word problem into an equivalent algebra problem.

The first step is to understand the problem. You may have to read the problem several times. Next, you will need to determine the unknown quantities and assign a variable to represent each one. The unknown quantities are what the problem asks you to find. They often appear at the end of the problem, following cue words such as "determine," "calculate," "find," or "how many." Define the unknown quantities as specifically and thoroughly as you can. State the units if these are applicable.

Practise Your Prior Skills

Often, an important part of understanding the problem is recognizing a familiar topic. Try these exercises as preliminary review.

1. A salesman drives on the highway for 45 min and travels 60 km. What formula can you use to calculate his average speed?

2. A total of $15 000 is invested at a simple interest rate of 8% per annum. How do you calculate the interest earned in 1 year?

**STUDENT
REFERENCE**

If you would like to see some examples of "interest" calculations or calculations of "average speed," look in the Student Reference.

Example 1 **Reword statements**

During a sale at a clothing store, 2 shirts and 1 sweater cost $60, but 3 shirts and 2 sweaters cost $104. Write equations that could be used to determine the sale price of a shirt and of a sweater.

SOLUTION

The cue word is "determine." Let x represent the sale price of 1 shirt in dollars and y represent the sale price of 1 sweater in dollars.

We can determine these two unknown quantities by finding two equations relating them. There are two statements in the problem.

Statement 1: Two shirts and 1 sweater cost $60.
Reword: The cost of 2 shirts plus the cost of 1 sweater is $60.

In dollars: $(2 \times x) + (1 \times y) = 60$

The equation is: $2x + y = 60$.

Statement 2: Three shirts and 2 sweaters cost $104.

Reword: The cost of 3 shirts plus 2 sweaters is $104.

$(3 \times x) + (2 \times y) = 104$

The equation is $3x + 2y = 104$.

These two equations form a linear system.

$$2x + y = 60$$
$$3x + 2y = 104$$

The language in *Example 1* is straightforward. For some problems it may be difficult to reword the statements and focus on the relationships in the problem. Whenever you can, draw a diagram to illustrate the problem.

Example 2 Draw a diagram to illustrate a problem

The perimeter of a standard tennis court is 69 m. The width is 13 m less than the length. Write equations that could be used to calculate the length and width of a standard tennis court.

SOLUTION

Let l represent the length of a standard tennis court in metres and w represent the width in metres.

Draw a diagram to illustrate the problem. Label all sides of the diagram.

We need to find equations that relate the length and the width of the tennis court.

The perimeter is the distance all around the court, so

$$2l + 2w = 69$$

The other information given in the question is:
The width is 13 m less than the length.

Since the width is 13 m less than the length, you must subtract 13 from the length to get the width.

$$w = l - 13$$

The linear system is:

$$2w + 2l = 69$$
$$w = l - 13$$

When the information seems complicated, a table may help to clarify the problem.

Example 3 Use a table to organize information

A person invested a total of $2000. Part of the $2000 was invested at 4% per annum and the rest at 5% per annum. After one year, the total interest earned was $95. Write equations that could be used to determine how much was invested at each rate.

SOLUTION

The unknown quantities are the principals invested at 4% and at 5% per annum.

Let x represent the principal, in dollars, invested at 4% and y the principal, in dollars, invested at 5%.

The simple interest earned, I dollars, is given by $I = Prt$, where P is the principal in dollars, r the annual interest rate expressed as a decimal, and t the time in years.

Create a table. Enter the data from the problem.

	Principal ($)	Interest Rate	Time (years)	Interest Earned ($)
First Investment	x	0.04	1	$0.04x$
First Investment	y	0.05	1	$0.05y$
Total	2000			95

Use the entries in the second and final columns to write the equations that represent the problem. Here is the linear system.

$$x + y = 2000$$
$$0.04x + 0.05y = 95$$

Sometimes, the problem contains information that is not immediately apparent. A combination of methods may help reveal this information.

Example 4 **Draw a diagram and use a table to interpret a problem**

Erin paddles steadily downstream for 1 h in a river that has a current of 4 km/h. The return trip takes her 2 h. Write an equation to determine Erin's average speed in still water.

SOLUTION

The unknown quantity to be determined is Erin's speed in still water. Let v represent Erin's speed in kilometres per hour in still water.

The equation for motion at a constant speed is $Distance = Speed \times Time$.

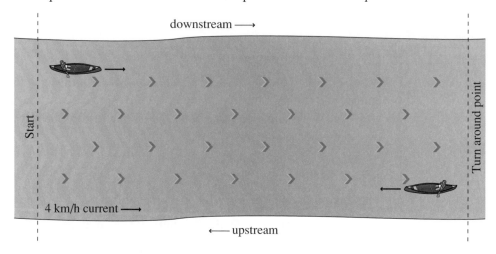

From the diagram, the return journey is the same distance as the outward journey. This distance is also unknown. Let d kilometres represent the distance Erin paddled.

On the outward trip, Erin travels downstream with the current. The current pushes her along. Her average resultant speed will be the sum of her speed in still water and the speed of the current, $(v + 4)$ km/h. Erin returns upstream against the current. Her average resultant speed is the difference between her speed in still water and the speed of the current, $(v - 4)$ km/h.

List the information in a table.

	Speed (km/h)	Time (h)	Distance (km)
Downstream	$v + 4$	1	d
Upstream	$v - 4$	2	d

The equations are: $(v + 4) \times 1 = d$ or $v + 4 = d$

$(v - 4) \times 2 = d$ or $2v - 8 = d$

1. Write a list of cue words that could mean "add." Write cue words that could mean "subtract," "multiply," and "divide."

2. Look at the problems in *Examples 1* to *4*. Could you translate each problem using only 1 variable? Which example do you think would have been easiest to translate using only 1 variable? Explain.

3. Why might it be easier to use 2 variables even though it is possible to translate the problem using only 1 variable?

EXERCISES

Checking Your Skills

In exercises 1 to 11, assign a variable to each unknown quantity. Then translate the problem into a system of linear equations that could be used to determine each unknown. **Do not solve the system**.

1. During a clearance sale, all the shirts are on sale at one price and all the sweaters at another price. Two shirts and 4 sweaters cost $98. One shirt and 3 sweaters cost $69. Write equations to determine the sale price for shirts and for sweaters.

2. At a sale, all CDs sell for one price and all tapes for another price. Three CDs and 2 tapes cost $72. One CD and 3 tapes cost $52. Write equations to determine the sale price for CDs and for tapes.

3. A sports club charges an initiation fee and a monthly fee. At the end of 5 months, a member had paid a total of $170. At the end of 10 months, she had paid a total of $295. Write equations to determine the initiation fee and the monthly fee.

4. Three footballs and 1 soccer ball cost $155. Two footballs and 3 soccer balls cost $220. Write equations to determine the price of a football and of a soccer ball.

5. Yasmin invested $2100 in the stock market. She purchased shares of World Oil stock at $7.50/share and Zinco Mines stock at $3.25/share. Yasmin purchased 450 shares altogether. Write equations to determine how many shares of each stock Yasmin purchased.

6. Jennifer had a total of $500 invested in high-yield investments. Part of the $500 was invested at 7% per annum and the rest at 10% per annum. After 1 year, the total interest earned was $44. Write equations to determine how much Jennifer invested at each rate.

7. Vien had a total of $800 invested. Part was invested at 4.5% per annum and the rest at 5% per annum. After 1 year, the total interest earned was $39.75. Write equations to determine how much was invested at each rate.

8. A light plane flies for 2 h with a 20 km/h tail wind. The return trip against the same wind takes 3 h. Write equations to determine the speed of the plane when there is no wind and the distance travelled.

9. A train leaves a station and travels west at 75 km/h. Two hours later, a second train leaves on a parallel track and travels west at 125 km/h. Write equations to determine when the trains will meet and how far from the station they will be at that time.

10. A canoeist paddles for 4 h downstream in a river with an 8 km/h current. The return trip takes 7 h. Write equations to determine the speed of the canoeist in still water and the distance travelled.

11. Mona had a total of $1250 invested. Part of the total was invested at 4% per annum and the rest at 6% per annum. At the end of 1 year, the two amounts invested earned an equal amount of interest. Write equations to determine how much Mona invested at each rate.

Extending Your Thinking

In these exercises, translate the problem into a linear system of equations, then solve the system graphically.

12. An aircraft travels 5432 km from Montreal to Paris in 7 h and returns in 8 h. The wind speed is constant. Determine the wind speed and the speed of the aircraft when there is no wind.

13. Five kilograms of tea and 8 kg of coffee cost a total of $58. The price of tea increases by 15% and that of coffee by 10%. The new total cost is $65.30. Determine the original cost of 1 kg of tea and 1 kg of coffee.

PROJECT

You have learned how to translate a word problem into a system of equations. You will use this skill in the Chapter Project and in the following project in the Project Book.

• Balancing Dietary Protein in Livestock Feeds

COMMUNICATING THE IDEAS

Choose one exercise above. Write to explain how it can be translated using one or two unknown quantities.

Solving Linear Systems by Substitution

It is not always possible to obtain the exact solution of a linear system by graphing. If the lines do not intersect on the grid lines, it is necessary to estimate the solution. Exact solutions can only be found algebraically. In this Chapter, you will study two algebraic methods for solving linear systems. This Tutorial deals with the substitution method and *Tutorial 3.5* presents the elimination method.

We cannot solve an equation with two variables. One problem-solving strategy is to manipulate a problem to make it simpler. Both the substitution and elimination methods for solving systems of equations involve manipulating the system to eliminate one of the variables.

Practise Your Prior Skills

In this Tutorial, you will rearrange equations, substitute algebraic expressions into equations, and solve linear equations. Try these exercises as preliminary review.

1. Simplify each expression by collecting like terms.

   a) $2(x + y) - 3x + 5y$ **b)** $5 - 3(y - x) + y$

   c) $4x - 5(x - 3y) + 3(x - y)$

2. Remove the fractions from each equation to obtain an equivalent equation. Do NOT solve.

   a) $\frac{1}{2}x + y = 3$ **b)** $x - \frac{3}{4}y = 2$ **c)** $\frac{1}{4}x + \frac{1}{2}y = 34$

3. Solve for x.

   a) $3x - 4 = 5x - 7$ **b)** $1 - 2(x - 4) = 11$ **c)** $0.04x = 2 - 3(2 + 0.2x)$

4. Rewrite each equation to isolate y.

   a) $3x + y = 12$ **b)** $5x - y = 8$ **c)** $-2x + 3y = 9$

STUDENT REFERENCE

If you wish to study examples of "collecting like terms," "formula rearrangement," or "solving linear equations," look in the Student Reference.

Example 1 Obtain an approximate solution by graphing and an exact solution by substitution

A helicopter flies at its maximum steady speed of 3 nautical miles per minute. When the helicopter is 22 nautical miles away, a boat sends up a distress flare. The pilot of the helicopter is told to change course immediately and head toward the boat. The equation that represents the helicopter's distance from the boat is $d = -3t + 22$, where d is the helicopter's distance from the boat in nautical miles, and t minutes is the time from the point at which the pilot changes course. The helicopter pilot can spot a flare 6 nautical miles away. How long is it from the moment the pilot changes course until she spots the flare?

SOLUTION

The pilot can spot a flare 6 nautical miles away, so when the flare is visible $d = 6$.

The system of equations to be solved is:

$$d = 6 \qquad ①$$
$$d = -3t + 22 \qquad ②$$

Method 1: Graph these lines on the same grid.

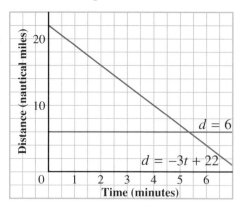

From the graph, an estimate of the point of intersection is (5.3, 6.0).

Check. Substitute $t = 5.3$ and $d = 6.0$ in the equation $d = -3t + 22$.

L.S. = 6   R.S. = $-3(5.3) + 22$
                  = 6.1

The two sides are not equal. This shows that (5.3, 6.0) is not the exact solution of the system.

The approximate time before the pilot spots the flare is 5.3 minutes.

To obtain an exact solution, proceed as follows.

Method 2: The system is $d = 6$ ①

$d = -3t + 22$ ②

Change the linear system to one equation in one variable.

At the point of intersection (the solution) the value of d from equation ① is the same as the value of d from equation ②, therefore we can substitute $d = 6$ into equation ②.

$$\boxed{d = 6}$$

$$\boxed{d} = -3t + 22$$

$$6 = -3t + 22$$

Solve this equation for t: $6 - 22 = -3t + 22 - 22$

$$-16 = -3t$$

$$t = \frac{16}{3}$$

Check the solution. Substitute $t = \frac{16}{3}$, and $d = 6$ in the original equations.

$d = 6$		$d = -3t + 22$	
L.S. = 6	R.S. = 6	L.S. = 6	R.S. = $-3(\frac{16}{3}) + 22$
			= 6

The pilot spots the flare after 5 min and 20 s.

The method of substitution can be used when solving any linear system in two variables. It is particularly appropriate when one of the equations has one variable already isolated.

Example 2 **Solve a system of linear equations by substitution**

A TV store has limited storage space. It receives an order of 300 new TV sets in two deliveries. The first delivery has 60 more TV sets than the second. Let f represent the number of TV sets in the first delivery, and s the number in the second delivery. The equations that model the situation are $f + s = 300$, and $f = s + 60$.

How many TV sets are in each delivery?

SOLUTION

The linear system is:
$$f + s = 300 \qquad ①$$
$$f = s + 60 \qquad ②$$

f is isolated in equation ② so substitute this expression for f into equation ①.
$$(s + 60) + s = 300$$

Now we have one equation in one variable.
$$2s + 60 = 300$$

Solve for s.
$$2s = 300 - 60$$
$$2s = 240$$
$$s = 120$$

Calculate the corresponding value of f. Substitute $s = 120$ into one of the original equations.

Choose equation ②.
$$f = 120 + 60$$
$$= 180$$

Check the solution. Substitute $f = 180$ and $s = 120$ into both of the original equations.

$f + s = 300$		$f = s + 60$	
L.S. = 180 + 120	R.S. = 300	L.S. = 180	R.S. = 120 + 60
= 300			= 180

The solution (180, 120) is correct.

The first delivery contained 180 TV sets, and the second delivery contained 120.

When solving a linear system, either variable can be replaced. Sometimes, a thoughtful choice can reduce the amount of work required.

Example 3 Solve a system of linear equations by substitution

For a figure skating competition, 12 000 tickets were sold. The tickets cost $35 for an adult and $20 for a student. The total value of the ticket sales was $307 500. Determine the numbers of adults and students who attended the competition.

SOLUTION

Let x represent the number of adult tickets sold, and y the number of student tickets sold.

Create a table to list the information given.

	Cost per Ticket ($)	Number of Tickets Sold	Value of Tickets ($)
Adult	35	x	$35x$
Student	20	y	$20y$
Totals		12 000	307 500

The third and fourth columns give the equations that model the problem:

Total numbers of tickets sold: $x + y = 12\ 000$ ①

Total value of tickets sold: $35x + 20y = 307\ 500$ ②

To determine the number of tickets sold at each price, we must solve this system.

Rearrange equation ① to isolate y: $y = 12\ 000 - x$

Substitute this expression for y in equation ②.

$$35x + 20(12\ 000 - x) = 307\ 500$$

Simplify. $35x + 240\ 000 - 20x = 307\ 500$

Collect like terms. $15x + 240\ 000 = 307\ 500$

Solve for x. $15x + 240\ 000 - 240\ 000 = 307\ 500 - 240\ 000$

$$15x = 67\ 500$$

$$\frac{15x}{15} = \frac{67\ 500}{15}$$

$$x = 4500$$

Solve for y.   Substitute $x = 4500$ into equation ①.

$$4500 + y = 12\ 000$$
$$y = 7500$$

Check the solution (4500, 7500).

Substitute $x = 4500$ and $y = 7500$ in the original equations.

$x + y = 12\ 000$	$35x + 20y = 307\ 500$
L.S. = 4500 + 7500 R.S. = 12 000 = 12 000	L.S. = 35(4500) + 20(7500) R.S. = 307 500 = 157 500 + 150 000 = 307 500

The solution (4500, 7500) is correct.

There were 4500 adults and 7500 students who attended the skating competition.

DISCUSSING THE IDEAS

1. Once a value has been determined for one variable, how is the corresponding value determined for the other variable?

2. Why is it necessary to check the solution in both original equations?

3. In *Example 2*, why do you think the equation $f = s + 60$ was chosen, rather than $f + s = 300$, to obtain a value for f? What would have been the result if $s = 120$ had been substituted into $f + s = 300$ instead?

4. In *Example 3*, why do you think the equation $x + y = 12\ 000$ was rearranged, rather than $35x + 20y = 307\ 500$? Suppose this other equation had been used. Would the same results have been obtained?

EXERCISES

Checking Your Skills

1. For which of these systems is $(-2, 5)$ a solution?

a) $15x + 4y = -10$
$25x - 6y = -80$

b) $3x + 2y = 4$
$5x - 3y = -5$

c) $-5x - 3y = -5$
$3x + 2y = 4$

2. Solve by substitution, then check.

a) $y = 105$
$-7x + y = 42$

b) $y = 1 + x$
$y = 4x - 5$

c) $y = 3x$
$x - 2y = 10$

d) $x = y + 7$
   $2x + y = -10$

e) $y = 7 - 3x$
   $5x - 2y = 24$

f) $y = 1 - x$
   $y - 3x = -11$

3. Solve each system by isolating one variable first, then check.

a) $x + y = 5$
   $2x - y = -4$

b) $x - y = 2$
   $4x + 2y = 16$

c) $x + y = 7$
   $3x + 4y = 24$

d) $x - y = 2$
   $3x + y = -14$

e) $x - y = 5$
   $3x + 4y = -6$

f) $x - y = 4$
   $2x + y = -4$

4. An airplane cruises at a constant velocity of 840 km/h during the 5430-km trip from Montreal to London, England. The equation that describes its motion is $d = -840t + 5430$, where d is its distance from London in kilometres, and t is the time in hours since the airplane reached its cruising velocity. The plane must start its descent when it is 90 km from London, so $d = 90$ when it starts its descent. How long has the plane been cruising when it starts its descent?

5. A car rental agency offers two rental plans for a certain class of car. Plan 1 is $60 per day with no charge for the number of kilometres driven. Plan 2 is $20 per day, plus $0.25 for each kilometre driven. You wish to rent a car for one day. The daily cost, C dollars, for driving d kilometres, is:
Plan 1: $C = 60$
Plan 2: $C = 0.25d + 20$

a) Which plan is better for a one-day, 200-km trip?

b) Solve the linear system. Determine how far you could drive so that the rental costs for each plan would be the same. What is this rental cost?

6. Pyramid Stables charges $20/h (including insurance) for trail rides. Sara's Stables charges $16/h, with a separate insurance fee of $12. Let the cost of the trail rides be C dollars and the number of hours be h. The equations relating cost to hours for each stable are $C = 20h$ and $C = 16h + 12$.

a) How many hours of trail rides would result in the same total costs for each stable?

b) Suppose you wish to go riding for 2 h. Which stable would you choose? Explain.

7. Ideally, the quantity of a crop that farmers harvest and sell at a given price should equal the quantity of the crop that consumers are willing to buy at that price. This is the law of supply and demand. The price of grapes is at least $1/kg and never more than $6.50/kg. The mass of grapes, G kilograms, that farmers will harvest (supply) is represented by $G = 5000p - 5000$, where p dollars is the selling price per kilogram. The quantity of grapes that consumers will purchase (demand) is represented by $G = -4000p + 26\,000$. Determine the price per kilogram where the supply of grapes equals the demand.

8. A fishing boat can sail to and from the fishing grounds at an average speed of 10 knots (nautical miles per hour). While the boat is fishing, it sails at an average speed of 3 knots. The total distance travelled during an 11-h period is 61 nautical miles. Let the time spent sailing to and from the fishing grounds be x hours, and the time spent fishing be y hours. An equation that represents the total distance travelled is $10x + 3y = 61$. An equation that represents the total time away from port is $x + y = 11$.

a) What time was spent sailing to and from the fishing grounds?

b) What time was spent fishing?

9. Part-time sales clerks at GenX Stereo Store are offered two methods of payment. Plan 1 pays $500 per month with a 4% commission on total sales. Plan 2 pays $700 per month with a 2% commission on total sales. Determine the value of sales for which both plans pay the same amount. How much would an employee earn at this level of sales? Follow the steps below to solve this problem.

a) Identify the unknown quantities and assign suitable variables.

b) Write a linear system that models the problem algebraically.

c) Solve the system by substitution.

d) What sales revenues would result in equal total earnings from these plans?

e) Which plan is better for a person who sells approximately $8000 worth of stereo equipment each month? What will the total earnings be?

10. In a cross-country ski race, competitors start the course 1 min apart, and are timed from start to finish. Duane starts exactly 3 min after Homer. Homer maintains a steady speed of 120 m/min, while Duane skis at 170 m/min.

a) Let d represent the distance from the start and t the time in minutes from Homer's start. Write a system of equations that represents the problem algebraically.

b) How long will it take Duane to catch up to Homer?

c) How far along the course are Homer and Duane when they meet?

11. A street vendor makes quarter-pound and half-pound burgers. Sales records show that in a typical month, the number of quarter-pound burgers sold is three times the number of half-pound burgers. The total monthly order for meat is 1250 pounds.

a) Copy and complete this table.

b) Write equations that model the problem.

	Number Sold	Amount of Meat
Quarter-pound burgers	x	
Half-pound burgers	y	
Total		

c) Determine how many quarter-pound burgers and half-pound burgers are made and sold each month?

d) What is the total number of burgers sold each month?

12. Liz bought four times as many candy bars as cans of pop. She spent $11.40. Suppose pop costs 48¢ a can and candy bars cost 45¢ each. How many of each item did Liz buy?

13. The cost to send a telegram is calculated using a flat fee for the first 10 words plus a set rate for each additional word. The cost to send a 12-word telegram is $13.50. The cost to send a 25-word telegram is $23.25. What are the flat fee and the set rate for each additional word?

14. Look at the problem in exercise 12. Can you think of a method to solve this problem that does not use equations? Solve the problem using this method.

Extending Your Thinking

15. A hockey team offers players the choice of two annual salary packages. Package A offers a base salary of x dollars plus a $1000 bonus for each goal scored. Package B offers a base salary of $10 000 less than Package A, but pays a bonus of $1500 for each goal scored. Determine the number of goals that must be scored in a season for both packages to pay the same amount.

PROJECT

You have solved linear systems in two variables by substitution. You will use this skill in the Chapter Project and in the following project in the Project Book:

• Balancing Dietary Protein in Livestock Feeds

COMMUNICATING THE IDEAS

List the steps you would use to solve a system of linear equations by substitution. Demonstrate that your list is correct using one of the exercises above.

Deploying a Parachute

In this stage of the Project, you will explore how long a skydiver can free fall at terminal velocity before the parachute is deployed. You will also determine the length of time it takes to reach the ground once the canopy is deployed. These photos show the standard free fall positions.

Terminal velocities vary for these different positions. Below are terminal velocity ranges for a skydiver wearing 9 kg of equipment.

Spread Stable Position: approximately 50 m/s to 54 m/s

Dive Position: approximately 56 m/s to 90 m/s

- Why do you think skydivers in the spread stable position fall at a slower rate than those in the dive position?

- You may already have learned that the minimum altitude for safe deployment of a parachute is approximately 760 m, and the rate of fall with an open parachute ranges from 3 m/s to 5 m/s, depending on the skydiver's mass and the type of parachute.

CHAPTER PROJECT

In the next stage of this Chapter Project, you will investigate how long it takes for a skydiver to accelerate to terminal velocity. *Tutorials 3.4* and *3.5* will help you develop an understanding of the related skills. You will return to this Chapter Project on page 158.

Work with a partner. Use a graphing calculator with these window settings.

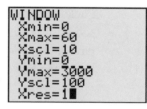

```
WINDOW
 Xmin=0
 Xmax=60
 Xscl=10
 Ymin=0
 Ymax=3000
 Yscl=100
 Xres=1■
```

1. Calculate when to deploy a parachute. Consider a skydiver who free falls from 3000 m in the spread stable position with a terminal velocity of 53 m/s.

    a) Write a linear equation in the form $y = mx + b$ that represents the skydiver's distance to the ground. Graph this line.

    b) Graph the line $y = 760$. What does this line represent?

    c) Determine the intersection point of these lines. What does this point represent?

    d) How much free fall time does the skydiver have at terminal velocity before the parachute must be deployed? Do not clear the equations in the Y= list. You will use them again in exercise 2.

Career Skills

Experimentation and adjustment of settings are skills used to optimize output in industry. Often, a guess has to be made based on past experience, and then adjustments are made.

2. Calculate how long it takes a skydiver with an open parachute to reach the ground. Consider the same skydiver with an open parachute who has a descent velocity of 4 m/s. The distance he is above ground is given by $y = -4x + b$.

a) Choose an appropriate value for b and graph your line. Use the same screen with the graphs displayed as in exercise 1.

b) Experiment with different values of b until the graph of the line representing the descent with an open parachute and the line representing the free fall intersect above the safe altitude of 760 m.

c) Choose an equation for the free fall that gives plenty of time for a free fall, and yet allows a safe descent with a parachute. Using this equation and the equation from part b, determine when the skydiver will deploy the parachute. How long will the skydiver fall at terminal velocity?

d) At what height did the skydiver deploy the parachute?

e) Use the x-intercept of the graph of the equation chosen in part c to determine how long it takes the skydiver to reach the ground once the parachute is opened. You may need to adjust your window settings.

Repeat exercises 1 and 2 for a skydiver in the dive position. Choose typical terminal velocities and parachute velocities.

All of the linear systems that you have studied so far have had exactly one solution. In this Tutorial, you will investigate linear systems that have no solution and systems that have many solutions. You will explore some important properties of linear systems in *Investigations 2* and *3*.

You will graph linear systems. The program LINES for the TI-83 calculator makes plotting systems of equations simple.

UTILITY

See Utility 24 for instructions on how to enter and run the LINES program using a TI-83 calculator. If you are using a different calculator, you must consult the User's Manual to amend the program for your calculator.

For each *Investigation*, use the standard window settings on the graphing calculator.

Investigation 1 The Number of Solutions of a Linear System

You will investigate how many solutions a linear system may have.

1. Graph the following system of equations:
$$-7x + y = 10$$
$$-14x + 2y = 20$$

a) What do you notice about the graphs? What are their slopes? What are their intercepts?

b) At how many points does the graph of the first equation intersect the graph of the second equation?

c) The solutions to a system of equations are the points of intersection of the graphs. How many solutions does this system have?

d) How are the equations alike? How are they different?

e) Make a prediction about the number of solutions of a system where one equation is a multiple of the other.

f) Check your prediction by creating another similar system of equations. Graph this system.

2. Graph the following system of equations.
$$2x - 5y = 15$$
$$2x - 5y = -5$$

a) What do you notice about the graphs? What are their slopes? What are their intercepts?

b) The solutions to a system of equations are the points where the graphs intersect. How many solutions are there?

c) How are the equations alike? How are they different?

d) Predict when a system of equations will have no solution.

e) Check your prediction with this system of equations.

$$3x + 2y = 8$$
$$3x + 2y = -4$$

f) Graph this linear system to see how many solutions it has.

$$4x - 3y = 12$$
$$8x - 6y = 30$$

g) If necessary, modify your prediction to write a statement to describe when a system of linear equations has no solution.

3. Graph the following system of equations.

$$2x - 3y = 3$$
$$5x + y = 16$$

a) What do you notice about the graphs?

b) At how many points does the graph of the first equation intersect the graph of the second equation?

c) How are the equations alike? How are they different?

A linear system may have one solution, no solution, or infinitely many solutions.

If a system has at least one solution, it is consistent. When a system has no solution it is inconsistent.

Intersecting lines

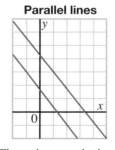

(a, b) is the only solution. system is consistent.

Parallel lines

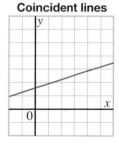

There is no solution. system is inconsistent.

Coincident lines

There are infinitely many solutions. The system is consistent.

Investigation 2   Properties of Linear Systems

In this *Investigation*, you will determine the effect of multiplying an equation by a constant.

1. Solve this linear system graphically.

$$5x + y = 16 \qquad ①$$
$$2x - 3y = 3 \qquad ②$$

2. A new system is created by multiplying equation ① by 4 and equation ② by 5.

$$20x + 4y = 64 \qquad ③$$
$$10x - 15y = 15 \qquad ④$$

Solve this new system graphically on the same grid as exercise 1.

3. Compare the results of exercises 1 and 2. What do you notice?

4. Use your knowledge from *Investigation 1* to explain why this occurs.

5. Write another linear system of equations with the same solution as these two systems. Check your prediction by graphing the new system.

6. Describe this property of linear systems.

Do not clear your graphs from the calculator or computer. You will use them in *Investigation 3*.

Investigation 3   Adding or Subtracting the Equations of a Linear System

You will investigate combining the equations of a linear system by adding or subtracting them.

1. Write another equation by adding the equations ① and ② of *Investigation 2*.

$$5x + y = 16 \qquad ①$$
$$+\ 2x - 3y = 3 \qquad ②$$

2. Graph the equation you obtained in exercise 1 on the same grid as in Investigation 2.

3. What do you notice? Explain.

4. Write another equation by subtracting equation ② of *Investigation 2* from equation ①.

$$5x + y = 16 \qquad ①$$
$$-(2x - 3y = 3) \qquad ②$$

5. Graph the equation you wrote in exercise 4 on the same grid as before.

6. What do you notice? Explain.

7. Describe the property of linear systems you have discovered.

In these *Investigations*, you should have discovered the following properties of linear systems:

Multiplying both sides of either equation of a linear system by a constant does not change the solution.

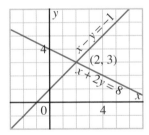
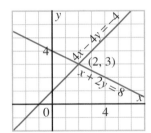

Adding or subtracting the equations of a linear system does not change the solution.

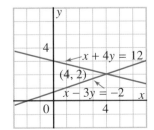
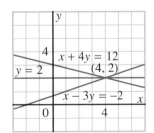

Check to determine if a point is a solution of a system.

Is $(-1, 1)$ a solution of the following system?

$$5x + 6y = 1$$
$$6x + 2y = -3$$

SOLUTION

$(-1, 1)$ is a solution of the system if the point lies on both lines. A point lies on a line only if its coordinates satisfy the equation of the line.

Substitute $x = -1$, and $y = 1$ in the equations.

$5x + 6y = 1$		$6x + 2y = -3$	
L.S. $= 5(-1) + 6(1)$	R.S. $= 1$	L.S. $= 6(-1) + 2(1)$	R.S. $= -3$
$= 1$		$= -4$	

The point with coordinates $(-1, 1)$ lies on the line $5x + 6y = 1$, but it does not lie on the line $6x + 2y = -3$.
Thus, $(-1, 1)$ is not a solution of the linear system.

DISCUSSING THE IDEAS

1. List three solutions to the system in exercise 1 of *Investigation 1*.

2. In *Investigation 2*, what is the solution of the system of equations ① and ② when both sides of equation ① are multiplied by -7 and equation ② remains the same?

3. In *Investigation 3*, what is the solution of the system consisting of the equations you wrote in exercises 1 and 4? Check your prediction.

4. Why is it important to specify that both sides of an equation should be multiplied by a constant for the solutions to remain the same? Why must the constant be non-zero?

5. Why is it necessary to check a possible solution of a system using both equations?

Checking Your Skills

1. For which of these systems is $(2, -3)$ a solution?

a) $x - y = 5$
$3x + 4y = -6$

b) $2x + y = 7$
$x - 3y = 10$

c) $4x - y = 11$
$-12x + 3y = -16$

2. Graph each system of equations to determine the number of solutions.

a) $4x + y = 9$
$3x + y = 7$

b) $x - 2y = -3$
$2x - 4y = -6$

c) $3x - 4y = 12$
$6x - 8y = 20$

3. The graphs of three lines are shown below.

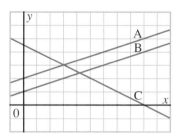

a) Which pairs of lines would create a system of equations with exactly one solution?

b) Which pairs of lines would create a system with no solution?

4. Determine whether each linear system has infinitely many solutions, no solution, or one solution.

a) $x + 2y = 6$
$x + 2y = 2$

b) $3x + 5y = 9$
$6x + 10y = 18$

c) $2x - 5y = 30$
$4x - 10y = 15$

5. Six equations are listed below.

$4x + 2y = 20$ $x - 3y = 12$ $5x - 15y = -60$
$2x + y = 10$ $6x + 3y = 5$ $2x - 6y = 24$

Using only these equations, write two different linear systems of two equations that have:

a) no solution

b) one solution

c) infinitely many solutions

6. Consider the equation $3x - 4y = 12$. Write a second equation to form a linear system that has:

a) no solution   **b)** one solution   **c)** infinitely many solutions

7. Consider this system of equations.

$$2x + 3y = 5 \qquad ①$$
$$6x + 7y = 1 \qquad ②$$

a) By what number would you multiply both sides of equation ① so that the coefficient on x is the same as in equation ②?

b) What is the result when you perform the multiplication described in part a? Label this equation ③.

c) What is the resulting equation when you subtract equation ② from equation ③? Solve this equation for y.

d) Once you know the value of y at the point of intersection, how do you find the value of x?

e) What value of x results from this procedure?

Extending Your Thinking

8. You used linear systems that have only one solution in *Investigations 2* and *3*. Determine whether the properties of linear systems that you discovered in these *Investigations* apply to a linear system that has:

a) infinitely many solutions   **b)** no solution

PROJECT

You will use the ideas you discovered in this Tutorial in the Chapter Project and in the following project in the Project Book:

• Balancing Dietary Protein in Livestock Feed

COMMUNICATING THE IDEAS

Suppose a linear system is given. Write to explain how you know, just by looking at the equations, the number of solutions that the system has.

Solving Linear Systems by Elimination

Solving a system of equations algebraically involves:

- reducing the system to one equation with only one variable
- solving this equation
- substituting this result into one of the original equations, or redoing the previous steps, to solve for the other variable

In this Tutorial, the one variable equation will be obtained using the method of elimination.

Example 1 **Solve a linear system by addition**

Susan can canoe upstream at 6 km/h and down-stream at 10 km/h. Her speed in still water is x kilometres per hour and the speed of the current is y kilometres per hour. The equations that represent this situation are $x + y = 10$ and $x - y = 6$.

a) Solve the system of equations to determine the speed of the current and Susan's speed in still water.

b) Check your answer.

SOLUTION

a) Since the coefficients of y are equal and opposite, we can eliminate y by adding the equations. According to the properties of linear systems you discovered in *Tutorial 2.4*, this will not change the solution.

$$\begin{array}{rl} x + y = 10 & \quad ① \\ +\quad x - y = 6 & \quad ② \\ \hline 2x = 16 & \quad ③ \\ x = 8 & \end{array}$$

Determine the value of y by substituting $x = 8$ in either of the original equations. Use equation $x + y = 10$.

$$8 + y = 10$$
$$y = 2$$

Susan paddles at 8 km/h in still water. The speed of the current is 2 km/h.

b) Check. Substitute $x = 8$ and $y = 2$ in both equations ① and ②.

x + y = 10		x − y = 6	
L.S. = 8 + 2 = 10	R.S. = 10	L.S. = 8 − 2 = 6	R.S. = 6

The solution (8, 2) is correct.

The procedure in *Example 1* may be explained graphically, as shown below.

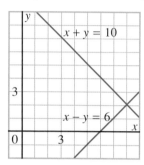 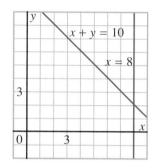 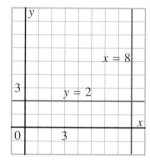

Example 2 **Multiply one equation by a constant, then subtract to eliminate**

A rock concert was attended by 8000 fans. Ticket prices were $50 and $30. The total revenue from ticket sales was $250 000.

a) How many $50 and $30 tickets were sold?

b) Check your answer.

S O L U T I O N

a) Let x represent the number of $50 tickets sold, and y the number of $30 tickets sold.

List the information in a table.

	Cost per Ticket ($)	Number of Tickets	Value ($)
High-priced-tickets	50	x	$50x$
Low-priced-tickets	30	y	$30y$
Total		8000	250 000

Use the last two columns in the table to generate the system of equations for the problem.

Total number of tickets sold: $x + y = 8000$ ①

Total value $50x + 30y = 250\ 000$ ②

To eliminate one of the variables, start by multiplying equation ① by a constant so that the coefficients of one of the variables are the same.

Multiply equation ① by 50 so that the coefficients of x will be 50 in both equations.

Multiply ① by 50. $50x + 50y = 400\ 000$
Copy, then subtract ② $- \quad (50x + 30y = 250\ 000)$
$$20y = 150\ 000$$

Solve for y. $y = 7500$

Substitute $y = 7500$ into equation ① and solve for x.
$$x + 7500 = 8000$$
$$x = 500$$

b) Check. Substitute $x = 500$ and $y = 7500$ into both equations ① and ②.

$50x + 30y = 250\ 000$	$x + y = 8000$

L.S. = 50(500) + 30(7500) R.S. = 250 000
    = 250 000
	L.S. = 500 + 7500 R.S. = 8000
	    = 8000

The solution is correct.

There were 500 tickets sold at $50 each, and 7500 tickets sold at $30 each.

Example 3 **Multiply each equation by an appropriate number, then add or subtract to eliminate a variable**

Andrea's Originals manufactures T-shirts with silk-screen prints of North West Coast aboriginal designs. She produces two types of T-shirts: a deluxe shirt with a 4-colour design, and a standard shirt with a one-colour design. One deluxe shirt costs $8 for materials and $30 for labour. One standard shirt costs $5 for materials and $12 for labour. Andrea's budget is $1700 for materials and $5700 for labour for one month. Solve by elimination to find how many of each type of shirt can be produced.

SOLUTION

Let d represent the number of deluxe T-shirts and s the number of standard T-shirts produced.

We have information about material costs and labour costs.

	Number of T-shirts	Material Costs	Labour Costs
Deluxe T-shirts	d	$8d$	$30d$
Standard T-shirts	s	$5s$	$12s$
Total		1700	5700

Material costs: $\qquad 8d + 5s = 1700 \qquad$ ①

Labour costs: $\qquad 30d + 12s = 5700 \qquad$ ②

To eliminate s, the coefficients must be the same. Since 12 is not a multiple of 5, make the coefficients a common multiple of 5 and 12. Use the lowest common multiple, 60.

Multiply ① by 12. $\qquad\qquad 96d + 60s = 20\ 400$

Multiply ② by 5, then subtract. $\quad -\ (150d + 60s = 28\ 500)$

$$-54d = -8100$$

Solve for d. $\qquad\qquad\qquad\qquad d = 150$

Substitute $d = 150$ in equation ①.

$$8(150) + 5s = 1700$$

Solve for s. $\qquad\qquad 1200 + 5s = 1700$

$$5s = 500$$

$$s = 100$$

Check the solution. Substitute $d = 150$ and $s = 100$ into equations ① and ②.

$30d + 12s = 5700$	$8d + 5s = 1700$
L.S. $= 30(150) + 12(100)$ R.S. $= 5700$ $= 5700$	L.S. $= 8(150) + 5(100)$ R.S. $= 1700$ $= 1700$

The solution is correct.

Angela can make 100 standard T-shirts and 150 deluxe T-shirts each month.

1. In *Example 1*, the two equations were added to eliminate *y*. What would have happened if we had subtracted the equations to eliminate *x*? Would we have obtained the same answers for *x* and *y*? Explain.

2. In *Example 2*, what could we have multiplied equation ① by
   a) to eliminate *x* by adding?
   b) to eliminate *y* by subtracting?
   c) to eliminate *y* by adding?

3. In *Example 2*, *y* = 7500 was substituted into equation ①. Why do you think ① was chosen? Would substituting *y* = 7500 into equation ② result in a different answer for *x*? Explain.

4. In *Example 3*, list 2 more multipliers that would eliminate *s* when you subtract.

5. Explain why it is easier to solve *Example 3* using the elimination method rather than the substitution method.

6. When do you add to eliminate a variable? When do you subtract?

7. Does it matter whether you eliminate *x* or *y*? Explain.

Checking Your Skills

1. Solve and check.
   a) $2x + 3y = 18$
      $2x - 3y = -6$
   b) $3x + 5y = 12$
      $7x + 5y = 8$
   c) $3x - 4y = 0$
      $5x - 4y = 8$

2. Solve and check.
   a) $3x + y = 18$
      $x + 2y = 11$
   b) $5x + 2y = 5$
      $3x - 4y = -23$
   c) $6x - 5y = -2$
      $2x + 3y = 18$

3. An airplane can travel at 800 km/h with a tailwind, and 730 km/h against the wind. Let the airplane's speed in still air be *s* kilometres per hour, and the wind speed be *w* kilometres per hour. A system of equations that represents the above information is $s + w = 800$ and $s - w = 730$. Solve the system to determine the wind speed and the speed of the plane in still air.

4. Green Thumb Garden Products Ltd. produces wheelbarrows and carts. A wheelbarrow has one front wheel. A garden cart has two wheels. The company has 500 wheels to make a total of 300 wheelbarrows and carts. Let w be the number of wheelbarrows and c the number of carts. An equation that shows there is a total 300 items is $w + c = 300$. An equation that shows there is a total of 500 wheels is $w + 2c = 500$. Solve the linear system by elimination to determine how many wheelbarrows and how many carts can be made.

5. The fuel consumption for a Mercedes-Benz is 11 L/100 km (0.11 L/km) for city driving, and 8 L/100 km (0.08 L/km) for highway driving. During one week, the car used 62 L of fuel to travel a total of 600 km both in the city and on the highway. Suppose the car travelled c kilometres in the city and h kilometres on the highway during that week. A system of equations that represents this situation is $c + h = 600$ and $0.11c + 0.08h = 62$. Solve the system to determine the distances driven in the city and on the highway.

6. The Leap Above Gymnastics Club is planning an end of season awards banquet. It will offer a choice of two main dishes: vegetarian lasagna at $8 a plate, and roast turkey at $12 a plate. The committee has a budget of $980 for 100 people. Let v represent the number of vegetarian lasagna plates and t the number of turkey plates to be served at the banquet.

a) Write an equation to represent the total number of people at the banquet.

b) Write an equation to represent the total cost of the banquet.

c) Solve the linear system by elimination to determine how many vegetarian lasagna plates and turkey plates can be served.

7. X-treme Snowboards manufactures a racing board and a high performance free-style board. The cost of manufacturing a racing board is $120 for materials and $180 for labour. The cost of manufacturing a free-style board is $100 for materials and $150 for labour. The company has a budget of $49 000 for materials and $73 500 for labour. It wishes to determine how many of each type of board to produce.

a) Define suitable variables to represent the unknowns.

b) Write a system of equations that represents the cost of labour and the cost of materials.

c) Determine how many of each board can be produced.

8. A disc jockey must have a total of 12 commercial breaks during a 1-h radio show. Each commercial break is either 30 s or 60 s. Suppose the total commercial time during a particular radio show was 10 min. How many 30-s and 60-s commercials were played during that hour?

9. The temperature of Earth's crust, T degrees Celsius, is a linear function of the depth, d metres, below the surface:
$T = ad + b$

In a mineshaft, the temperature is 23°C at a depth of 240 m. At 620 m, the temperature is 31°C.

a) Use the information given to write a system of equations in the unknowns a and b.

b) Solve this system of equations. Give your answers to 2 decimal places.

c) Write T as a function of d.

d) The world's deepest mine is 3581 m deep. Calculate the temperature at the bottom of this mine.

10. Any material that has a property that varies with heat can be used to establish a temperature scale. The most familiar example is the height of a column of mercury in a thermometer. There are other ways of finding the temperature. For example, read the pressure in a gas thermometer, or measure the voltage produced in a thermocouple. To establish a scale, you must decide on two fixed points. You then establish an equation that relates the temperature to a reading of the given quantity. Two convenient fixed points are 0°C (the melting point of ice) and 100°C (the boiling point of water). You wish to calibrate a thermocouple for temperatures between 0°C and 100°C. The temperature T, is a linear function of the thermocouple voltage, v. The general equation of this function is $T = mv + b$. By experiment you determine that in melting ice, $T = 0$°C and the voltage is 1.55 mV. In boiling water, $T = 100$°C and the voltage is 4.78 mV.

a) Use the experimental data given to generate a system of equations in the unknowns m and b.

b) Solve the system from part a. Substitute the resulting values of m and b into the general equation to get the calibration equation.

c) Use the calibration equation to determine the temperature, in degrees Celsius, that produces a voltage of 3.00 mV.

11. A coffee shop uses two different types of coffee to make a house blend. A dark French roast costing $4.95 per pound is mixed with a lighter Kenyan roast costing $3.75 per pound. The two types of coffee must be mixed together to make 50 pounds of the house blend. The house blend will cost $4.35 per pound.

a) State the unknown quantities and define suitable variables for them.

b) Write equations to represent the mass of coffee and the cost of coffee.

c) Solve the linear system by elimination to determine the mass of each kind of coffee that should be used.

Extending Your Thinking

12. A saline solution is a solution of salts in water. A nurse needs 4 L of an 8% saline solution by volume. She must mix the standard 10% and 5% saline solutions to obtain this. Let *x* litres be the volume of 10% solution and *y* litres the volume of 5% solution.

a) Write an equation for the total number of litres of solution that the nurse uses.

b) Write an equation that represents the total amount of salt in the solution.

c) How much of each solution will the nurse use?

13. An alloy is a mixture of metals. Jewellers often melt metals of different purity to make their products. A jeweller needs to make 500 g of a 50% silver alloy. She has a 60% silver alloy and a 35% silver alloy.

a) Write a linear system that models the problem.

b) What mass of each alloy was used to produce the final alloy?

PROJECT

In this Tutorial, you learned how to solve a linear system by elimination. You will use this skill in the Chapter Project and in the following project in the Project Book:

• Balancing Dietary Protein in Livestock Feeds

DISCUSSING THE IDEAS

In this chapter, you have learned three methods for solving a linear system: graphing, substitution, and elimination. Is one method always easier, or does it depend on the particular linear system you are solving? Choose examples from the exercises in the Tutorials to illustrate when it might be easiest to use each method.

Skydiving to Terminal Velocity

The equations you used at the beginning of your study on skydiving were linear. While descending at terminal velocity, or with an open parachute, the skydiver's velocity is constant because of air resistance. How long does a skydiver take to reach the constant terminal velocity? This depends on the skydiver's mass and on the position of the fall.

1. Free Fall in the Dive Position

A skydiver who free falls in the head-down dive position has an acceleration due to gravity that is very close to 9.8 m/s^2. She may fall a distance of 367.8 m before she reaches her terminal velocity of 84.9 m/s. In a jump from an airplane at an altitude of 3450 m, her height, h metres, above the ground during this free fall is given by $h = -4.9t^2 + 3450$. Determine graphically how many seconds it takes the skydiver to reach her terminal velocity.

2. Free Fall in the Spread Stable Position

A skydiver falling in the spread stable position is affected by air resistance. It takes about 12 s to reach an average terminal velocity of 52.8 m/s. Skydiving manuals contain Free Fall Tables. These tables give data on the distance a skydiver falls at various times until terminal velocity is reached. The Free Fall Table to the right shows the cumulative distance fallen in the spread stable position to a terminal velocity of 52.8 m/s.

Consider the skydiver who jumps from an altitude of 3450 m.

- Create a table in your graphing calculator, showing times in list L1 and corresponding height above the ground in list L2, during the free fall.

- Use the [STAT] [CALC] menu of your calculator to determine a quadratic function that best fits the data.

- Plot the graph of the regression function on the same grid as that for the head-down dive position in exercise 1.

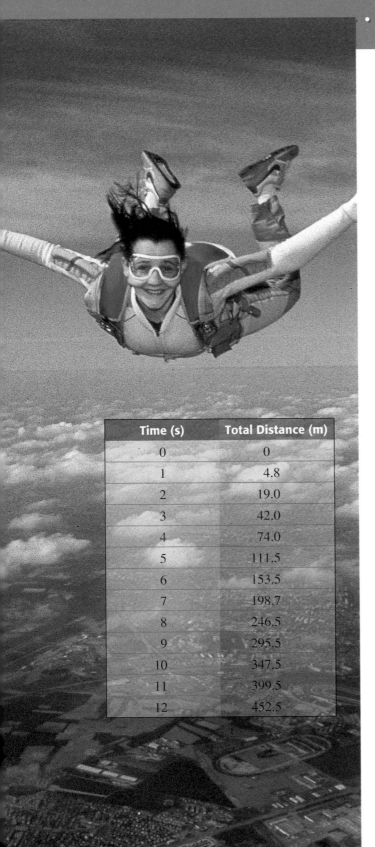

Time (s)	Total Distance (m)
0	0
1	4.8
2	19.0
3	42.0
4	74.0
5	111.5
6	153.5
7	198.7
8	246.5
9	295.5
10	347.5
11	399.5
12	452.5

3. Create your skydiving information poster. It should include the following:

- A vertical scale to show altitude every 100 m, up to 4000 m. Indicate the points on the line that correspond to a skydiver making a typical jump. Show an initial height of your choice, the altitude at which terminal velocity is reached, the altitude at which the parachute is deployed, and the minimum safe altitude for deploying a parachute. For each stage of the jump, include the time in the air, and the skydiver's speed. In the same diagram, include information for a skydiver in the spread stable position.

- Graphs that show the different stages of the jump.

- Drawings or photographs that illustrate the spread stable position and the dive position.

- Any other photographs or drawings you found.

Career Skills

The ability to communicate technical information in an interesting way is a relevant skill in today's workplace. Salespeople and technical planners often have to make presentations that explain the capabilities and uses of equipment to an audience of non-specialists.

What Do I Need To Know?

Tutorial	Skills and Concepts	Important Results and Formulas
3.1	• Solve a system of linear equations in two variables by graphing	• A solution of a linear system is an ordered pair that satisfies all the equations • Solutions may be found by graphing the lines on the same grid. If the lines intersect, the coordinates of the intersection point(s) are a solution of the system
3.2	• Model a situation algebraically with a linear system	
3.3	• Solve systems of linear equations in two variables by substitution	• Reduce a linear system to an equation in one variable by substitution from one equation of the system into the other equation • Determine the value of the remaining variable by substitution
3.4	• Understand that there might be one, many, or no solutions to a linear system depending on the equations • Understand that multiplying both sides of an equation in a linear system by a non-zero constant does not change the solution of the system • Understand that adding or subtracting the equations of a system does not change the solution of the system	• A linear system is consistent if it has one solution or infinitely many solutions; the graphs either intersect at one point or are the same line • A linear system is inconsistent if there is no solution; the graphs are distinct parallel lines
3.5	• Solve a system of linear equations in two variables using elimination	• Reduce a linear system to an equation with one variable by adding or subtracting multiples of the equations • Determine the value of the remaining variable by substitution

What Should I Be Able To Do?

You have used several different methods to solve linear systems and non-linear equations. You will use all of these methods in this review. Part A is investigative, part B has contextual problems, and part C gives you an opportunity to reflect on the Chapter Project.

Use the reference sections of the book as necessary.

Part A

You will need grid paper, a ruler, and a graphing calculator.

1. Before a manufacturing business expands its operations, it is important to investigate how additional capital investment will affect costs. You will investigate how increased production may lower costs, change the break-even point, and increase profits.

   a) A business manufactures widgets. The *fixed cost* for this business is currently $10 000 each month, and each widget costs $8 to produce. Each widget is sold for $10. Write an equation that represents the total cost, C dollars, of producing n widgets each month. Write an equation to represent the revenue, R dollars, from selling n widgets each month.

   b) Plot the graphs of the equations you wrote in part a on the same grid. Use your graph to determine how many widgets must be sold for the business to break even. What are the production costs and revenues at this point?

   c) The business plans to expand its production by purchasing a new, and more efficient widget-making machine. This investment will result in the fixed monthly costs increasing to $50 000, but each widget will now only cost $5 to produce. Write an equation that represents the new costs, N dollars, each month. Plot the graph of the new costs on the same grid as part a.

   d) Use your graph to estimate how many widgets must be sold each month before the purchase of the new equipment becomes cost effective. (At what point do the costs using the new equipment equal the costs using the old equipment?)

   e) Use the TRACE and CALC functions on your calculator to determine the new break-even point.

   f) Verify your results by calculating the new break-even point algebraically.

   g) Calculate the profit on the sale of 20 000 widgets for each type of equipment. How much more profit can be made once the new equipment is installed?

   h) Assume the company sells an average of 15 000 units each month. Should the company purchase the new equipment? Explain.

i) To stay competitive, the company is considering decreasing the selling price to $8.50 per unit when the new equipment is used. How many units must be sold to break even at this price? Would you recommend decreasing the price to $8.50? Explain.

Part B

2. Solve the linear system graphically.

$2x - y = 8$

$x + 2y = 21$

3. Solve the linear system by substitution, then check.

$y = 1 - 3x$

$2x + 3y = 11$

4. Solve the linear system by elimination.

$4x + y = -5$

$2x + 3y = 5$

5. Elena has the choice of two cellular phone plans.

Company A: $25 per month with 30 min free calling time, and 55¢ per minute or part thereof.

Company B: $50 per month charge, and 20¢ per minute or part thereof.

The equations that represent these plans are:

$C = 0.55(n - 30) + 25$, where $n > 30$

$C = 0.20n + 50$, where C is the cost in dollars for n minutes of calling time used each month.

a) Use a graphing calculator to determine the number of minutes of calling time used each month for both plans to cost the same. What is this cost?

b) Which plan should Elena choose if she speaks for 100 min on average each month?

6. The perimeter of a rectangular garden plot is 20 m. The length is 3 m greater than the width. Write equations that represent this situation. Use substitution to calculate the length and width of this garden plot.

7. A total of 200 people attended a school play. Ticket prices were $10 for adults, and $6 for students. The total revenue from ticket sales was $1680.

a) Create a table that lists this information.

b) Write two equations that represent the situation.

c) Determine the number of adults and the number of students who attended the play.

8. A small home-based chair manufacturer produces handcrafted stools and kitchen chairs. The materials for a stool cost $12 and the labour costs $20. The cost of making a chair is $15 for materials and $25 for labour. Each month, the manufacturer budgets $960 for materials and $1600 for labour.

a) Write equations that represent this situation.

b) Determine the number of stools and chairs that can be produced each month.

9. For each of the following systems, determine, without solving, the number of solutions.

a) $2x + 3y = 5$
$3x - 2y = 7$

b) $6x + 12y = 21$
$2x + 4y = 7$

c) $5x - 2y = 12$
$4y - 10x = 6$

10. A diver dives into the sea in Alcapulco from a height of 35 m. His height, h metres, above the water t seconds after leaving the cliff is given by $h = -4.9t^2 + t + 35$. Use a graphing calculator to determine how long he is in the air before he hits the water.

Part C

The Chapter Project combines many skills and concepts in a single problem. Here is a sampling of student work from different stages of the project. Review these samples to gain insights into your own project work.

Here is a copy of a student's work. Has he explained the terms he has used? Do you think his estimates of heights above the ground at which a skydiver reaches terminal velocity are reasonable? Has he illustrated skydiving from below 4000 m in a clear and interesting way?

Representation of a Skydiver in the "Dive" position

Starting height of 3600m, reaching terminal velocity after 367.8 m. Terminal velocity 85 m/s, speed when parachute deployed is 4 m/s. Minimum deployment height is 760 m.

Time (s)	Height (m)
0	3600
1	3595.1
2	3580.4
3	3555.9
4	3521.6
5	3477.5
6	3423.6
7	3359.9
8	3286.4
8.66	3232.2
10.66	3062.2
12.66	2892.2
14.66	2722.2
16.66	2552.2
18.66	2382.2
20.66	2212.2
22.66	2042.2
24.66	1872.2
26.66	1702.2
28.66	1532.2
30.66	1362.2
32.66	1192.2
34.66	1022.2
36.66	852.2
37	823.3
57	743.3
77	663.3
97	583.3
117	503.3
137	423.3
157	343.3
177	263.3
197	183.3
217	103.3
237	23.3
242.825	0

This data represents the skydivers increase in speed until he reaches terminal velocity

This data represents the skydiver at terminal velocity

This data represents the skydiver once the parachute has been deployed

Sky diver at 3600 in the Dive

Representation of a Skydiver in the "Spread Stable" position

Starting height of 3600m, reaching terminal velocity after 452.4 m. Terminal velocity 53 m/s, speed when parachute deployed is 4 m/s. Minimum deployment height is 760 m.

Time (s)	Height (m)
0	3600
1	3595.2
2	3581
3	3558
4	3526
5	3488.5
6	3446.5
7	3401.3
8	3353.5
9	3304.5
10	3252.5
11	3200.5
12	3147.5
15	2988.5
18	2829.5
21	2670.5
24	2511.5
27	2352.5
30	2193.5
33	2034.5
36	1875.5
39	1716.5
42	1557.5
45	1398.5
48	1239.5
51	1080.5
54	921.5
57	762.5
77	682.5
97	602.5
117	522.5
137	442.5
157	362.5
177	282.5
197	202.5
217	122.5
237	42.5
247.625	0

This data represents the skydivers increase in speed until he reaches terminal velocity

This data represents the skydiver at terminal velocity

This data represents the skydiver once the parachute has been deployed

Sky diver at 3600 in the Spread Stable

Chapter Project - Skydiving

Deploying a Parachute

1. a) $y = -53x + 3000$
   b) The minimum height at which the skydiver must deploy his parachute.
   c) $x = 42.26$, $y = 760$ (42.26,760) This represents the time spent at terminal velocity before the minimum height for parachute deployment is reached.
   d) 42.26 seconds

2. a) $y = -4x + 3000$. The slope is -4, negative because the skydiver is getting closer to the ground.
   b) $y = -4x + 1000$. Free falls for 40.82 s, opens parachute at 836.73 m.
   c) 250 seconds
   d) The skydiver will be at terminal velocity for 40.82 seconds, and will have an open parachute for 209.18 s.

For the "Dive" position, the following information was determined.
An average equation for the skydiver is $y = -73x + 3000$.
It will take 30.68 seconds to reach the minimum parachute deployment height
Using the same speed for a deployed parachute (4 m/s), and the same equation ($y = -4x+1000$), the skydiver will be at terminal velocity for 28.99 seconds, will deploy the parachute at 884.06 m, and will have the parachute open for 221.01 seconds.

Skydiving To Terminal Velocity

1. $3450 - 367.8 = -4.9t^2 + 3450$
   $3082.2 = -4.9t^2 + 3450$
   $-4.9t^2 = 367.8$
   $t^2 = 75.06$
   $t = 8.66$ seconds

2. $y = -2.03t^2 - 15.19t + 3462.19$

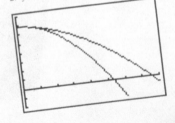

4

Linear Programming

Overview

PROJECT

You should complete at least one project that uses the skills you learn in this chapter. Recommended projects in the Project Book are:

- Diamond Mining
- Farm Planning
- Maximizing Music Profits

Analyzing a Snack Food

An important part of a healthy lifestyle is making proper food choices. We must eat well for our bodies to grow, remain healthy, and have the energy needed for the day's activities. When we increase our activity level, our nutritional needs increase accordingly. Canoeists, hikers, and other outdoor enthusiasts often take along a "trail mix" on excursions as a nutritious snack. Trail mix usually contains nuts, seeds, and dried fruit.

In this Chapter Project, you will investigate the nutritional content of one trail mix. Based on this analysis, and the nutritional information of various components, you will plan an improved trail mix that can be produced for minimum cost.

CHAPTER PROJECT

To complete this Chapter Project you will need to set up linear systems of inequalities that model problem situations and solve the systems. Complete *Tutorials 4.1* to *4.4* to develop an understanding of the related skills. You will return to this Chapter Project on page 198.

Here are some questions to consider:

- What are the general nutritional needs of people?

- What are the nutritional needs of people who are physically active for the majority of the day?

- Some fats are essential for proper growth and health. What are the differences between "good" and "bad" fats?

- What factors contribute to trail mix being considered a good nutritional snack?

Research nutrition and trail mixes. The Internet, your library, magazines, and outdoor equipment suppliers are possible sources of information. Write a short outline of what is required for trail mix to be considered a good nutritional snack.

FYI Visit: www.awl.com/canada/school/connections

You can start your research from our Internet site: Click on <u>MATHLINKS</u>
followed by the *Applied Mathematics 11* logo. Select a topic under Nutrition.

The Graph of a Linear Inequality

In this chapter you will learn to solve graphically certain types of *optimization problems*, such as "which foods should I eat to get the best combination of nutrients but minimize my calorie intake?" Problems such as this, which ask for the best solution subject to certain conditions, occur in many different settings. *Linear programming* is the process of solving optimization problems that can be represented by a system of linear inequalities. A linear inequality, such as $3x - 2y < 1$, is similar to a linear equation, but the equals sign has been replaced with one of four inequality signs: $>$, $<$, $\geq$, $\leq$.

As a first step to solving some of these problems, you will graph linear inequalities in two variables.

Practise Your Prior Skills

You will work with inequalities. Try these exercises as preliminary review.

1. Each inequality below is followed by a list of numbers. Determine which numbers are solutions of the inequality.

  a) $2x - 5 < 11$ 6, 8, 10

  b) $3x + 1 \geq 10$ 2, 3, 4

2. Write an inequality that is represented by each graph.

  a)

  $$-1 \quad 0 \quad 1 \quad 2 \quad 3 \quad 4 \quad 5$$

  b)

  $$-1 \quad 0 \quad 1 \quad 2 \quad 3 \quad 4 \quad 5$$

  c)

  $$-3 \; -2 \; -1 \quad 0 \quad 1 \quad 2 \quad 3$$

3. Graph each inequality.

  a) $b \geq 2$ **b)** $s < -1$

  c) $m \leq 3.5$ **d)** $y > -3.5$

4. Solve and check each inequality.

  a) $2x > -8$ **b)** $5 + x \geq 3$

  c) $-\frac{1}{3}y \geq 4$ **d)** $2x + 11 < 5$

  e) $2x + 5 < 3x - 1$

5. Rewrite each equation to solve for y. Give the slope and the y-intercept of each line.

  a) $2x + 3y - 6 = 0$ **b)** $x - 2y = 6$

6. Graph each line.

a) $2x - 3y + 6 = 0$ **b)** $x - y = 1$

An equation in one variable can be graphed on a coordinate grid. Recall that $x = 5$ is a vertical line through $(5, 0)$. Similarly $y = -3$ is a horizontal line through $(0, -3)$.

Investigation 1 Graphing Half-Planes

You will graph inequalities in one variable on a coordinate grid. Use grid paper.

1. Draw a coordinate grid.

2. Draw the line which represents the equation $x = 3$.

3. Do all of the points on the line satisfy the equation in exercise 2?

4. The line divides the plane into two regions, or *half-planes*. Shade the region to the left of the line. Write a statement about the x-coordinates of all points in this half-plane.

5. Write a statement about the x-coordinates of all the points to the right of the line.

6. On a new grid, draw the line $y = 2$.

7. Shade the region that contains all the points whose y-coordinates satisfy the inequality $y > 2$.

8. Use a different method of shading to indicate the region where all the points have y-coordinates that satisfy $y < 2$.

9. Describe how to draw the graph of $x > 4$. Do all of the points on the line $x = 4$ satisfy the inequality? Suggest ways you could draw the line to indicate this.

10. How could you draw the graph of $y \leq 1$?

Is there a simple way to determine the graph of an inequality that contains two variables? You will investigate a way to do this.

Graphing an Inequality in Two Variables

In this Investigation you will determine the graph of the inequality $x + 3y \geq 3$. Use grid paper.

1. Draw a coordinate grid.

2. Graph the equation $x + 3y = 3$. Use any method you wish.

3. Choose any 4 points on the line. Determine the coordinates of each point.

4. Test the coordinates of each point to see if they satisfy the inequality $x + 3y \geq 3$. Do all the points on the line $x + 3y = 3$ satisfy the inequality $x + 3y \geq 3$? Explain.

5. On the coordinate grid, mark any 4 points in the half-plane above the line, and any 4 points in the half-plane below the line. Label each point with its coordinates.

6. Substitute the coordinates of each point in turn into the left side of the inequality $x + 3y \geq 3$. Compare each result to the right side, 3. Circle any points on your grid that satisfy the inequality.

7. Make a conjecture about the location of all points that satisfy the inequality $x + 3y \geq 3$.

8. Predict the inequality that all points in the half-plane below the line would satisfy.

9. Suggest a method for graphing a linear inequality in two variables.

10. Check your prediction. Graph $2x + y < 4$.

You have confirmed in *Investigations 1* and *2* that a line divides the coordinate plane into two half-planes, each of which is the graph of an inequality obtained by replacing = with either > or <.

DISCUSSING THE IDEAS

1. You drew the graphs in the Investigations on grid paper. Explain how to draw the graph of the inequality $y < 4$ on a graphing calculator.

UTILITY

If you have never changed the graphing style of your graphing calculator, Utility 21 tells you how to do it on a TI-83. If you are using a different calculator, refer to its User's Manual.

2. You cannot enter the equation $x = 2$ into the Y= list of a graphing calculator. Discuss how to draw a vertical line on a calculator.

If you need to review the drawing capability of the TI-83, check the User's Mannual.

3. Explain why the graph of $2x + y < 4$ is the region below the line.

4. Discuss possible ways you could show on a diagram that the points on the line $2x + y = 4$ are not part of the graph of the inequality $2x + y < 4$.

5. How would the graph of $2x + y < 4$ change if the < sign was replaced by ≤?

6. One way to graph a linear inequality is to first graph the corresponding equation, then shade a region on one side of the line. Explain how to tell which side of the line to shade.

7. If you were asked to graph the inequality $y > x^2 + 1$, you might start by drawing the graph of the equation $y = x^2 + 1$. Where do you think the points that satisfy the inequality are relative to the graph? Check your predictions using a graphing calculator.

PROJECT

In this Tutorial, you investigated the graph of an inequality. You will use this in the Chapter Project and the following projects in the Project Book.

- Diamond Mining
- Farm Planning
- Maximizing Music Profits

COMMUNICATING THE IDEAS

Write a letter to a friend that explains how important it is to be able to graph a linear equation quickly and accurately when graphing a linear inequality.

In *Tutorial 4.1* you investigated the graph of a linear inequality. In this Tutorial you will use your knowledge of half-planes to graph linear inequalities in two variables.

Here is a procedure you can use to graph a linear inequality.

- Graph the line obtained by replacing the inequality sign with an equals sign. This line is the boundary between two half-planes.
  - If the inequality sign is ≤ or ≥, the points on the line belong to the graph. Use a solid line to indicate this.
  - If the inequality sign is > or < the points on the line do not belong to the graph. Use a broken line to indicate this.

- Solve the inequality for y in the form $y > mx + b$, or $y < mx + b$, where y is positive. Recall, when you multiply or divide both sides of the inequality by a negative number, the inequality sign changes direction. The half-plane above the line is the graph of the corresponding > inequality, the half-plane below is the graph of the corresponding < inequality.

- Choose a test point in one half-plane. Substitute the coordinates of the test point into the inequality and evaluate the expression.
  - If a true statement results, the test point belongs to the required graph and so will all the other points in this half-plane. This is the graph of the inequality. Shade this half-plane.
  - If a false statement results, the region on the other side of the line is the graph of the inequality, so shade it.

Linear inequalities can be graphed on a coordinate grid and on a graphing calculator. *Example 1* demonstrates both these methods.

Example 1 **Graph a linear inequality**

Graph each inequality.

a) $2x + y > 6$

b) $y - x < 3$

SOLUTION

a) Use a coordinate grid.

First graph the equation $2x + y = 6$, with a broken line. Use the intercepts. The y-intercept is 6 and the x-intercept is 3, giving the points $(0, 6)$ and $(3, 0)$.

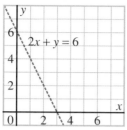

Solve the inequality $2x + y > 6$ for y.

$y > 6 - 2x$

The graph of the inequality should be the half-plane above the line. To check this, choose any point in the identified region. Choose $(8, 8)$. Substitute the values $x = 8$ and $y = 8$ into the inequality.

L.S. $= 2(8) + 8$ R.S. $= 6$
$\quad\ = 24$

L.S. $>$ R.S.
The inequality is satisfied.

The points on the line do not satisfy the inequality. The broken line indicates that these points are not part of the solution. Shade the region above this line.

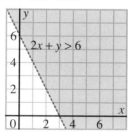

b) Use the graphing calculator.

Replace the inequality sign with an equals sign to get $y - x = 3$.

If you have never used a graphing calculator to graph an inequality, Utility 21 shows you how to change the graph style on a TI-83. If you are using a different calculator, refer to its User's Manual.

The equation $y - x = 3$ must be entered into the Y= list. Rearrange the equation to solve for y.

$$y - x + x = 3 + x$$
$$y = 3 + x$$

Enter this equation into the calculator.

To identify the correct half-plane, solve the inequality for y.

$$y - x < 3$$
$$y < 3 + x$$

The graph of the inequality $y - x < 3$ is the half-plane below the line with equation $y - x = 3$.

To check this, choose a test point. Choose $(0, 0)$. Substitute $x = 0$ and $y = 0$ into the original inequality.

L.S. $= 0 - 0$ R.S. $= 3$
        $= 0$

L.S. $<$ R.S.

The inequality is satisfied.

To change the graph style to that shown in the window below left, go to the Y= screen, move the cursor to the left of Y1, and press [ENTER] 3 times until the lower triangle symbol appears. Press [GRAPH] to display the graph shown on the right. Press [ZOOM] **6** to set the standard [WINDOW] settings.

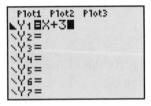
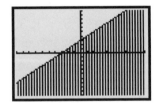

Inequalities may occur when we model a problem algebraically. The graph of the inequality is a pictorial representation of the solution.

Example 2 Solve an inequality by graphing

A mixture is to be created using sunflower seeds and raisins. Sunflower seeds contain 4 mg of iron per 100 g and raisins contain 2 mg of iron per 100 g. The mixture must contain at least 20 mg of iron. This can be represented by the inequality $4x + 2y \geq 20$, where x represents the number of 100-g units of sunflower seeds used and y represents the number of 100-g units of raisins used.

a) Explain why the inequality ≥ is used as opposed to >.

b) Graph all possible solutions for this mixture.

c) Describe 2 possible combinations of sunflower seeds and raisins that meet the criteria stated above.

SOLUTION

a) The mixture must contain at least 20 mg of iron. This means that 20 mg, or more, of iron is acceptable. The sign ≥ indicates that all mixtures containing 20 mg, or more, of iron are possible solutions of this problem.

b) The mixture cannot contain a negative amount of either ingredient, so consider only the first quadrant of the coordinate plane.

Graph the line $4x + 2y = 20$.

Use a table of values. Calculate the intercepts of the line.

x	y
0	10
5	0

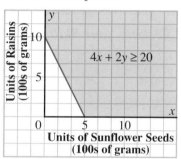

Use a solid line to indicate that ordered pairs on the line are solutions. Label the axes. Since the point (0, 0) is not on this line, use it to determine which half-plane represents the graph of the inequality.

Substitute $x = 0$ and $y = 0$ into the inequality $4x + 2y \geq 20$.

$$\text{L.S.} = 4(0) + 2(0) \qquad\qquad \text{R.S.} = 20$$
$$= 0$$
$$\text{L.S.} < \text{R.S.}$$

The point (0, 0) does not satisfy the inequality.

The solutions of this inequality lie above or on the line. This region is shaded and the line remains a solid line.

c) Mark any 2 points on the line or in the shaded region. These are *feasible solutions*. Points on the intersection of grid lines are easiest.

Point A (3, 4) represents 3 units of sunflower seeds and 4 units of raisins, that is, 300 g of sunflower seeds and 400 g of raisins.

Point B (4, 12) represents 400 g of sunflower seeds and 1200 g of raisins.

1. Why is an inequality such as $2x + 3y \leq 5$ called a linear inequality in two variables?

2. Explain why $(0, 0)$ is often chosen to be the test point. When must you use a different point as the test point?

3. If you were to graph the inequality $3x + 5y < 60$, should you use a solid or a broken line as the boundary? Justify your answer.

4. Wilma graphs the inequality $x > 0$, considering it to be an inequality in one variable. Frank graphs the same inequality, considering it to be an inequality in two variables. How will the two graphs differ?

EXERCISES

Checking Your Skills

1. Graph each inequality on a coordinate grid.

   a) $x < 2$ **b)** $y \geq -2$

   c) $y > 0$ **d)** $x \leq 0$

2. Copy each diagram below. Draw the boundary line and shade the solution of each inequality.

   a) $2x + y \leq 10$ **b)** $x + 4y > 12$

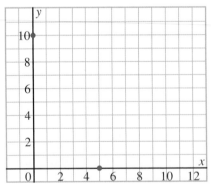 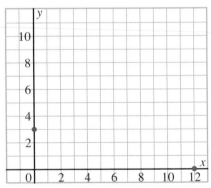

3. Graph each inequality on a coordinate grid. Describe 2 possible solutions of each inequality.

   a) $y \leq 2x - 3$ **b)** $y \leq x - 2$

   c) $4y < x - 3$ **d)** $2y \geq -x + 5$

   e) $y + 3x \geq 9$ **f)** $2y - x < 2$

   g) $3x - 2y > 6$ **h)** $4x - 5y + 20 \leq 0$

4. Use technology to graph each inequality. Use the standard window settings.

a) $y \geq x + 1$

b) $y < 3x - 4$

c) $2y > 3x - 5$

d) $4y < 5x + 12$

5. Use technology to graph each linear inequality. Use the standard window settings.

a) $y \leq 4$

b) $y + 1 > 0$

6. Use technology to graph each inequality. Choose suitable window settings.

a) $x - 2y \geq 4$

b) $5x + 2y > 10$

c) $2x + y < -4$

d) $2x - 7y \leq 14$

7. A company makes motorcycles and bicycles. In any given week, a total of no more than 400 vehicles can be made. An inequality that represents this is $x + y \leq 400$, where x represents the number of motorcycles and y the number of bicycles made in 1 week.

a) Explain why the inequality sign is $\leq$.

b) Explain why x and y are *discrete* variables. What does this mean about the graph of the inequality?

c) Draw a graph to show the number of motorcycles and bicycles that could be made in 1 week.

If you need to review discrete and continuous variables see *Tutorial 1.2*.

8. Terry plans to spend up to 10 h reviewing science and English in preparation for examinations. An inequality that represents this is $x + y \leq 10$, where x represents the number of hours spent on science and y the number of hours spent on English.

a) Explain why x and y are *continuous* variables.

b) Draw a graph to show how much time Terry could spend on a review of each subject.

9. A cycle dealer wishes to purchase touring cycles for $300 each and racing cycles for $400 each. She plans to spend not more than $8400. She buys x touring models and y racing models. An inequality that represents this is $300x + 400y \leq 8400$, which can be simplified to $y \leq 21 - 0.75x$.

a) Explain how the inequality was simplified.

b) Show the solution of this inequality graphically.

c) A *feasible solution* is one that satisfies all the conditions of the problem, including the obvious ones that are not stated. Explain why the feasible solutions of this problem are ordered pairs of whole numbers. Describe two possible solutions.

10. One type of cake requires 150 g of flour. Another requires 75 g of flour. At most, 2.25 kg of flour is available. An inequality that represents the problem is $0.15x + 0.075y \leq 2.25$.

a) Use a graphing calculator to graph this inequality.

b) Explain how this graph can be used to obtain the feasible solutions to the problem, and describe two possible solutions.

Extending Your Thinking

11. An 80-ha farm is to be planted with corn and wheat. Planting and harvesting costs, for which no more than $12 000 are available, are $300/ha for corn and $100/ha for wheat. Draw a graph to show the area of each crop that can be planted.

PROJECT

In this Tutorial, you learned how to graph an inequality in two variables. You will use this in the Chapter Project and the following projects in the Project Book.

- Diamond Mining
- Farm Planning
- Maximizing Music Profits

COMMUNICATING THE IDEAS

The graphing calculator can shade a region above or below a line, and a line can be drawn as a broken line. Write to explain why it may be preferable to graph an inequality on grid paper.

The Solution of a System of Linear Inequalities

In *Chapter 3* you studied systems of linear equations in two variables. The solution is the point(s) of intersection of the lines.

Recall from *Tutorial 4.1* that the graph of any linear equation is a straight line that divides the plane into two half-planes. The half-planes are the graphs of the corresponding inequalities.

A system of linear inequalities can consist of two or more inequalities, and the solution is the region where the corresponding half-planes intersect or overlap.

Example 1 **Graph a system of linear inequalities**

A region is defined by these inequalities.

$$x \geq 0$$
$$y \geq 1$$
$$2x + y < 4$$

Graph this region.

SOLUTION

Graph each inequality on the same grid.

- The graph of $x \geq 0$ is the set of points on the y-axis and in the half-plane to the right of it.

- The line $y = 1$ is horizontal with y-intercept 1. The graph of $y \geq 1$ is this line together with the half-plane above it.

- To graph the line with equation $2x + y = 4$, determine the intercepts.

x	y
0	4
2	0

Solve the inequality $2x + y < 4$ for y:

$y < 4 - 2x$

The graph of $2x + y < 4$ is the half-plane below the line.

Use $(0, 0)$ as a test point. Substitute $x = 0$ and $y = 0$ into the inequality.

L.S. $= 2(0) + 0$ R.S. $= 4$
       $= 0$

L.S. $<$ R.S.

The point $(0, 0)$ satisfies the inequality.

• Use a different colour or a different type of shading for each half-plane.

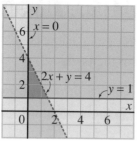

The solution is the region covered by all three half-planes.

Shading all of the half-planes can be very messy. Often we will shade only the region that is common to all three half-planes. This region is the intersection of the three half-planes.

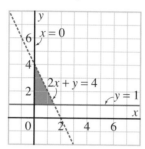

Example 2 **Graph a system of inequalities using technology**

A sporting goods manufacturer makes footballs and soccer balls. Each football takes 3 min on a cutting machine and 1 min on a stitching machine. A soccer ball takes 3 min on the cutting machine and 4 min on the stitching machine. Let x represent the number of footballs and y the number of soccer balls made in 1 h or less.

a) Explain why these inequalities represent this situation.

$$x \geq 0$$
$$y \geq 0$$
$$x + y \leq 20$$
$$x + 4y \leq 60$$

b) Draw a graph to illustrate these inequalities.

c) Use the graph to write two possible solutions of the system of inequalities.

SOLUTION

a) The number of footballs or soccer balls cannot be negative.

$x \geq 0$ ①

$y \geq 0$ ②

The time taken on each machine can be shown in a chart.

	Football	**Soccer Ball**
Variable	x	y
Time Taken for 1 Ball on a Cutting Machine	3 min	3 min
Time Taken for 1 Ball on a Stitching Machine	1 min	4 min

The total time on the cutting machine for the footballs and the soccer balls is less than or equal to 60 min.

$3x + 3y \leq 60$, which simplifies to

$x + y \leq 20$ ③

The total time on the stitching machine for the footballs and the soccer balls is less than or equal to 60 min.

$x + 4y \leq 60$ ④

b) Graph the system.

- The graph of $x \geq 0$ is the set of points on the line $x = 0$ (the y-axis), and the half-plane to the right of it.

- The graph of $y \geq 0$ is the set of points on the line $y = 0$ (the x-axis), and the half-plane above it.

- The inequality $x + y \leq 20$ can be rewritten as $y \leq -x + 20$. The graph of the inequality is the line $y = -x + 20$ together with the half-plane below it.

- Solve the inequality $x + 4y \leq 60$ for y.

$4y \leq 60 - x$

$y \leq \dfrac{60 - x}{4}$

The graph of the inequality $x + 4y \leq 60$ is the line $y = \dfrac{60 - x}{4}$ together with the half-plane below it.

- To graph these inequalities using a graphing calculator:

Enter the following equations into the Y= list.

$y = -x + 20$

$y = \dfrac{60 - x}{4}$

$y = 0$

- For the graphing styles, choose the lower triangles for the equations $x + y = 20$ and $x + 4y = 60$, since the graph is the lower half-plane. Choose the upper right triangle for $y = 0$, since the graph is the upper half-plane.

- The graph of the inequality $x \geq 0$ cannot be drawn in this way, since it is not the graph of a function. A vertical line can be drawn on the graphing calculator, but the half-plane cannot be shaded. The easiest way to deal with the inequality $x \geq 0$ is by choosing Xmin = 0 for the graphing window.

- A suitable window and the graph of the system of inequalities are shown below.

 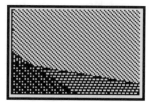

c) Only whole numbers of footballs and soccer balls can be produced, so x and y should be whole numbers. Only those points within the overlap region with integral coordinates are feasible solutions. A graphing calculator cannot show this. Choose two points within, or on the boundary of, the region.

By inspection, (10, 10) and (20, 0) are feasible points.
The manufacturer could produce 10 footballs and 10 soccer balls or 20 footballs and 0 soccer balls.

You can see from the graph in *Example 2* that when many half-planes overlap, it is quite difficult to distinguish the region that shows the solution to the system of inequalities. One answer to this problem is to shade the complementary or opposite half-planes. This way, the region of solution is unshaded and clearly visible. This is called *reverse shading*. The graph below shows the solution to *Example 2* using reverse shading.

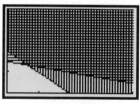

reverse shading

Example **3** **Solve a system of linear inequalities using technology and reverse shading**

A target is described by these inequalities.

$$x \geq 0$$
$$y \geq 0$$
$$5x + 8y \leq 10$$

The coordinates represent length in metres. What is the shape and area of the target?

SOLUTION

Use a graphing calculator.

- The graph of $x \geq 0$ is the set of points on the line $x = 0$ (the y-axis), and the half-plane to the right of it.

- The graph of $y \geq 0$ is the set of points on the line $y = 0$ (the x-axis), and the half-plane above it.

- To graph the inequality, first solve for y.

$$8y \leq -5x + 10$$
$$y \leq \frac{-5x + 10}{8}$$

Enter the equation $y = \frac{-5x + 10}{8}$ into the Y= list of the calculator.

The graph is the half-plane below the line. To use reverse shading, shade the part of the screen that is NOT the solution to the inequality $5x + 8y \leq 10$. Choose the upper triangle from the graphing styles.

```
Plot1  Plot2  Plot3
▼Y₁◼(-5X+10)/8■
 \Y₂=
 \Y₃=
 \Y₄=
 \Y₅=
 \Y₆=
 \Y₇=
```

Since $x \geq 0$ and $y \geq 0$, the solution is contained in the first quadrant. Choose Xmin = 0 and Ymin = 0 in the window settings.

A suitable window setting is shown below left. The *unshaded* region of the graph on the right shows the ordered pairs (x, y) that satisfy all three inequalities.

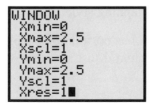

```
WINDOW
 Xmin=0
 Xmax=2.5
 Xscl=1
 Ymin=0
 Ymax=2.5
 Yscl=1
 Xres=1■
```

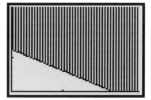

reverse shading

The shape of the target is a right triangle.

To determine its area, we must determine the length of the legs. Use TRACE to determine the x- and y-intercepts. The y-intercept is 1.25 and the x-intercept is 2.

$$\text{Area} = \frac{1}{2}(1.25)(2)$$
$$= 1.25$$

The area of the target is 1.25 m^2.

DISCUSSING THE IDEAS

1. The diagram below shows a system of inequalities. It has been graphed using regular shading. The plane is divided into four distinct regions. Explain which region represents the solution to the system of inequalities. Explain why the other regions do not represent solutions to the system.

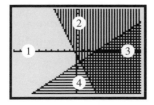

2. In *Example 3*, suppose the < sign was replaced with ≤ and the two ≥ signs were replaced with >. What change, if any, would there be in the graph?

3. Explain what reverse shading is and why it is used.

4. In *Example 3*, what is the inequality that is satisfied by the *shaded* region of the calculator screen? Why do you think the name "reverse shading" is used?

5. Explain the connection between the inequality sign and the choice of upper or lower triangle shading for the graphing style.

6. A system of two linear inequalities has no solution. Explain how this can be so. Sketch a graph of such a system. Must a system of three linear inequalities have a solution?

Checking Your Skills

1. These graphs were produced by a graphing calculator set for reverse shading. The equations of the lines at the boundaries of the shaded regions are shown. Replace the = signs with either > or < to generate the inequalities that correspond to each unshaded region.

a) $y = 2x + 3$
$y = 0.5x + 1$

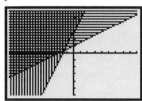

reverse shading

b) $y = -1.5x - 2.5$
$3y = 2x - 3$

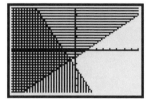

reverse shading

2. Write the inequality that represents the shaded region on each graph.

a)

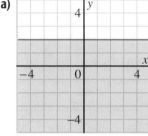

b)

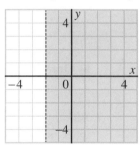

c)

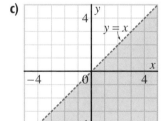

3. On grid paper, graph the region defined by each system of inequalities.

a) $x \leq 0$
$x \geq -3$
$y \leq 0$

b) $x \geq 0$
$x \leq 5$
$y \leq x + 2$

c) $x \geq 0$
$y \geq 0$
$y \leq 2x + 3$

4. Determine the solution to each system of inequalities

a) $x + y < 2$
$2x - y \le 4$
$x \ge 0$
$y \ge 0$

b) $y - x \ge -4$
$x \ge 0$
$y < 0$

c) $50x + 200y < 2000$
$2x - y < 40$
$x > 0$
$y > 0$

5. Use a graphing calculator to graph the solution to this system of inequalities.

$3x - y > 4$

$2x + y \le 6$

6. A store manager has storage available for 10 appliances. A dishwasher takes 20 min to unpack and set up, and a refrigerator requires 10 min. The manager estimates that she has 70 min of employee time available in a day for unpacking and setting up. Let x represent the number of dishwashers and y represent the number of refrigerators.

a) Explain why a system of inequalities that represents the situation is:

$x \ge 0$
$y \ge 0$
$x + y \le 10$
$2x + y \le 7$

b) Draw a graph that shows the numbers of each kind of appliance that can be unpacked and set up from storage in a day.

7. A company makes two types of stereo speaker systems. The number of worker-hours required for assembly and carpentry are shown.

	Speaker System A	Speaker System B
Variable	x	y
Worker-hours for Assembly	3	4
Worker-hours for Carpentry	2	6

Available labour allows a maximum of 480 worker-hours per week for assembly and a maximum of 540 worker-hours for carpentry. Let x represent the number of type A speaker systems, and y the number of type B systems made in one week. A system of inequalities that represents this situation is:

$x \ge 0$ $\qquad$ $3x + 4y \le 480$
$y \ge 0$ $\qquad$ $2x + 6y \le 540$

a) Explain why this system represents the situation.

b) Graph the system to determine the numbers of each type of stereo speaker system that can be made in a week.

c) Does this situation represent discrete or continuous variables? Explain.

8. A company makes motorcycles and bicycles. The physical dimensions of the work area limit the number of both kinds of vehicles that can be made in one day.

No more than 20 motorcycles can be made.
No more than 30 bicycles can be made.
No more than 40 vehicles in all can be made.

Let x represent the number of motorcycles and y the number of bicycles made in one day.

a) Write a system of inequalities that represent this situation.

b) Graph the ordered pairs that show the numbers of motorcycles and bicycles that can be made in one day.

Extending Your Thinking

9. Graph each system.

a) $x + y \geq 7$
$x - 3y \geq 12$
$y - 3x \geq -6$

b) $x - 2y < 12$
$x - 3y > 6$
$2y + 5x \geq 10$

10. A dog owner wants to build a rectangular dog run using no more than 20 m of fencing. She wants the run to have an area of at least 20 m².

a) Write a system of inequalities to represent this scenario.

b) Use technology to determine if it is feasible to satisfy both of the given conditions.

PROJECT

In this Tutorial you have graphed systems of linear inequalities. You will use this skill in the Chapter Project and the following projects in the Project Book.

- Diamond Mining
- Farm Planning
- Maximizing Music Profits

COMMUNICATING THE IDEAS

Write a paragraph to explain how graphing a system of linear inequalities is similar to, yet different from, graphing a system of linear equations.

Modelling a Problem Situation

In *Tutorial 3.2* you learned to model certain problems algebraically using a system of linear equations. In this Tutorial, you will determine a system of inequalities that represents a situation, and graph it using technology.

Many of the methods you learned earlier can be used here: rewording statements, summarizing information in tables, drawing diagrams. This time, you will not only have to create an algebraic expression but also decide on the appropriate inequality sign for the sentence. For example, "at least," "not less than," and "a minimum of" all mean "greater than or equal to" and the appropriate sign is $\geq$. "No more than," "a maximum of," and "not greater than" all mean "less than or equal to" and the appropriate sign is $\leq$.

Example 1   Developing an exercise program

Marie likes to swim and play tennis. In 1 h Marie burns 600 calories swimming or 450 calories playing tennis. Swimming costs \$4/h and tennis costs \$6/h. In one week, Marie wishes to burn at least 5000 calories and spend no more than 10 h exercising. She is willing to pay up to \$48 per week. Can Marie devise an appropriate weekly exercise program of playing tennis and swimming? Describe a possible program for Marie.

SOLUTION

We must determine the number of hours Marie will spend swimming and playing tennis each week. Assign a variable to each of the unknown quantities.

Let x represent the number of hours Marie swims per week and let y represent the number of hours she plays tennis per week. These two variables are subject to conditions, called *constraints*.

Information about the constraints can be summarized in a table.

	Swimming	Playing Tennis	Total
Variable	x	y	
Time (h)	x	y	≤ 10
Cost/h ($)	4	6	
Total Cost ($)	$4x$	$6y$	≤ 48
Calories/h	600	450	
Total Calories	$600x$	$450y$	≥ 5000

An implicit constraint is obvious, but not specifically mentioned. For example, in practical situations, the variables are always positive.

- Time spent exercising cannot be negative.

  $x \geq 0$ ①

  $y \geq 0$ ②

- Time spent exercising in a week: the total time Marie spends exercising in a week has to be less than or equal to 10 h.

  $x + y \leq 10$ rearrange to isolate y

  $y \leq 10 - x$ ③

- Cost of activities in a week: the total amount Marie spends on these two activities in one week has to be less than or equal to $48.

  $4x + 6y \leq 48$, which simplifies to

  $2x + 3y \leq 24$ rearrange to isolate y

  $y \leq \dfrac{24 - 2x}{3}$ ④

- Calories burned through exercising: the total energy Marie expends in a week has to be greater than or equal to 5000 calories.

  $600x + 450y \geq 5000$, which simplifies to

  $12x + 9y \geq 100$ rearrange to isolate y

  $y \geq \dfrac{100 - 12x}{9}$ ⑤

Setting the window on the graphing calculator as shown below left satisfies constraints ① and ②. Enter constraints ③, ④, and ⑤ into the calculator using reverse shading as shown below right.

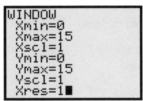

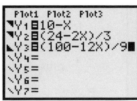

The solution of the system of inequalities is represented by the unshaded region in the diagram shown below.

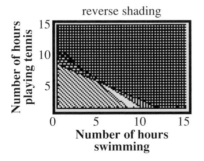

reverse shading

It is possible for Marie to design an exercise program that satisfies all the constraints within the problem.

One possible program is 9 h swimming and 1 h playing tennis.

Example 2 | **Manufacturing sportswear**

A sporting goods manufacturer makes swimsuits and leotards. To make a swimsuit requires 2 min on the cutting machine and 1 min on the stitching machine. A leotard requires 2 min on the cutting machine and 4 min on the stitching machine. How many swimsuits and leotards can be made in 1 h or less?

SOLUTION

The unknown quantities are the number swimsuits and leotards that can be made in 1 h. Assign a variable to each unknown quantity.

Let x represent the number of swimsuits made in 1 h and let y represent the number of leotards made in 1 h. These variables are subject to the following constraints:

- Time on the cutting machine: the total time on the cutting machine for both garments is less than or equal to 1 h.

  - Each swimsuit requires 2 min on the cutting machine, so x swimsuits need $2x$ min on the cutting machine.

  - Each leotard requires 2 min on the cutting machine, so y leotards need $2y$ min on the cutting machine.

  - A total of $2x + 2y$ minutes are spent on the cutting machine. The constraint is that this total time must be less than or equal to 60 min:
    $2x + 2y \leq 60$, which simplifies to
    $$x + y \leq 30 \qquad \text{rearrange to isolate } y$$
    $$y \leq 30 - x \qquad ①$$

- Time on the stitching machine: the time on the stitching machine for both garments is less than or equal to 1 h.

  - Each swimsuit requires 1 min on the stitching machine, so x swimsuits need $1x$ min on the stitching machine.

  - Each leotard requires 4 min on the stitching machine, so y leotards need $4y$ min on the stitching machine.

  - A total of $x + 4y$ min are spent on the stitching machine. This total time must be less than or equal to 60 min.
    $$x + 4y \leq 60 \qquad \text{rearrange to isolate } y$$
    $$y \leq \frac{60 - x}{4} \qquad ②$$

192   CHAPTER 4   LINEAR PROGRAMMING

- The implicit constraints are that the number of swimsuits and leotards made cannot be negative.

$$x \geq 0 \qquad \text{③}$$
$$y \geq 0 \qquad \text{④}$$

- The numbers of swimsuits and leotards produced must be whole numbers. This cannot be represented using inequalities, but must be reflected in the solution of the problem.

Use the graphing calculator to determine the region that satisfies all inequalities.

A suitable window setting is shown below. This satisfies constraints ③ and ④.

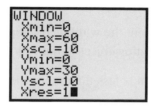

Remember to enter constraints ① and ② into the calculator using reverse shading. The graph of all of these constraints is shown below.

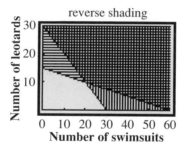

The solution of the system of inequalities is the unshaded region in the diagram.

Only the ordered pairs with integral coordinates are solutions of the problem. These are the feasible points. The coordinates of the points on the boundary of the region can be determined using the TRACE and CALC features of the TI-83.

Now suppose that you are the director of the factory where the clothing is made. Among all the possible solutions in *Example 2*, which is the best? This is the topic of the next Tutorial.

Example 3 Solve a problem using a non-linear system of inequalities in two variables

A desktop publisher has to design formats for rectangular data tables and uses graphing grids as a design tool. Use reverse shading to indicate the region on the graph that represents the possible dimensions of rectangles in which the length is less than twice the width, the perimeter is at most 48 cm, and the area is at least 32 cm^2.

SOLUTION

The unknown quantities are the dimensions of a rectangle. Assign a variable to each unknown quantity.

Let x represent the width and y represent the length of a rectangle. These dimensions are subject to the following constraints:

- The length is less than twice the width.
  $y < 2x$ ①

- The perimeter is at most 48 cm.
  $2x + 2y \le 48$, which simplifies to
  $x + y \le 24$ rearrange to isolate y
  $y \le 24 - 2x$ ②

- The area is at least 32 cm^2.
  $x \times y \ge 32$ rearrange to isolate y
  $y \ge \frac{32}{x}$ ③

- The implicit constraints are that the dimensions cannot be negative.
  $x \ge 0$ ④
  $y \ge 0$ ⑤

Graph the system of inequalities on a graphing calculator. Use reverse shading to determine the region that satisfies all the inequalities. Suitable window settings are shown below left. Set Xmin = 0 and Ymin = 0 to satisfy constraints ④ and ⑤. Enter the equations as shown below right.

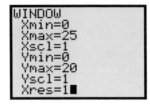

The graph of the system of inequalities is shown below.

The unshaded region shows all the combinations of length and width that satisfy all the constraints.

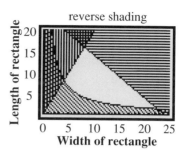

DISCUSSING THE IDEAS

1. In *Example 1*, can Marie spend a fraction of an hour on an activity, or must she swim or play tennis in full-hour increments only?

2. In *Example 2*, are all of the ordered pairs in the unshaded region possible solutions to the problem? Explain.

3. What is meant by an implicit constraint?

4. In a modelling problem such as the ones in this Tutorial, how do you decide which quantities should be represented by variables?

EXERCISES

Checking Your Skills

1. A company makes motorcycles and ATVs. The physical dimensions of the work area limit the numbers of both kinds of vehicle that can be made in one day. No more than 25 motorcycles or 35 ATVs can be made in one day. No more than 50 vehicles in all can be made in one day.

   a) What quantities should x and y represent for this problem?

   b) What constraints are given in this problem? Write an inequality for each constraint.

   c) What implicit constraints exist for the variables? Write an inequality for each implicit constraint.

   d) Draw a graph that shows the possible number of vehicles that can be made in one day.

2. Larry is an athlete in training. He plays basketball and golf. He burns about 600 Cal/h playing basketball and 350 Cal/h playing golf. Larry will spend at most 12 h per week exercising and he wants to burn at least 5000 Cal per week during his exercise.

a) What quantities should x and y represent for this problem?

b) Write a system of inequalities for this problem.

c) Draw a graph to show the time Larry could spend on each activity in a week.

3. A company manufactures 2 kinds of flashlight: type A with rechargeable batteries and type B without. In one day, the company can make at most 50 type A flashlights and 60 type B. Type A requires 3 work hours to produce and type B requires 2 work hours. The workforce provides a maximum of 180 work hours each day.

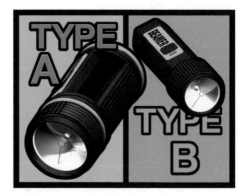

a) What should a and b represent in this problem?

b) Write a system of inequalities that represents this situation.

c) Draw a graph to determine the region that satisfies all inequalities and illustrate the numbers of each type of flashlight the company can produce in a day.

4. Holly likes to walk and swim. She burns about 500 Cal/h on a brisk walk and 600 Cal/h swimming. It costs $4/h to swim at the local pool. Holly estimates that she can spend no more than 5 h per week exercising and she is willing to spend up to $12 per week. She wants to burn at least 2900 Cal per week exercising.

a) What quantities should x and y represent for this problem?

b) Write a system of inequalities for this problem.

c) Draw a graph to determine if it is possible for Holly to develop an exercise program.

5. A storeowner wishes to purchase bicycles to stock his store. Mountain bikes cost $200 each and touring bikes cost $160 each. He wants to buy at least 10 of each model but does not want to spend more than $4400 in total. Develop a system of inequalities to determine how many bicycles the storeowner can buy under these circumstances.

6. A manufacturer produces two types of tents. Tent A requires 20 min of machine time, 20 min of skilled labour, and 40 min of unskilled labour to produce. Tent B requires 30 min of machine time, 40 min of skilled labour, and 20 min of unskilled labour to produce. In one day the company has a maximum of 24 h of machine time available, 28 h of skilled labour, and 30 h of unskilled labour. A minimum of 10 of each type of tent must be produced every day.

a) Develop a system of inequalities to determine if it is possible for the company to produce 50 or more tents in a day. Graph the solution to this system of inequalities.

b) If there are possible solutions, select one and explain how it fits the constraints.

7. A farmer plans to build a rectangular pen. The length of the pen must be greater than the width, the perimeter can be no more than 120 m, and the area must be at least 280 m^2.

a) Develop a system of inequalities to represent the constraints in this problem.

b) On a graph, indicate the region that represents the possible dimensions of the pen.

Extending Your Thinking

8. A 1000-g mixture of snack food is to be created with raisins, sunflower seeds, and peanuts. Use the information in the chart below to determine if it is possible to create a mixture that contains at least 50 g of dietary fibre but no more than 1000 mg of sodium. Let x represent the number of 100-g units of sunflower seeds and let y represent the number of 100-g units of raisins. (Hint: You may end up with a system of inequalities involving 3 variables. Use one of the constraints to reduce the number of variables to 2.)

	100 g of Sunflower seeds	100 g of Raisins	100 g of Peanuts
Dietary fibre (g)	10	5	2
Calcium (mg)	70	50	70
Iron (mg)	4	2	20
Sodium (mg)	4	20	10
Vitamin C (mg)	1	3	0

PROJECT

In this Tutorial, you learned how to design a system of linear inequalities to model problem situations. You will use this in the Chapter Project and in the following projects in the Project Book.

- Farm Planning
- Maximizing Music Profits

COMMUNICATING THE IDEAS

Write a list of steps to determine the feasible points of a region for a problem such as the ones you have solved in this Tutorial.

Finding Feasible Snack Mixes

At the start of this project, you researched trail mixes and the nutritional requirements of physically active people. In this section you will design a trail mix. Work in a group of 3.

Your company plans to develop and market a trail mix for hikers, bikers, and canoeists. It must contain 2 different ingredients and have at least 25% less fat than other trail mixes. Your company's present trail mix is analyzed to the right.

Nutritional content for 100 g:	
Calories	485
Protein	13.8 g
Total Fat	33.2 g
(Saturated Fats	5.9 g)
Carbohydrate	29.6 g
Dietary Fibre	9.3 g

CHAPTER PROJECT

To complete this Chapter Project, you must solve an optimization problem. Complete *Tutorial 4.4* to develop an understanding of the technique. You will need these skills when you return to the Chapter Project on page 210 and for the following projects in the Project Book.
• Diamond Mining
• Farm Planning
• Maximizing Music Profits

1. Would you recommend increasing the dietary fibre, carbohydrates, or protein of your mixture compared to the present trail mix? Write a paragraph defending your choice.

2. Propose three possible trail mixes that satisfy the following conditions:

  • The trail mix has at least 1000 g in total of the two ingredients.

  • At least 200 g of each ingredient must be used in trail mix.

  • The mixture contains 25% less fat than the present trail mix.

  • One of dietary fibre, carbohydrates, or protein should be increased by at least 5% over the present trail mix.

3. Your company has access to the ingredients in the following table. The nutritional information for 100 g of each item is also provided. For each of your proposed trail mixes, show graphically that it is feasible for the trail mix to satisfy each of the above conditions. Include a mathematical description of the conditions you have imposed on the trail mix.

	Semisweet Chocolate	Milk Chocolate	Raisins (Seeded)	Raisins (Seedless)	Sunflower Seeds Hulled, Dry-roasted	Peanuts, Raw	Peanuts, Dry Roasted with salt	Peanuts, Oil Roasted, with salt
Calories	479	513	296	300	582	567	585	581
Protein (g)	4.2	6.9	2.52	3.2	19.33	25.8	23.68	26.35
Total fat (g)	30	30.7	0.54	0.46	49.8	49.24	49.66	49.30
Total carbohydrate (g)	63.1	59.2	78.47	79.13	24.07	16.14	21.51	18.93
Dietary fibre (g)	5.9	3.4	6.8	4.0	11.1	8.5	8.0	9.2
Calcium (mg)	32.0	191.0	28	49.0	70.0	92.0	54.0	88.0
Iron (mg)	3.13	1.39	2.59	2.08	3.8	4.58	2.26	1.83
Sodium (mg)	11.0	82.0	28.0	12.0	3.0	18.0	813.0	433.0
Vitamin C (mg)	0.0	0.40	5.4	3.3	1.4	0.0	0.0	0.0
Cholesterol (mg)	0.0	22.0	0.0	0.0	0.0	0.0	0.0	0.0
Saturated fats (g)	17.75	18.48	0.178	0.150	5.219	6.834	6.893	6.843

Save your results. Your company is still negotiating the cost of each ingredient with suppliers. Once this is known, you will determine how much of each ingredient should be used in your trail mix to minimize its cost. Based on your results, you will then be asked to share and defend your recommendation for the best composition of this trail mix.

Career Skills

To analyze the nutritional value of a trail mix requires organizational skills and attention to detail. Working with others to complete a task is an essential skill that is highly valued by employers.

Optimization Problems

In the previous Tutorials, you learned how to model certain problem situations using systems of linear inequalities, and to determine the solution of a system of linear inequalities. But how do we choose one ordered pair from the many that are available in the solution region? Usually, the problem relates to maximizing or minimizing some specified quantity such as profit, and this determines the ordered pair needed.

The graph below shows the possible numbers of swimsuits and leotards that could be produced, given the constraints in *Example 2* of *Tutorial 4.4*. The solution region has the shape of a polygon whose vertices are labelled A, B, C, and D. Although all the ordered pairs with integral coordinates in the region are possible solutions, not all are desirable. For example, manufacturing no swimsuits and no leotards, although possible, would not result in profit for the company. Assuming the company would like to produce as large a profit as possible, how many swimsuits and leotards should it make? The answer depends on the profit made on each item.

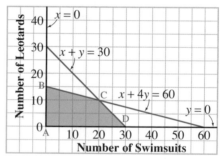

The Investigation below shows you how to determine a profit.

Maximizing Profits

Assume that the company in *Example 2* of *Tutorial 4.4* makes a profit of $10 on a swimsuit and $15 on a leotard. Recall that x represents the number of swimsuits made and y represents the number of leotards.

1. Copy the diagram above onto grid paper.

2. Write a formula for the profit, P dollars, earned by the company if it manufactures x swimsuits and y leotards.

3. Suppose we want a profit of $60. Use the formula from exercise 2, and substitute 60 for P. Graph the resulting line on your diagram. Write the equation on the line.

4. Plot the points (6, 0), (4.5, 1), (3, 2), and (0, 4) on the line. Interpret these points in terms of how many swimsuits and leotards are made. Which points are feasible?

5. Repeat exercise 3 for each of the following profits, *P*: 120, 180, 240, 300, 360. On each resulting line, select a few points. Interpret these points in terms of the numbers of swimsuits and leotards made.

6. How are the profit lines from exercises 3 and 5 related?

7. Use any patterns in your diagram to predict which ordered pair in the solution region corresponds to the maximum profit, and which corresponds to the minimum profit. Confirm by calculation that your prediction is correct.

8. Repeat exercises 1 to 7. Assume that the company earns $10 profit on each swimsuit it makes and $5 profit on each leotard. Select profit values that you think are reasonable.

9. Compare the maximum and minimum profits in exercise 8. Compare the locations of the points that correspond to the maximum and minimum profits.

10. What conclusion can you draw from this Investigation?

You probably noticed in the *Investigation* that the profit lines were parallel in each case. You may also have noticed that if you move toward the upper right of the diagram, perpendicular to the profit lines, the profits increase steadily from one line to the next. Thus, the maximum profit occurs at a point on the boundary of the solution region, somewhere in the right-hand side of the region, provided that this is a feasible point. A similar argument shows that the minimum profit occurs at a point on the boundary of the solution region, somewhere in the lower-left side of that region.

A function such as the profit function in the *Investigation*, is called an *objective function*. A linear programming problem requires the maximum or minimum value of an objective function. When the objective function is linear, its maximum and minimum values in a solution region occur at vertices of that region.

The maximum value of an objective function occurs at a vertex of the solution region.

The minimum value of an objective function occurs at a vertex of the solution region.

The vertices may not be feasible points for the particular problem, in which case the maximum or minimum value will occur at a feasible point just inside the region.

> Steps for solving optimization problems
>
> 1. Read the problem, determine the unknown quantities, and assign variables.
>
> 2. From the information given, write a system of linear inequalities in terms of the variables you introduced in step 1.
>
> 3. Determine a formula for the objective function in terms of the variables you introduced in step 1.
>
> 4. Solve the system of linear inequalities and graph the solution region. Determine the coordinates of the vertices of the solution region.
>
> 5. Determine the value of the objective function at each vertex of the solution region. Both the maximum and the minimum values of the objective function are among the values found in this step.

The lines resulting from substituting specific values for the objective function could be parallel to a side of the solution region. In that case, the maximum or minimum values of the objective function may occur at every point along that side of the solution region, including the vertices at the ends of the side.

Example 1 | Minimizing vitamin costs

A doctor advises a patient to take vitamin supplements to provide at least 35 mg of Vitamin C, but no more than 600 mg of calcium daily. Each brand A pill contains 100 mg of calcium and 5 mg of Vitamin C. Each brand B pill contains 150 mg of calcium and 10 mg of Vitamin C. Each brand A pill costs 4¢ and brand B costs 9¢.

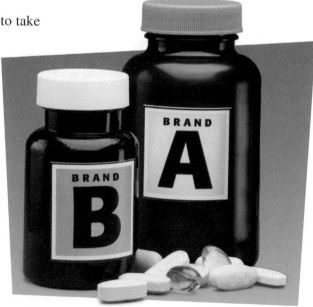

a) Suppose the patient takes x brand A pills and y Brand B pills every day. Write an expression to represent the daily cost of taking these pills.

b) Write a system of inequalities to represent the constraints in this problem.

c) Graph the system.

d) How many of each type of pill should the patient take daily to minimize the cost of taking vitamins?

SOLUTION

a) Let C cents represent the daily cost. The objective function is:
$$C = 4x + 9y$$

b) The inequalities are developed below.
- The first two constraints are implicit, because the number of pills cannot be negative:

$$x \geq 0 \qquad \qquad ①$$
$$y \geq 0 \qquad \qquad ②$$

- Brand A contains 5 mg of Vitamin C per pill, so x pills contain $5x$ mg of Vitamin C. Brand B contains 10 mg of Vitamin C per pill, so y pills contain $10y$ mg of Vitamin C. The total amount must be at least 35 mg. The inequality is:

$5x + 10y \geq 35$, which simplifies to
$$x + 2y \geq 7 \qquad \text{rearrange to isolate } y$$
$$y \geq \frac{7 - x}{2} \qquad ③$$

- Brand A contains 100 mg of calcium per pill, so x pills contain $100x$ mg. Brand B contains 150 mg of calcium per pill, so y pills contain $150y$ mg. The total amount of calcium must be no more than 600 mg, so

$100x + 150y \leq 600$, which simplifies to
$$2x + 3y \leq 12 \qquad \text{rearrange to isolate } y$$
$$y \leq \frac{12 - 2x}{3} \qquad ④$$

c) Constraints ① and ② limit the graph to the first quadrant of the coordinate plane. Reverse shading was used to graph this system.

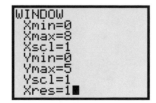

The graph for this system gives the constraint polygon shown below. Use TRACE and CALC features to determine the coordinates of the vertices of the region. These are shown on the grid.

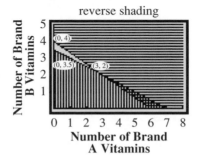

reverse shading

Number of Brand B Vitamins (vertical axis)

(0, 4)
(0, 3.5)
(3, 2)

0 1 2 3 4 5 6 7 8
Number of Brand A Vitamins

To determine the optimal value, calculate the value of the objective function $C = 4x + 9y$ at each vertex of the polygon.

Vertex	Value of $C = 4x + 9y$	Maximum/ Minimum
(0, 3.5)	$C = 4(0) + 9(3.5)$ $= 31.5$	
(0, 4)	$C = 4(0) + 9(4)$ $= 36$	maximum
(3, 2)	$C = 4(3) + 9(2)$ $= 30$	minimum

By taking 3 brand A pills and 2 Brand B pills daily, the patient will minimize the cost of taking vitamins.

Example 2 **Maximizing revenue**

A parking lot has 540 m² available to park vehicles. On average, cars need 9 m² and buses need 36 m² for parking. No more than 45 vehicles can be parked in the lot at one time. The charge to park cars is $7.50 a day and to park buses is $25 a day. How many cars and how many buses should be parked at one time to produce the maximum revenue?

SOLUTION

Let x represent the number of cars and y represent the number of buses parked in the lot for the day.

- The daily revenue, R dollars, is given by the equation:
  $R = 7.5x + 25y$

This is the objective function.

- The first two constraints are implicit, because the number of cars or buses parked in the lot cannot be negative:
  $$x \geq 0 \qquad\qquad ①$$
  $$y \geq 0 \qquad\qquad ②$$

- Each car needs 9 m², so x cars will occupy $9x$ m². Each bus occupies 36 m² so y buses occupy $36y$ m². The total area must not exceed 540 m², so
  $9x + 36y \leq 540$, which simplifies to
  $$x + 4y \leq 60 \qquad\qquad \text{rearrange to isolate } y$$
  $$y \leq \frac{60 - x}{4} \qquad ③$$

- A maximum of 45 vehicles may park at one time in the lot during the day, so
  $$x + y \leq 45 \qquad\qquad \text{rearrange to isolate } y$$
  $$y \leq 45 - x \qquad\qquad ④$$

The first two constraints limit the graph to the first quadrant of the coordinate plane. By defining the viewing window as shown below left, only the first quadrant of the coordinate plane will be displayed. The other constraints are entered into the calculator as shown below right.

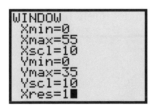

The graph for this system gives the constraint polygon shown below right. Reverse shading was used when graphing this system.

To determine the optimal value of the objective function, calculate its value at each vertex of the polygon. The coordinates of the vertices can be determined using the TABLE, CALC, or TRACE features.

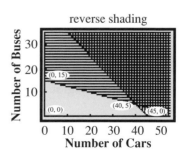

To determine the maximum daily revenue, calculate the value of the objective function $R = 7.5x + 25y$ at each vertex.

Vertex	Value of $R = 7.5x + 25y$	Maximum/ Minimum
$(0, 0)$	$R = 7.5(0) + 25(0)$ $= 0$	minimum
$(0, 15)$	$R = 7.5(0) + 25(15)$ $= 375$	
$(40, 5)$	$R = 7.5(40) + 25(5)$ $= 425$	maximum
$(45, 0)$	$R = 7.5(45) + 25(0)$ $= 337.5$	

The maximum daily revenue of $425 occurs when 40 cars and 5 buses are parked in the lot.

DISCUSSING THE IDEAS

1. Explain the following terms in the context of a linear programming problem: solution, optimal solution.

2. Reverse shading was used to draw the solution region shown below. The solution region extends indefinitely upward and to the right.

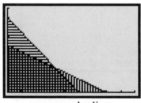

reverse shading

Is it possible for an objective function to have both a minimum value and a maximum value in this region? Justify your response.

3. Suppose the boundary lines of a solution region are all broken lines. Can an objective function have a maximum or minimum value in the solution region? Explain.

Checking Your Skills

1. Find the optimal value for each objective function given its constraint polygon.

    a) $C = 3x + 5y$

    b) $T = x + 4y$

    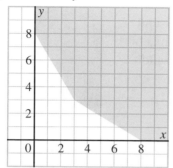
    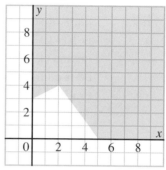

2. Graph the system of inequalities given below. Determine the optimal values for the objective function $T = 5x + 7y$.

    $$x \geq 0$$
    $$y \geq 0$$
    $$2x + y \leq 12$$
    $$x + 2y \leq 12$$

3. A small clothing company manufactures two types of jackets. The first type of jacket requires 20 min of cutting time and 10 min of sewing time. The second requires 10 min of cutting time and 15 min of sewing time. In one day, the company has a maximum of 12 h of cutting time and 8 h of sewing time. The company makes a profit of $20 each on the first type of jacket and $15 each on the second type of jacket. How many of each type of jacket should the company produce in a day to maximize its profits?

4. A mathematics contest for high school students has two categories of questions. Each question in section A takes approximately 4 min to solve and is worth 6 marks. Each question in section B takes approximately 6 min to solve and is worth 10 marks. You must answer at least 12 questions on the exam and the time limit is 1 h. How many questions should you answer from each section to obtain the maximum score? Assume that you get every answer correct.

5. You have been asked to create at least 1000 g of a mixture of sunflower seeds and raisins. The mixture must contain at least 75 g of dietary fibre, but no more than 40 mg of iron. Use the chart below to determine how many units of sunflower seeds (1 unit is 100 g) and how many units of raisins (1 unit is 100 g) should be used to minimize the cost of producing this mixture.

	100 g of Sunflower seeds	100 g of Raisins
Dietary fibre (g)	10	5
Calcium (mg)	70	50
Iron (mg)	4	2
Sodium (mg)	4	20
Vitamin C (mg)	1	3
Cost (cents)	12	10

6. A driver attempts to travel as far as possible by car using at most 108 L of fuel. When the car travels at 100 km/h it uses 9 L of gas per hour. When it travels at 90 km/h it only uses 6 L of gas per hour. The total travelling time must be no more than 15 h. What is the maximum distance the car can travel?

7. A company manufactures two types of hats. The first type of hat requires 6 min of cutting time and 1 min of sewing time. The second type of hat requires 2 min of cutting time and 4 min of sewing time. In each 2-h time slot, the company has a maximum of 75 min of cutting time and 40 min of sewing time for the production of hats. The company makes a profit of $8 on each of the first type of hat and $5 on each of the second type of hat made.

a) Determine how many of each type of hat the company should produce in each 2-h time slot to maximize its profits.

b) Is the result in part a reasonable? If not, explain how you would choose a reasonable number of hats of each type to produce.

Extending Your Thinking

8. Brand A breakfast cereal and brand B breakfast cereal are both enriched with vitamins P and Q. The information about these vitamins follows.

	Cereal A	Cereal B	Recommended Daily Intake
Vitamin P	1 unit/oz	2 units/oz	10 units
Vitamin Q	5 units/oz	3 units/oz	30 units
Cost	$0.12 /oz	$0.18 /oz	

Find the mass of each type of cereal that you should consume to ensure that you get the recommended daily intake of vitamins P and Q at lowest cost.

PROJECT

In this Tutorial, you learned how to solve optimization problems using linear programming. You will use this skill in the Chapter Project and the following projects in the Project Book.

- Farm Planning
- Maximizing Music Profits

COMMUNICATING THE IDEAS

Explain why it is important to find the coordinates of the vertices of the solution region when you are using linear programming to solve an optimization problem. Give a step-by-step procedure for determining the coordinates of the vertices of the solution region.

Determining the Best Trail Mix

In previous work on the Chapter Project, your group found 3 possible compositions for your company's new trail mix. Your company has negotiated the following prices for 100 g of each of the following ingredients.

Ingredient	Price per 100 g (¢)
Semisweet chocolate	21
Milk chocolate	22
Raisins (seeded)	9
Raisins (seedless)	10
Sunflower seeds, hulled dry roasted	10
Peanuts, raw	7
Peanuts, dry roasted with salt	8
Peanuts, oil roasted with salt	7.5

- Determine how much of each ingredient should be used in the trail mix to minimize the cost of ingredients. How does the composition of this trail mix compare to the 3 trail mixes you selected previously? Show the formula for the objective function and your calculations.

- Use the quantities that will minimize the cost of ingredients to determine the nutritional content of the trail mix. Compare this to the nutrient content of each of the 3 trail mixes you selected previously. Express the nutritional content for each based on 100 g of each trail mix.

- Decide which trail mix the company should adopt. Write a paragraph to explain the advantages of this trail mix as opposed to the others.

Your completed project will consist of your initial research, the analysis of the 3 trail mixes you considered, your analysis to determine the trail mix that minimizes cost, and your final recommendations for a trail mix with good nutrition and low cost.

Career Skills

Careful analysis of data is a skill used by people employed in the research and development departments of all manufacturing industries. Food processing companies employ food technologists, biochemical technologists, nutritionists, and technical writers.

What Do I Need To Know?

Tutorial	Skills and Concepts	Important Results and Formulas
4.1	• Investigate the graph of a linear inequality	• If $y \geq 0$, the graph of $y > ax + b$ is the half-plane above the line $y = ax + b$ • If $y \leq 0$, the graph of $y < ax + b$ is the half-plane below the line $y = ax + b$ • The points on the line $y = ax + b$ satisfy both inequalities $y \geq ax + b$ and $y \leq ax + b$ • A test point can be used to determine the half-plane that represents the solution of an inequality
4.2	• Graph a linear inequality in two variables	
4.3	• Graph systems of linear inequalities on grid paper • Graph systems of linear inequalities using technology • Determine if a feasible solution exists for a given system of constraints	• The solution of a system of inequalities is the region where all of the half-planes that are the graphs of the individual inequalities overlap • Reverse shading helps to identify the region of overlap of the half-planes
4.4	• Design systems of linear inequalities to model problem situations	
4.5	• Solve maximum/minimum problems using linear programming	• The objective function attains its maximum and minimum values at the vertices of the region of feasible solutions

What Should I Be Able To Do?

When you have completed the work in *Chapter 4*, you should be able to solve the problems that follow. Part A is investigative in nature. As you work through the exercises, refer to the *Student Reference*, *Utilities*, and the *Tutorials* as necessary.

Part A

You will need a metre stick or tape measure.

In this investigation, you will determine how many desks and tables should be in your classroom so that this seating covers a minimum area.

1. Should a classroom have desks or tables? Assume that at least 3 desks must be in the room to accommodate independent work and at least 1 table must be available for group work. The room must have seating for at least 30 students and the seating cannot occupy more than 70% of the room's area. Let x represent the number of desks in the room and let y represent the number of tables in the room.

   a) Determine the area of your classroom.

   b) Determine the area occupied by 1 classroom desk and 1 table. Be sure to measure this area when people are seated at the desk or table.

   c) Write an expression for the area, S, occupied by seating in the classroom. This is the objective function.

   d) Write a system of inequalities for this problem. There will be at least 4 inequalities. Include possible constraints.

   e) Determine the number of desks and tables so that a minimum area is taken up by seating.

   f) What other facts may need to be considered when you solve this problem?

Part B

2. On grid paper, graph each system of inequalities.

   a)
   $$x \geq 0$$
   $$y \geq 0$$
   $$x < 10$$
   $$x + y \geq 15$$

   b)
   $$x \geq 0$$
   $$y \geq 0$$
   $$2x + y \geq 10$$
   $$x + 2y \geq 10$$

3. On grid paper, graph the region that satisfies these inequalities.

$$x \geq 2$$
$$x \leq 8$$
$$y \geq 0$$
$$y \leq 6$$
$$3x + 4y \leq 36$$

a) Determine the coordinates of the point(s) that maximize the objective function $P = x + 3y$ applied to the given system.

b) Determine the minimum value of the objective function $C = y - x$ applied to the given system.

4. The school is holding a volleyball tournament. Ticket prices for each game are $4 per student and $5 per adult. Tournament organizers estimate that they will need at least $100 in revenue per game to make a profit, but do not expect game revenues to exceed $500. Let x represent the number of students attending a tournament game and y represent the number of adults.

a) The revenue needed to make a profit can be modelled by the inequality $4x + 5y \geq 100$. Graph this inequality.

b) The inequality $4x + 5y < 500$ can be used to model the expected game revenue. Graph this inequality.

5. A factory produces two types of cooler, A and B, each of which is processed by two machines, M and N. Cooler A requires 2 h on machine M and 4 h on machine N. Cooler B requires 4 h on machine M and 2 h on machine N.

a) Let x represent the number of cooler A and y the number of cooler B produced daily. Explain why the following system of inequalities represents the situation.

$$x \geq 0$$
$$y \geq 0$$
$$2x + 4y \leq 24$$
$$4x + 2y \leq 24$$

b) Graph the system of inequalities in part a.

c) Describe two possible numbers of coolers that the factory could produce in a day.

6. Siri estimates that jogging for 1 hour burns 600 calories of energy, and cycling for 1 hour burns 400 calories of energy. Siri wishes to burn at least 4800 calories each week but can spend a maximum of 10 h exercising. If Siri spends x hours a week jogging and y hours a week cycling, we can represent the constraints using the following system of inequalities:

$$x \geq 0$$
$$y \geq 0$$
$$x + y \leq 10$$
$$600x + 400y \geq 4800$$

a) Explain why this system represents the situation.

b) Graph the system of inequalities on grid paper to determine if it is feasible for Siri to burn 4800 calories by exercising 10 h a week.

c) Check your result using the graphing calculator.

7. A homeowner is building an exercise pen for his dog. The length of the pen can be no more than twice the width, the area must be at least 3 m^2, and the perimeter cannot be greater than 8 m.

a) Determine a system of inequalities that represents these constraints.

b) On a graph, show the region that represents the possible dimensions of the pen.

8. A farmer plans to plant 80 ha of farmland with corn and wheat. The farmer has $12 000 available for planting and harvesting costs. The farmer estimates that it will cost approximately $300/ha to plant and harvest the corn and approximately $100/ha to plant and harvest the wheat. The expected profit for corn is $300/ha, whereas the profit for wheat is $200/ha.

a) Write an expression to represent the expected profit if the farmer plants x hectares of corn and y hectares of wheat.

b) Write a system of inequalities to represent the constraints in this problem.

c) Determine the area of each crop that should be planted to maximize the farmer's profits.

9. An aircraft has seats for 48 passengers. Those willing to pay first class fare can take 60 kg of baggage each. Economy class passengers can take 20 kg each. The aircraft can carry no more than 1440 kg of baggage. For a journey, the first class fare is $1000, and the economy fare $500. Determine the number of first class and economy passengers that gives maximum revenue.

Here is a sample of a student's work on the Chapter Project.

10. Is the student's choice of the 3 mixes reasonable? Do the trail mixes meet the criteria given?

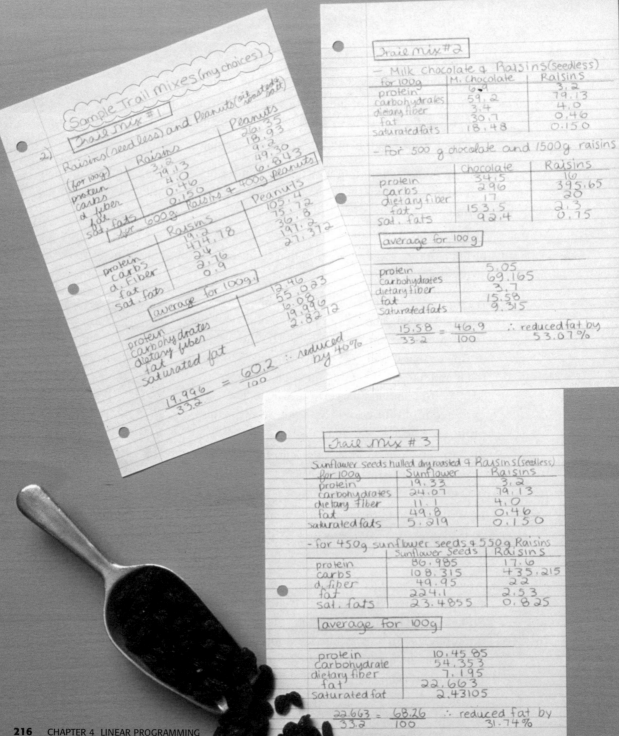

11. The same student presented the following cost analysis to justify her recommendation for the composition of the new trail mix. Is the analysis correct?

Determining the Best Mixture

Mixture #1

x = raisins (seedless)
y = peanuts (oil roasted and salted)
c = cheapest cost
mc = my cost

Cheapest Cost	Cost of My Mixture
10x + 7.5y = c	10x + 7.5 = mc
10(2) + 7.5(8) = c	10(6) + 7.5(4) = mc
20 + 60 = c	60 + 30 = mc
80¢ = c	90¢ = mc

Mixture #2

x = milk chocolate
y = raisins (seedless)
c = cheapest cost
mc = my cost

cheapest Cost	Cost of My Mixture
22x + 10y = c	22x + 10y = MC
22(2) + 10(8) = c	22(5) + 10(5) = MC
44 + 80 = c	110 + 50 = MC
$1.24 = c	$1.60 = MC

Mixture #3

x = sunflower seeds hulled dry roasted
y = raisins (seedless)
c = cheapest cost   MC = my cost

Cheapest Cost	Cost of My Mixture
10x + 10y = C	10x + 10y = MC
10(5) + 10(5) = C	10(4.5) + 10(5.5) = MC
50 + 50 = C	45 + 55 = MC
$1.00 = C	$1.00 = MC

Determining the Best mixture (using cheapest cost)

Mixture #1
for 200 grams of Raisins and 800 grams of Peanuts

	Raisins	Peanuts
protein	6.4	210.8
carbohydrates	158.26	151.44
dietary fibers	8	73.6
fat	0.92	394.4
saturated fats	0.3	54.744

- average for 100 grams

protein	21.72
carbohydrates	30.97
dietary fibers	8.16
fat	39.532
saturated fats	5.5044

Mixture #2
for 200 grams of chocolate and 800 grams of raisins

	Chocolate	Raisins
protein	13.8	25.6
carbohydrates	118.4	633.04
dietary fibers	6.8	32
fat	61.4	3.68
saturated fats	39.96	1.2

- average for 100 grams

protein	3.94
carbohydrates	75.144
dietary fibers	3.88
fat	6.508
saturated fats	4.116

Mixture #3
for 500 grams of sunflower seeds and 500 grams of raisins

	sunflower seeds	raisins
protein	96.65	16
carbohydrates	120.35	395.65
dietary fibers	555.5	20
fat	24.9	2.3
saturated fats	26.095	0.75

- average for 100 grams

protein	11.265
Carbohydrates	51.6
dietary fibres	57.55
fat	25.13
saturated fats	2.6845

12. Read the student's recommendation. Were her conclusions appropriate?

(3)

Determining the Best Mixture

I think that our company should adopt mixture number 3 (from my mixtures). I think this for many reasons. First, the cheaper mixtures are great for their prices, but their nutritional values are not that great at all. The amount of fat in the mixtures is very high. They do not meet the decrease of 25 %.

The two other mixtures of mine (numbers 1 and 2) are both good regarding the decrease in fat, but the amounts of protein, dietary fibers and carbohydrates are not very good. In all of the mixtures I made, the amount of carbohydrates are very high.

In my opinion I feel that the best mixture to adopt would be mixture number 3 (of mine). Another reason for picking it would be that the cost difference between the cheapest version and it is that there is none. They are exactly the same price. You can not make it any cheaper and it meets all of the requirements.

Those are the reasons for why I feel that mixture number 3 would be the best one to adopt.

5

Finance

You should do at least one project that uses the skills you have learned in this chapter. Recommended projects in the Project Book are:

- Restaurant Prices
- The Graduation Trip
- Buying or Leasing a Car
- Hot Dog Stand
- The Rule of 72
- Net Pay

Overview

Living Independently

For some students, graduation from high school means moving away from home to find employment or to undertake post-secondary education. As part of the process of becoming independent, you have to make many decisions, some of which will be financial. Planning to move out is often an exciting time in a person's life.

CHAPTER PROJECT

To complete this Chapter Project you will need to use information about income, payroll deductions, and living expenses. Complete *Tutorials 5.1* to *5.3* to learn about methods of payment for work, deductions from pay cheques, and expenses. You will return to this project on page 242.

In this Chapter Project you will investigate the cost of living independently. In this part of the project, you will write about the circumstances of someone planning to live independently. You may choose to plan for yourself, or for someone else, real or imaginary. Write a description of the person moving out. Include the name, age, where the person will live, occupation, probable income, and lifestyle. Here are some initial points to consider.

- Where might you live? What will it cost?

- What is your income likely to be?

- What transportation will you use?

- What are some of the costs of day-to-day living?

- Will you be borrowing money or using credit cards? What are the costs involved?

FYI Visit: www.awl.com/canada/school/connections

You can start your research from our Internet site: Click on <u>MATHLINKS</u> followed by the *Applied Mathematics 11* logo. Then select a topic under Living Independently.

Have you ever thought about the different methods employers use to calculate earnings? In this Tutorial you will investigate several different, common methods of determining gross pay.

Practise Your Prior Skills

In the work that follows, you will perform calculations using percent. Try these exercises as preliminary review.

1. Write each percent in decimal form.

   a) 12%   **b)** 7%   **c)** 150%   **d)** 6%

2. a) Calculate 12% of $32 576.

   b) Calculate 3% of $136.65.

3. What percent of $740 is $36? Give the answer to the nearest whole number.

STUDENT REFERENCE

If you need to review working with percent, look in the Student Reference under "percent."

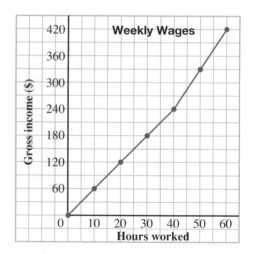

Investigation 1   **Interpreting a Wage Graph**

You will explore the graph of the income of a fast food restaurant employee for 1 week's work.

This graph shows the gross income that a fast food restaurant pays an employee for 1 week's work.

1. At what point does the slope of this graph change?

2. Suggest some reasons why the slope changes.

3. Calculate the slope of each part of the graph.

4. What does each slope represent?

5. Suppose an employee worked a total of 70 h during the week. Determine his gross income. Explain how you calculated your answer.

The money an employee earns before deductions is called *gross income* or *gross earnings*. Businesses pay their employees at regular time intervals, known as **pay periods**. Common pay periods are weekly, biweekly (once every 2 weeks), semi-monthly (twice each month), and monthly.

Employers pay employees in different ways.

- *Salary*: A fixed amount of money earned over a specified time period, such as a month or a year. Usually there is no overtime pay for someone on salary.

- *Wage*: Money earned hourly, or daily. Overtime and gratuities may also be included in a person's wage.

- *Commission*: Earnings based on a percent of an employee's sales during the pay period; may be paid in combination with a salary or wage.

- *Graduated commission*: Earnings based on commission; the rate of commission increases or decreases when sales reach a certain level.

- *Piecework*: Earnings based on the number of items produced.

Example 1 **Determine gross earnings including overtime**

Crystal works full time at a gas station. She is paid $7.50/h plus time-and-a-half for overtime, which is any time over 40 h a week. Calculate her gross earnings for a week in which she worked 46 h.

SOLUTION

Crystal worked 46 h in total: 40 of these were regular hours and the remaining 6 were overtime.

Regular earnings:
Hours worked × Hourly wage = 40 × $7.50
= $300.00

Overtime earnings:
Hours worked × Hourly wage × Overtime rate
= 6 × $7.50 × 1.5
= $67.50

Total earnings:
Regular earnings + Overtime earnings
= $300.00 + $67.50
= $367.50

Crystal's gross earnings for the week were $367.50.

Example 2 Calculate graduated commission

Dale works at a furniture store where she earns a graduated commission. She earns 9% commission on the first $10 000 worth of furniture she sells, and 12% commission on all sales exceeding $10 000. In May, Dale's sales were $21 675. Calculate her gross earnings for the month.

SOLUTION

Since Dale earns a graduated commission, and her sales exceeded $10 000, calculate her earnings in two parts. She will earn 9% on the first $10 000 and 12% on the remaining $11 675.

First $10 000:
9% of $10 000 = 0.09 × $10 000
            = $900

Remaining $11 675:
12% of $11 675 = 0.12 × $11 675
            = $1401

Total earnings:
$900 + $1401 = $2301
Dale's gross earnings for May were $2301.

Example 3 Compare earnings plans

Troy has job offers from two clothing stores. Store A will pay $7.25/h. Store B will pay a base salary of $800 plus 4% commission on sales. Both stores want Troy to work 160 h per month. Above what level of sales will Troy make more money in Store B?

SOLUTION

Determine the gross earnings that Troy might expect from each store.

Store A pays an hourly wage with no other remuneration.

Monthly earnings for Store A:
= Hours worked × hourly wage
= 160 × $7.25
= $1160

Store B pays a salary plus 4% commission. This means that Troy's earnings will vary, depending on his sales.

Monthly earnings for Store B:
= Base salary + (0.04 × Monthly sales)
= $800 + (0.04 × Monthly sales)

From this equation, create a table of values and graph to show how Troy's earnings depend on his sales.

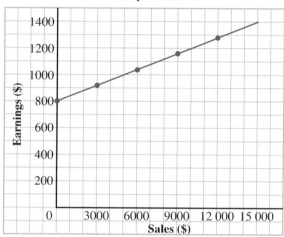

How Troy's Earnings Depend on Sales

Sales	Earnings
0	800
3 000	920
6 000	1040
9 000	1160
12 000	1280

From the table and graph, for monthly sales of $9000 Troy earns $1160. This is equal to his monthly earnings at Store A.

If Troy can regularly exceed $9000 in monthly sales, his gross pay at Store B will be higher; otherwise he should work at Store A.

DISCUSSING THE IDEAS

1. Explain the difference between earning a salary and earning a wage.

2. List some jobs where employees get paid

  a) a wage   **b)** a commission   **c)** a salary

3. Explain some of the advantages and disadvantages of the following pay methods: salary, piecework, straight commission, and graduated commission.

4. Why would a company structure its commission payment as a graduated commission?

5. Describe how a person who is paid a straight commission, and who has monthly payments to make, might have to plan their financial needs differently from someone who is paid an hourly rate.

EXERCISES

Checking Your Skills

1. What are the advantages to an employer of paying her salespeople a commission instead of a salary? What are the advantages to her salespeople?

2. What is the difference between biweekly and semi-monthly pay periods?

3. A company pays all its employees weekly. Is it possible that it ever issues pay cheques more than 52 times a year? fewer than 52 times? Explain.

4. Geri earns a base salary of $900 a month plus 5% commission on total sales. Last month she had a total of $26 324 in sales. Estimate her gross earnings. Write to describe how you determined your estimate.

5. Caroline is hired to arrange flowers. She is paid $2.50 for every arrangement or $12/h. Caroline estimates she could create about four arrangements an hour. Which payment scheme would you recommend and why?

6. Calculate the gross earnings for each person. Identify each payment method.
   a) Joe works in a restaurant 27 h a week. He is paid $7.50/h and receives $134 in tips.
   b) Sze Mun worked 46 h last week. She was paid $11.50/h and double time for overtime. Her normal workweek is 40 h.
   c) Jack, a salesperson at an appliance store, earns 12% commission. Last week his sales totalled $5675.
   d) Megan plants trees. She is paid 25¢ for every tree she plants. One week she planted 4350 trees.
   e) Marlene works in a computer store. She earns a graduated commission of 3% on her first $15 000 in sales and 5% on sales over $15 000. Last week she sold $32 150 worth of merchandise.
   f) Duncan, a salesperson, receives $200 a week plus 4% commission. Last week he sold $4780 worth of merchandise.
   g) Frank, a salesperson, is paid $1800 a month and is expected to have monthly sales of $25 000. He is paid 8% commission on any sales beyond this amount. Last month, Frank's total sales were $36 740.

7. Select one part of exercise 6. Write a paragraph to explain how you calculated the gross earnings.

8. May works as a server. She earns $6.25/h and keeps 70% of the tips she receives. The other 30% is shared among the hostess, bus people, and cooks. May worked 34 h last week and received $254 in tips, before sharing. What was her gross pay?

9. Eric is offered a job as a server at two restaurants. The Fish House pays $6.50/h and a server averages $34 a day in tips. The Tea House pays $7.25/h and a server averages $28 a day in tips. If Eric considers the gross pay, which job should he take? What other factors might he want to consider?

10. Jay has just accepted a job in computer sales. The company offers a base salary of $900 plus 6% of his monthly sales, or a straight commission of 9%.

a) Draw a graph to show gross earnings against sales. Plot both situations on the same grid. You could use a graphing calculator or a spreadsheet.

b) Use the graph to advise Jay.

c) What other information might help Jay make a decision?

Extending Your Thinking

11. Pauline earns $9.50/h plus extra for overtime. Her normal workweek is 40 h. Last week she worked 51 h. Her gross earnings were $641.25. What is Pauline's overtime rate of pay?

PROJECTS

In this Tutorial you have worked with different methods of calculating earnings. You will use these skills when you return to the Chapter Project, and for the following projects in the Project Book.

• Restaurant Prices

• Hot Dog Stand

COMMUNICATING THE IDEAS

Your aunt plans to open a computer store. She is unsure how to pay her staff. Write a letter to your aunt to explain how paying the staff a commission might be more favourable to her than paying staff a fixed hourly rate.

Have you ever thought about who pays for the roads on which we drive, the school you attend, or the medical care we use when we are sick? Taxpayers fund all of these services. In this Tutorial you will study payroll deductions.

Here is a typical pay stub for the first pay period of the year.

Company Name: One Better		For the period ending: **15/01/00**		
Employee's Name	**Total Hours**		**Deductions**	**Year to Date**
Louis Robitaille	82	Income Tax	202.05	202.05
Regular Pay	**Year to Date**	EI	28.94	28.94
75×12.75	956.25	CPP	35.00	35.00
$= 956.25$		RRSP	100.00	100.00
Overtime		Union dues	17.02	17.02
7×25.50	178.50			
$= 178.50$		Total Deductions	383.01	383.01
Total Gross Earnings		Net Earnings	751.74	751.74
1134.75	1134.75			

On the left, the pay stub indicates Louis' gross earnings for the current pay period and for the year to date. On the right, the pay stub shows a number of payroll deductions that are subtracted from the gross earnings for the current pay period and the year to date. Louis' take-home pay is his net earnings. An employer is responsible for making these deductions from each employee's 2000 gross earnings:

- *Canada Pension Plan (CPP)*: Any employee between 18 and 70 years of age must contribute to CPP, up to $1186.50 per year. The employer must contribute an equal amount on behalf of the employee. After the age of 60, an individual may apply for CPP contributions to be waived. The CPP is a government-run pension plan for working Canadians.

- *Employment Insurance Premiums (EI)*: In almost all employment situations, the worker has insurable earnings and pays into the Employment Insurance fund up to $994.50 per year. The employer must pay 1.4 times the amount contributed by the employee. The fund insures the worker against unemployment situations such as disability and job loss, and provides an income in case of maternity leave.

- *Income Tax*: Both the federal and provincial governments tax personal income, based on the employee's claim code as indicated on her or his TD1 form. The TD1 form is completed by anyone receiving employment income.

The final year to date totals for earnings and deductions will be used to compile the T4 slip, which the employee uses to calculate income tax.

For the situations in this text, insurable earnings are equal to gross earnings.

Other possible payroll deductions include union dues, professional dues, life insurance premiums, medical insurance premiums, parking fees, alimony or child support payments, Registered Pension Plan (RPP) contributions, and Registered Retirement Savings Plan (RRSP) contributions. Some of these deductions are tax-exempt: the government does not tax any income directed toward these contributions.

Taxable income is gross income minus any of the following tax-exempt deductions: union dues, RPP, RRSP.

Example 1 Calculate net earnings

Joseph owns a convenience store in Saskatchewan. He pays his manager, Angie, every 2 weeks. She has gross earnings of $1160. Her TD1 claim code is 1, and she pays $125 every 2 weeks into an RPP. Calculate Angie's deductions and her net earnings.

SOLUTION

Use the 1999 payroll deduction tables for Saskatchewan. A portion of these tables is shown on pages 286 to 289. Businesses may use these printed tables, or they may get a computer program from Revenue Canada to calculate these deductions.

- To determine the CPP deduction, go to the pages that specify biweekly pay periods in section B of the payroll deduction tables. Look for the pay range that includes Angie's $1160 gross income. The CPP deduction is indicated to the right, in grey.

From - De To - A	CPP	From - De To - A	CPP	From - De To - A
1138.47 - 1138.75	35.14	1159.04 - 1159.32	35.86	1179.61 - 1179.89
1138.76 - 1139.03	35.15	1159.33 - 1159.60	35.87	1179.90 - 1180.18
1139.04 - 1139.32	35.16	1159.61 - 1159.89	35.88	1180.19 - 1180.46
1139.33 - 1139.60	35.17	**1159.90 - 1160.18**	**35.89**	1180.47 - 1180.75
1139.61 - 1139.89	35.18	1160.19 - 1160.46	35.90	1180.76 - 1181.03

Angie's CPP deduction is $35.89, assuming she has not yet paid $1186.50 for 1999.

- To determine the EI deduction, turn to section C in the payroll deduction tables. There is one table that covers all pay periods. Find the appropriate pay range, and read the corresponding deduction.

From - De	To - A	EI premium	From - De	To - A	EI premium	From - De	To - A	EI premium
1129.61 -	1129.99	28.81	1157.85 -	1158.23	29.53	1186.08 -	1186.47	30.25
1130.00 -	1130.39	28.82	1158.24 -	1158.62	29.54	1186.48 -	1186.86	30.26
1130.40 -	1130.78	28.83	1158.63 -	1159.01	29.55	1186.87 -	1187.25	30.27
1130.79 -	1131.17	28.84	1159.02 -	1159.41	29.56	1187.26 -	1187.64	30.28
1131.18 -	1131.56	28.85	1159.42 -	1159.80	29.57	1187.65 -	1188.03	30.29
1131.57 -	1131.96	28.86	**1159.81 - 1160.19**		**29.58**	1188.04 -	1188.43	30.30
1131.97 -	1132.35	28.87	1160.20 -	1160.58	29.59	1188.44 -	1188.82	30.31
1132.36 -	1132.74	28.88	1160.59 -	1160.98	29.60	1188.83 -	1189.21	30.32
1132.75 -	1133.13	28.89	1160.99 -	1161.37	29.61	1189.22 -	1189.60	30.33

Angie's EI deduction is $29.58, provided she has not yet paid $994.50 for 1999.

- To determine the income tax deduction, first determine Angie's taxable income. Remember that her RPP contribution is tax-exempt.

$$\text{Taxable income} = \text{Gross income} - \text{RPP}$$
$$= \$1160 - \$125$$
$$= \$1035$$

Now go to the pages in the tables that correspond to biweekly pay periods. Look for the pay range that includes $1035, then locate the appropriate claim code in that row. This is Angie's deduction.

Pay		0	1	2	3	4	5	6	7
From	Less than								
915. -	931.	241.00	176.50	168.60	152.80	137.10	121.75	104.55	89.25
931. -	947.	245.25	180.75	172.85	157.05	141.25	125.85	109.45	94.15
947. -	963.	249.55	185.05	177.15	161.35	145.50	130.00	114.35	99.05
963. -	979.	253.80	189.30	181.40	165.60	149.75	134.10	118.80	103.45
979. -	995.	258.05	193.55	185.65	169.85	154.05	138.25	122.90	107.60
995. -	1011.	262.30	197.80	189.90	174.10	158.30	142.50	127.00	111.70
1011. -	1027.	266.55	202.05	194.15	178.35	162.55	146.75	131.10	115.80
1027. - 1043.		**270.80**	**206.30**	198.40	182.60	166.80	151.00	135.20	119.90
1043. -	1059.	275.05	210.55	202.65	186.85	171.05	155.25	139.45	124.00
1059. -	1075.	279.50	214.80	206.90	191.15	175.30	159.50	143.70	128.10

Angie's income tax deduction is $206.30.

- To calculate Angie's net earnings, add all the payroll deductions and subtract this amount from her gross earnings.

$$\text{Total deductions} = \$125.00 + \$206.30 + \$29.58 + \$35.89$$
$$= \$396.77$$

$$\text{Net earnings} = \text{Gross earnings} - \text{Total deductions}$$
$$= \$1160.00 - \$396.77$$
$$= \$763.23$$

Employees do not normally have access to the payroll deduction tables, so it may not always be possible to calculate net earnings. However, to plan your spending, you need some idea of what your net earnings will be. To estimate net earnings, we can use the following approximations.

EI   3% of gross earnings, to a maximum of $994.50 annually

CPP   3% of gross earnings, to a maximum of $1186.50 annually

Income tax* 18% of annual taxable income from $7000 to $30 000
              29% of annual taxable income from $30 000 to $60 000
              39% of annual taxable income above $60 000

*In practice, if taxable income is closer to the lower end of the range, the estimate will be high. If taxable income is closer to the higher end of the range, the estimate will be low.

Example 2 Estimate net earnings

Suppose Angie wanted to estimate her net earnings before receiving her pay cheque. Estimate her net earnings using the information in the box that follows *Example 1*.

SOLUTION

- EI and CPP deductions are each approximately 3% of $1160.
  $0.03 \times \$1160 = \$34.80$

- To determine the percent to use to calculate income tax, find Angie's annual taxable income. From *Example 1*, her taxable income is $1035 every 2 weeks.

  Annual taxable income $= 26 \times \$1035$
  $= \$26\,910$

  Angie's annual taxable income is between $7000 and $30 000. She can expect to pay approximately 18% income tax each pay period.
  $0.18 \times \$1035 = \$186.30$

  Since Angie's annual taxable income is close to $30 000, this estimate may be low.

- To estimate Angie's net earnings, add all the payroll deductions and subtract this amount from her gross earnings.

  Total deductions $= \$125.00 + \$34.80 + \$34.80 + \$186.30$
  $= \$380.90$

Estimated net earnings = Gross earnings − Total deductions
$$= \$1160.00 - \$380.90$$
$$= \$779.10$$

Angie's net earnings for the biweekly pay period can be estimated at $780, or less.

Example 3

Estimate net earnings

Naz earns a monthly salary of $3425. Each month, in addition to the mandatory deductions, she pays $45 in union dues, $225 into an RPP, and $20 for parking. Estimate her net earnings.

SOLUTION

- Naz's CPP and EI deductions are each approximately 3% of her gross income.
  $$0.03 \times \$3425 = \$102.75$$

- To calculate her taxable income, subtract RPP contributions and union dues, which are tax exempt.

  Taxable monthly income = Gross monthly income − (Union dues + RPP)
  $$= \$3425 - (\$45 + \$225)$$
  $$= \$3155$$

  Total taxable income = Taxable monthly income × 12
  $$= \$3155 \times 12$$
  $$= \$37\ 860$$

  Her taxable income is between $30 000 and $60 000, so Naz's income tax deduction will be approximately 29% of her taxable monthly income.

  Income tax = 0.29 × $3155.00
  $$= \$914.95$$

  Since Naz's annual taxable income is close to the lower end of the $30 000 – $60 000 range, this estimate may be high.

- To estimate Naz's net earnings, add all the payroll deductions and subtract this amount from her gross earnings.

  Total deductions = $20.00 + $45.00 + $225.00 + $102.75 + $102.75 + $914.95
  $$= \$1410.45$$

  Net earnings = Gross earnings − Total deductions
  $$= \$3425.00 - \$1410.45$$
  $$= \$2014.55$$

  Naz's net earnings will be about $2015.

1. Explain the differences among gross earnings, taxable earnings, and net earnings.

2. Suppose you were hired for a job today. Which payroll deductions would be made from your pay?

3. How could a person reduce the amount of income tax she pays without changing the gross pay or the claim code?

EXERCISES

Checking Your Skills

1. Look at Louis Robitaille's pay stub on page XX. What will Louis' employer pay for CPP and EI?

2. What is a TD1 form? Why is it important that an employee fill out one?

3. Why do the payroll deduction tables differ from province to province?

4. Examine the payroll deduction tables on pages 286 to 289. Describe how each of the following deductions changes.
   a) CPP, as income increases
   b) income tax, as income increases
   c) EI, as gross income increases
   d) income tax, as TD1 claim code increases

5. Use the payroll deduction tables to determine the required deduction.
   a) CPP, monthly gross income $1160
   b) EI, monthly gross income $1130.45
   c) CPP, monthly gross income $1117.35
   d) income tax, biweekly taxable income $1156, claim code 1
   e) income tax, claim code 10, biweekly taxable income $1601.98
   f) EI, monthly gross income $1165.32

6. Explain how contributing to an RRSP or RPP affects CPP, EI, and income tax deductions.

7. Jackie and Keith have identical gross earnings. However, Jackie's gross earnings are for 2 weeks of work whereas Keith's are for 1 month.
   a) Which person will have higher CPP deductions over the year?
   b) Which person will have higher EI deductions over the year?

c) Suppose Jackie and Keith have the same claim code. Which person will pay more income tax?

d) Consider your answers to parts a to c. Do you think this is fair? Why?

8. a) Use the payroll deduction tables. Calculate the net earnings for Sandra, whose gross biweekly earnings are $1184. Each pay period, she pays $50 into an RRSP as well as a life insurance premium of $10. Her claim code is 3.

b) When Sandra's family situation changes, she changes her claim code from 3 to 8. Use her new claim code to recalculate her net earnings.

9. Tim earns a biweekly salary of $1169. He has a claim code of 1 and pays $20 in union dues each pay period.

a) Calculate Tim's biweekly net earnings.

b) Tim receives a raise of $5 a week. Use Tim's new biweekly salary to recalculate his net earnings.

c) Write to explain why Tim's net earnings changed by less than $10.

10. Alina earns $1320 a week. Each week she pays $100 into an RRSP and $10 for parking.

a) Estimate Alina's weekly net earnings.

b) Will this estimate be higher or lower than the actual net earnings? Why?

c) Some employees at Alina's workplace have asked to increase their RRSP contribution to $200 a week. Assuming that this amount is within her contribution limit, would this be beneficial for Alina? Why?

11. Jim earns a salary of $2325 semi-monthly. He pays $150 every pay period into an RPP, as well as a medical insurance premium of 1.5% of his gross income.

a) Estimate Jim's net earnings.

b) Would you expect Jim's actual net earnings to be higher or lower than your estimate? Explain your answer.

12. You have a job offer from a grocery store. The job pays $8.25/h, and you will work 25 h a week. You will be paid every 2 weeks.

a) Calculate your gross earnings for one pay period.

b) Estimate your net earnings.

c) What percent of your gross earnings will you receive in your pay cheque?

Extending Your Thinking

13. Copy this table.

Claim Code	Income Tax Deducted ($)	Percent of Taxable Income Deducted (%)
0		
1		
2		
3		
4		
5		
6		
7		
8		
9		
10		

a) Refer to pages 286 to 289. Complete the table for a Saskatchewan resident who earns a biweekly taxable income of $1740.

b) Plot a graph of income tax deducted against claim code. Place the claim code on the horizontal axis.

c) Describe how the income tax deducted changes as the claim code increases.

d) Draw a line of best fit, and determine the equation of this line.

PROJECTS

In this Tutorial you have investigated payroll deductions. You will use this knowledge when you return to the Chapter Project and in the following projects in the Project Book.

- Restaurant Prices
- Hot Dog Stand
- Net Pay

COMMUNICATING THE IDEAS

A friend writes you a letter stating, "I've been offered a great job that pays $15/h. They want me to work 80 h a month, which means I will receive $1200 a month." Write a paragraph responding to your friend's statement outlining what you think the net earnings will be.

Often, people experiencing financial difficulties have not planned their spending. A *budget* is a written plan outlining how you will spend your money. A budget allows you to analyze your spending in light of your financial goals.

To develop a budget, you must identify your *expenses*. Expenses include all items or services for which you pay. When you identify expenses, it is helpful to distinguish between necessities and desires.

Most people plan personal budgets based on monthly spending. However, you must also budget for expenses that come up once or twice a year, such as car and home insurance, residential taxes, or holidays.

Example 1   **Foreign exchange**

Rick is planning a three-week vacation to visit his relatives in Norway 10 months from now. The air travel will cost $1200. His relatives have suggested he bring NOK 6000 (Norwegian kroner) for spending money. The current exchange rate is NOK 1 for Can $0.19.

a) Determine the total cost of the trip.

b) How much should Rick save each month to plan for this vacation?

SOLUTION

a) Since Rick is visiting relatives, assume he will only have to pay for his air travel and take along spending money. His relatives have suggested NOK 6000 spending money. Convert this amount to Canadian dollars.

NOK 1 = Can $0.19
NOK 6000 = 6000 × Can $0.19
NOK 6000 = Can $1140

The total cost of the trip is: $1200 + $1140 = $2340.

b) Rick has 10 months to save $2340. He should save $234 each month for the trip.

When first you leave home, you will have new expenses — groceries, furniture, kitchenware, linens, and so on. In order to set a realistic budget, it is useful to be able to compare prices.

Example 2 Compare prices using unit pricing

A store is selling a box of 12 125-mL containers of yogurt for $3.49 for a total of 1500 mL. The same yogurt can be purchased in a large 500-mL container for $1.09.

a) Which purchase provides the better value?

b) Explain when it might be more economical in the long term to buy the item with the higher unit price.

SOLUTION

a) Compare the cost of 100 mL of yogurt.
Offer 1: 12 125-mL containers for $3.49

1500 mL for $3.49

100 mL for $\frac{\$3.49}{15}$ or $0.23

Offer 2: a 500-mL container for $1.09

100 mL for $\frac{\$1.09}{5}$ or $0.22.

The 500-mL container is the better value, since the unit price is lower.

b) It may be more economical to purchase the item with the higher unit price if any yogurt from the large container would be wasted. Wasteage would increase the effective unit price and the bulk purchase might no longer be the better value.

Some responsibilities that come with home ownership are mortgage payments, property taxes, and utilities.

Property owners pay taxes to their local government. These taxes help support education, libraries, and other municipal services.

Property Tax

Property tax depends on the assessed value of the property and the local *mill rate*. The assessed value of a property is a percent of its fair market value. The mill rate is set locally: one mill is equal to $\frac{1}{1000}$ of $1. This formula is used:

$$\text{Property tax} = \frac{\text{Assessed value} \times \text{Mill rate}}{1000}$$

Example 3 **Calculate the property tax**

The Meyers' property has a fair market value of $124 000. In their area, the assessed value of a property is 75% of fair market value. The current mill rate is 28 mills.

a) Determine the Meyers' property tax for the year.

b) How much should the Meyers budget each month for this expense?

SOLUTION

a) The assessed value is 75% of the fair market value.

Assessed value $= 0.75 \times \$124\ 000$

$= \$93\ 000$

$$\text{Property tax} = \frac{\text{Assessed value} \times \text{Mill rate}}{1000}$$

$$= \frac{\$93\ 000 \times 28}{1000}$$

$$= \$2604$$

The Meyers' property tax is $2604.

b) The Meyers have 12 months to budget for this expense.

$\$2604 \div 12 = \$217$

They should budget $217 monthly.

DISCUSSING THE IDEAS

1. What are the three quantities that determine the amount of property tax a homeowner must pay?

2. The fair market value of property in a community is reviewed regularly. Suppose the fair market values of all properties increase, but local government expenses do not change. What would you expect to happen to the mill rate in that community?

3. List as many sources as you can where you may obtain current listings for foreign exchange rates.

4. A person travelling from Canada to the United States received an exchange rate of US $0.65 for Can $1. Explain how you can calculate the exchange rate for a person travelling on the same day from the United States to Canada.

Checking Your Skills

1. When shopping for groceries or other household items, we often make decisions about which items are most economical. Estimate which item is the better buy. Check your estimate using a calculator.

   a) tomato soup: $0.54 for 284 mL, or $1.39 for 907 mL

   b) grated cheese: $2.98 for 400 g, or $1.98 for 255 g

   c) breakfast cereal: $2.19 for 450 g, or $6.99 for 1.4 kg

   d) macaroni dinner: 12 for $9.99, or the first 6 for $0.69 each and the next 6 for $0.96 each

2. A department store sells a box of 12 videocassettes for $49.99. The same tapes can also be purchased in packages of 3 for $13.99.

   a) Which purchase provides the better value?

   b) Is it always wise to purchase the more economical package? Explain.

3. An electricity company offers an equalization plan that charges a customer a fixed amount every month. At the end of the year, the company calculates the difference between customer usage and the amount paid, and charges or rebates the difference to the customer. This chart summarizes the electricity bills for the Dirksen family over 1 year. Near the end of this year, the family learned that electricity rates would increase by 4% effective January 1st.

January	$155.43	July	$ 75.64
February	$137.78	August	$ 74.73
March	$ 34.31	September	$ 75.56
April	$ 99.56	October	$ 87.77
May	$ 87.11	November	$ 95.69
June	$ 79.42	December	$119.79

   a) Compare the amounts for February, March, and April. Suggest some reasons for the differences.

   b) The Dirksens decide to use the equalization plan. What monthly amount should the company charge?

   c) Explain how joining this plan would make budgeting easier.

4. The Lees own two cars and their home. This table summarizes the non-monthly expenses associated with their cars and home.

March 30	Car licence	$ 150
April 15	Car insurance	$ 625
May 20	Home insurance	$ 520
June 30	Property taxes	$ 2060
November 15	Car licence	$ 170
November 30	Car insurance	$ 870

a) The Lees decide to save money each month to pay for these expenses. How much money do they need to set aside each month?

b) Suppose the Lees save the monthly amount you calculated in part a. Will they be able to pay for all these expenses if they begin to put money aside January 1? Explain your answer.

5. Miki's property has an assessed value of $73 900. Last year's mill rate was 31.8 mills.

a) Determine Miki's property tax for last year.

b) Suppose the mill rate is increased by 3 mills. Determine the increase in Miki's property tax.

c) How much should Miki set aside each month to budget for the increased property taxes?

d) Many banks allow customers with a mortgage to include property tax payments with their mortgage payments. Suggest some advantages to this option.

6. A farmer owns land that has a fair market value of $225 000. The assessed value is 70% of the fair market value. The mill rate is 14.3 mills. How much should the farmer budget each month for property taxes?

7. Two friends are planning a vacation in Alaska. They want to include a one-day coastal cruise that costs US $139 per person. The friends estimate that the total cost for this cruise will be approximately Can $350 for two people, and they budget accordingly. When they leave for their trip, Can $1 is worth US $0.72.

a) Estimate the cost of the cruise in Canadian dollars. Have the two friends budgeted enough money? Explain your answer.

b) Calculate the cost, in Canadian dollars, of the one-day cruise.

8. The Sants are planning a 4-day ski vacation at Whitefish, Montana. They estimate daily costs of US $125 for lift tickets and US $120 for accommodation and food. They plan an additional Can $500 for travel and incidental expenses. When they plan their budget, US $1 is worth Can $1.40. The Sants have 6 months to save for the vacation. How much money should they set aside each month?

9. Suppose the value of the Canadian dollar increases relative to the American dollar. Is this beneficial for Canadians planning an American vacation? Explain.

10. A person travelling from Canada to the United States received an exchange rate of 71%. The same day, a person travelling from the United States to Canada received an exchange rate of 140.8%. Write to explain how this is possible.

11. A Canadian is travelling from the Netherlands to Britain. She knows that one Dutch guilder is equivalent to Can $0.71, whereas one British pound is equivalent to Can $2.24. She has 200 guilders and wants to exchange them for British pounds. How many British pounds should she receive?

12. Suppose the mill rate is increased by 2 mills. Will all taxpayers experience an equal increase in their property taxes? Justify your answer.

Extending Your Thinking

13. The inflation rate measures how the cost of living changes. If the inflation rate one year is 2%, it means that it costs 2% more than it did in the preceding year to maintain an equivalent standard of living. Given an average annual inflation rate of 4%, estimate the cost of each item 60 years from now.

  a) $0.60 for 1 L of gas   **b)** $8 for admission to a movie

  c) $22 000 for a new car   **d)** $100 000 for a new home

PROJECTS

In this Tutorial you have worked on some of the expenses of living independently. You will use this knowledge when you return to the Chapter Project and in the following projects in the Project Book.

- Restaurant Prices
- Hot Dog Stand
- The Graduation Trip
- Buying or Leasing a Car

COMMUNICATING THE IDEAS

A recent immigrant has just bought a house. He has never paid property taxes before. Write a short note to explain property taxes.

The Cost of Running a Car

Many people see a car as part of their dream of an independent future. You can buy a car, in which case it belongs to you, or you can lease a car that belongs to a leasing company. Either way you will also have additional costs for registration, insurance, maintenance, and gas. Investigate the cost of running a car by completing the steps below. Assume you can buy a Saturn SL1 for $18 253, plus taxes. Alternatively, examine local advertisements, choose a car you would like to own, and include details of financing. Cut out and keep the advertisement.

1. Calculate the cost of buying the car. Use appropriate taxes for your province.

2. Your grandmother gives you a gift of $8800 to use as a down payment for the Saturn. The Saturn dealer tells you that to buy the car the monthly payment for 36 months will be $365.81. How much will you pay in total?

3. The dealer also gives you the option of leasing the car for 36 months, using the same down payment. The monthly payment will be $106.65, including taxes. After 3 years you may buy the car for $8531, plus taxes. How much is the total lease payment? If you buy the car at the end of the lease, how much does the car cost you in total?

4. Determine the annual registration fee in your province.

5. The cost of insurance varies widely, depending on factors such as: where you live and how you use the car; your age, sex, and driving record; and whether you have had a driver-training course. Research insurance costs and try to estimate the cost for your insurance.

CHAPTER PROJECT

Complete *Tutorials 5.4* to *5.8* to develop the relevant skills for the last stage of this Chapter Project. You will return to the Chapter Project on page 278.

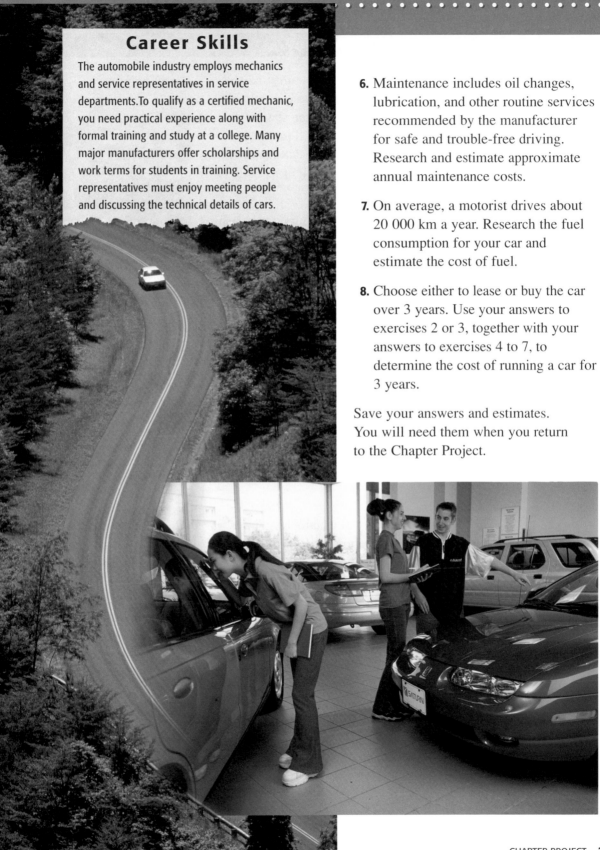

Career Skills

The automobile industry employs mechanics and service representatives in service departments. To qualify as a certified mechanic, you need practical experience along with formal training and study at a college. Many major manufacturers offer scholarships and work terms for students in training. Service representatives must enjoy meeting people and discussing the technical details of cars.

6. Maintenance includes oil changes, lubrication, and other routine services recommended by the manufacturer for safe and trouble-free driving. Research and estimate approximate annual maintenance costs.

7. On average, a motorist drives about 20 000 km a year. Research the fuel consumption for your car and estimate the cost of fuel.

8. Choose either to lease or buy the car over 3 years. Use your answers to exercises 2 or 3, together with your answers to exercises 4 to 7, to determine the cost of running a car for 3 years.

Save your answers and estimates. You will need them when you return to the Chapter Project.

To manage your affairs well, you must be able to keep track of your money. You can only make sensible decisions if you know the state of your finances. In this Tutorial, you will investigate how to keep track of your personal finances and how a small business keeps track of its daily finances.

When you open a chequing account with a bank or trust company, you may receive a passbook or the bank may send you a monthly statement showing its record of your account.

Chris Haddad
49 Spire Hillway,
Cooksville, MB, M7B 2S3

Account no. 4325193
Number of enclosures 2
Period ending 15/10/98

Account description	Debits	Credits	Date	Balance
Balance forward			15/09	523.14
Cash withdrawal	50.00		17/09	473.14
Cheque 034	62.18		20/09	410.96
Deposit		341.60	29/09	752.56
Maintenance fee	9.75		01/10	742.81
Withdrawal	40.00		04/10	702.81
Cheque 035	137.64		05/10	565.17
Withdrawal	60.00		10/10	505.17
Withdrawal	40.00		12/10	465.17

Date	No.	Description	Credit	Debit	✔	Balance
		Balance forward				523.14
Sept. 17		Withdrawal		50.00		473.14
Sept. 18	34	The Electronic Store		62.18		410.96
Sept. 29		Deposit	341.60			751.56
Oct. 3	35	Clothing Express		137.46		614.10
Oct. 4		Withdrawal		40.00		574.10
Oct. 12		Withdrawal		40.00		534.10
Oct. 15	36	Bike and Skate		83.12		450.98

The bank's arithmetic will usually be correct, but there could be incorrect charges. If you don't report errors promptly, the bank's statement will be taken as correct. It is a good idea to record all transactions in a transaction record. Record all deposits and withdrawals such as cheques and direct debits made with a debit card. If you get into the habit of doing this at the time the transaction is made, you will not forget about it and you will have a complete record of your transactions.

When you receive your bank statement, it will show your account's activity from the date of the last statement up to the date it was printed. It could be a week or more from printing until you receive the statement, so you may have recorded later transactions in your transaction record. You should check whether both records agree up to the date of the bank statement. This process is called *reconciling your account*.

There are different ways to reconcile a statement. The Investigation that follows shows you one way.

Reconciling a Bank Statement

1. Ask your teacher for a copy of the statement and transaction record above. Look in the transaction record for each item on the bank statement. Check off each item on the statement if it has been recorded.

2. Add any entry that appears on the bank statement and is not in the transaction record. Add any further entries, such as bank fees or interest, reported on the statement.

3. Start with the final balance on the bank statement. Account for transactions in the transaction record that have not yet cleared at the bank: add uncleared deposits and subtract uncleared cheques or withdrawals.

4. Compare the result from step 3 with the final balance in the transaction record. The two numbers should be the same. If they are not, check:
   - Did you copy the entries in the transaction record correctly?
   - Did you make a mathematical error when revising the balance?

Balancing the Till

You will investigate a method of keeping track of the cash of a small business.

Many people today have small businesses. The Chemainiac Shop in Chemainus, B.C. is a gift shop. Beverly, the owner, uses the following method to reconcile the cash register statements each day.

1. At the beginning of the day, the cash register at the shop has a certain amount of cash in it, called a *float*. Why is a float necessary? Why is it important to know the amount of the float?

2. At the end of the day, how can the amount of cash taken in that day be determined?

3. Many people make their purchases using credit cards or they make direct debit transactions using debit cards. In determining the daily revenue, how should you deal with the value of these card transactions?

4. Customers sometimes return merchandise for a refund. When calculating the daily sales, how should you deal with the total value of refunds?

5. Consider the table on the following page. It is the till statement for a day in July. The Float column shows how much money was in the till at the beginning of the day and the Take column shows the money at the end of the day.

Float		Take	
	Value ($)		Value ($)
50 × 1¢ =	0.50	65 × 1¢ =	0.65
30 × 5¢ =	1.50	29 × 5¢ =	1.45
30 × 10¢ =	3.00	37 × 10¢ =	3.70
20 × 25¢ =	5.00	39 × 25¢ =	9.75
10 × $1 =	10.00	9 × $1 =	9.00
10 × $2 =	20.00	12 × $2 =	24.00
2 × $5 =	10.00	11 × $5 =	55.00
5 × $10 =	50.00	11 × $10 =	110.00
5 × $20 =	100.00	12 × $20 =	240.00
		2 × $50 =	100.00
Total Float		**Total Cash**	
		Cheques	252.31
		Direct Debit	188.14
		Credit Card	15.63
			105.00
			95.00
		Subtotal	
		Refunds	12.39
		Total Take	

6. Find the total value of the float.

7. Complete the table. Is the subtotal equal to the value of the day's sales? Why or why not? What is the total value of the day's sales? Explain why this differs from the subtotal.

8. Determine the net sales revenue for the day.

9. The till prints 2 copies of the transaction: one is a receipt for the customer, the other on a tape is for the owner's record. What further checks should the owner do at the end of the day?

10. If the take from the till and the tape do not balance, what procedures do you think the owner should follow?

1. Why is it important to keep your personal bank register updated?

2. Why should you include direct debit transactions made with a debit card in your transaction record?

3. Many retail stores reconcile cash register takes with the duplicate sales receipts at the end of every day. Why may the two not balance?

Checking Your Skills

1. For banking purposes, a debit item represents a withdrawal from an account and a credit item represents a deposit into an account. Copy and complete the statement below in your notebook or on a spreadsheet. Determine the final balance.

Account description	Debits	Credits	Date	Balance
Balance forward			11/8	1195.12
Cheque 200	789.36		12/8	
Cheque 201	316.26		15/8	
Deposit		704.54	16/8	
Service charges	9.95		16/8	
Cheque 202	587.24		17/8	
Deposit		812.56	18/8	

2. Use the transaction record and the bank statement below. Reconcile the chequing account for May. If the balance is incorrect, identify any errors and describe how to correct them. Assume that the entries on the bank statement are correct.

Date	No.	Description	Credit	Debit	✔	Balance
		Balance forward				$525.00
4/5	124	David's Gift Shop		19.00		
9/5		Pay cheque	116.00			
13/5	125	B.C. Tel		43.00		
14/5	126	Pete's Garage		58.00		
18/5	127	Bookstore Unlimited		50.00		
26/5	128	United Way		25.00		
28/5	129	Wayside Apartments		275.00		
30/5		Pay cheque	1000.00			

The bank statement for the account is below.

Account description	Debits	Credits	Date	Balance
Balance forward			1/5	525.00
Deposit		116.00	9/5	641.00
Cheque 124	19.00		9/5	622.00
Cheque 125	43.00		14/5	579.00
Printed cheques	8.00		15/5	571.00
Cheque 126	68.00		16/5	503.00
Cheque 127	50.00		23/5	453.00
Service charge	12.00		31/5	441.00

3. Consider the table below. It is the till statement for one day in August.

Float		Take	
	Value ($)		Value ($)
$76 \times 1¢ =$	0.76	$89 \times 1¢ =$	0.89
$36 \times 5¢ =$	1.80	$37 \times 5¢ =$	1.85
$41 \times 10¢ =$	4.10	$57 \times 10¢ =$	5.70
$44 \times 25¢ =$	11.00	$39 \times 25¢ =$	9.75
$23 \times \$1 =$	23.00	$10 \times \$1 =$	10.00
$20 \times \$2 =$	40.00	$19 \times \$2 =$	38.00
$7 \times \$5 =$	35.00	$15 \times \$5 =$	75.00
$9 \times \$10 =$	90.00	$21 \times \$10 =$	210.00
$5 \times \$20 =$	100.00	$12 \times \$20 =$	240.00
$0 \times \$50 =$		$3 \times \$50 =$	150.00

The value of credit card and debit card transactions was $653.63 and cheques amounted to $440.45. There were no refunds that day. Determine the total take for the day.

4. The following petty cash transactions for a small business occurred during the first week of March.

4/3	$100 cheque was received to establish the petty cash fund.
5/3	Bought $12.50 worth of postage stamps.
5/3	Spent $10 to have a parcel delivered by taxi.
6/3	Spent $6.50 for lunch.
7/3	Paid a courier service $25 for deliveries.
7/3	Bought flowers for opening day, $28.
8/3	Replenished the petty cash fund, $25.
9/3	Purchased postage stamps, for $21.50.

Determine if a final balance of $20 is correct. If not, provide an explanation for the difference, and indicate possible ways to correct the problem.

5. Create a table similar to the one below. You may wish to set up a spreadsheet. Complete the table to determine the cost of credit for using a department store charge account for the period shown. For each month determine the balance due, then add the credit charge to determine the new balance. Monthly credit charges are 1.4% of the balance due.

Month	Previous Balance	− Payment Made	+ Payment Made	= Balance Due	+ Credit Charges	= New Balance
Feb.	$314.65	$100.00	$193.75		$5.72	$414.12
Mar.		$150.00	$59.60			
Apr.		$140.00	$421.83			$618.62
May	$618.62	$200.00	$39.65			
June		$250.00	$58.11			
July		$150.00	$77.21			
Aug.		$120.00	$163.09			

Extending Your Thinking

6. Set up a spreadsheet to serve as a transaction record. Your spreadsheet should automatically calculate the balance after each transaction. How would you use your spreadsheet to reconcile a bank statement?

PROJECTS

In this Tutorial, you learned to reconcile a till statement and a monthly bank statement. You will need to know how to keep track of money for the Chapter Project and the following projects in the Project Book.

- Restaurant Prices
- Hot Dog Stand

COMMUNICATING THE IDEAS

Write instructions to a new store clerk explaining how to reconcile the till.

Interest

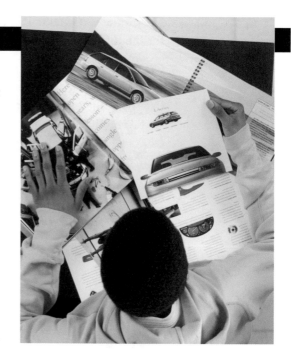

As you think about living independently, you can see that it is necessary to manage your money carefully. You need to have savings for unexpected expenses and for large purchases, such as a car or a house. One very common method of saving is to deposit money into a bank account. When you do this, you are lending your money to the bank. In return the bank pays you *interest*. This is the money paid for the use of your money.

Investigation 1

Simple Interest

You will investigate the amount of simple interest earned on an investment of $100 for different periods of time.

Suppose you make a $100 investment that earns simple interest at 4% per year.

1. How much interest would you earn in 1 year?

2. How much interest would you earn in 2 years? 5 years? 10 years?

3. How much interest would you earn in 6 months? 3 months? 1 month?

4. For a year with 365 days, write to explain how you could calculate the interest earned in 40 days.

5. Write a general method for calculating interest over any time period.

When interest is calculated once only, at the end of the investment period, the interest is called *simple interest*. It is used today only over short periods of time, usually up to one year. The formula for calculating the amount of simple interest, *I*, in dollars is

$$I = Prt,$$

where *P* dollars is the amount invested, called the *principal*, *r* is the annual interest rate as a decimal, and *t* is the time in years.

Example 1 | **Calculate the amount for simple interest**

Terry invests $350 on March 1 by opening a savings account. The annual interest rate is 1.5%. Interest is calculated at the end of the month on the minimum balance in the account that month.

a) Calculate the amount that will be in the account on April 1 if Terry makes no other transactions.

b) Calculate the amount that will be in the account on April 1 if Terry withdraws $100 on March 20.

SOLUTION

a) Terry's minimum balance during March is $350.
Use the formula $I = Prt$.
Substitute $P = 350$, $r = 0.015$, and $t = \frac{1}{12}$ year.
$I = 350 \times 0.015 \times \frac{1}{12}$
$\quad = 0.44$, rounded to the nearest cent

The amount, A, in the account is the principal plus the interest, or $P + I$.
$A = \$350.00 + \$0.44$
$\quad = \$350.44$.

On April 1, $350.44 is in Terry's account.

b) The minimum balance during March is now $350 − $100, or $250.
To calculate the interest for March, substitute $P = 250$, $r = 0.015$, and $t = \frac{1}{12}$ into the formula
$I = Prt$.
$I = 250 \times 0.015 \times \frac{1}{12}$
$\quad = 0.31$, rounded to the nearest cent

The interest earned is $0.31 and the amount in the account on April 1 is $250.00 + $0.31, or $250.31.

If you invest money for longer periods of time, the interest calculated is *compound interest*. In this case, the interest earned during a specified time period is added to the principal. The new amount, which includes the principal and the interest, then earns interest during the next time period. This periodic recalculation and addition of the interest to the principal continues for the duration of the investment.

The process of converting interest into principal is called *compounding*.

Practise Your Prior Skills

In the Investigation that follows, you will work with exponents. Try these exercises as preliminary review.

1. Use exponents to rewrite each expression in the shortest way you can. Do not evaluate.

a) $340(1.3)(1.3)(1.3)$ **b)** $2(y)(y)$

2. Write the following as a single power of x.

a) $(x^3)(x^5)$ **b)** $(x)(x^5)$ **c)** 1

STUDENT REFERENCE

If you need to review "exponents," look in the Student Reference section.

In the following Investigation you will work with compound interest.

Investigation 2

Compound Interest

Suppose you invest $1000. The bank offers you an annual interest rate of 5%, compounded annually, if you agree to leave the account unchanged for 6 years.

1. Set up a table, either on a spreadsheet, on your graphing calculator, or in your notebook. Use the following column headings:

Year	Principal for Year	Interest	Amount at End of Year

2. Enter the principal for year 1 of $1000.

3. Calculate the interest earned at the end of the first year and the amount at the end of the first year.

4. What is the principal for year 2?

5. Calculate the entries for the remaining rows of the table.

6. Graph the data in columns 1 and 4.

7. Look at the entries for year 2. You can determine the amount at the end of the year in a single calculation, by multiplying the principal at the beginning of the year by a certain factor. What is this factor?

8. Verify that the same factor works for each row.

9. Copy and complete the table below.

Year	Amount at End of Year
1	$1000(1.05) = 1000(1.05)^1$
2	$1000(1.05)(1.05) = 1000(1.05)^2$
3	
4	
5	
6	

Evaluate each amount to verify that it is the same as the equivalent entry in the last column of the table in exercise 1.

10. Write an expression to calculate the amount if the investment were to continue to the end of year 9.

Look at the pattern in the table in exercise 9 of *Investigation 2*. In each row, the principal is multiplied by the factor 1.05. Note that $1.05 = 1 + 0.05$, and 0.05 is the decimal form of the interest rate for the compounding period.

In general, to calculate the amount, the principal is multiplied by a factor, called the *compounding factor*, $(1 + i)^n$.

$A = P(1 + i)^n$, where

A is the accumulated or future amount

P is the principal or present amount

i is the interest rate per compounding period expressed as a decimal

n is the number of compounding periods

Many graphing calculators can perform financial calculations. The TI-83 is one of these. It has a feature called the TVM (Time Value of Money) Solver.

UTILITY

If you have never used a graphing calculator to make financial calculations, Utility 22 explains how to do this on the TI-83 calculator. If you are using a different calculator, consult the User's Manual.

Example 2 **Determine the accumulated amount**

Germaine deposited $30 in an account earning 4.75% interest, compounded annually. Determine the amount at the end of 8 years.

SOLUTION

Method 1: Use the compound interest formula:

$$A = P(1 + i)^n$$

Substitute $P = \$30$, $i = 0.0475$, and $n = 8$.

$$A = 30(1 + 0.0475)^8$$
$$= 43.486\ 405\ 16$$

The amount at the end of 8 years is $43.49.

Method 2: Use the graphing calculator.

To access the TVM Solver on the TI-83, press $\boxed{\text{2nd}}$ $\boxed{x^{-1}}$, then $\boxed{\text{ENTER}}$.

The screen display for this calculation is shown below.

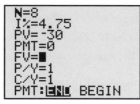

The variables represent the following quantities.

N: total number of payment (compounding) periods

I%: annual interest as a percent

PV: present value (principal)

PMT: payment each period

FV: future amount

P/Y: number of payments per year

C/Y: number of compounding periods per year

The calculator displays either positive or negative quantities for PV, PMT, and FV. A positive value indicates the amount is earned. A negative value indicates the amount is invested. Enter –30 for PV since this is the amount Germaine invested.

To find the future value, move the cursor to FV and press [ALPHA] [ENTER].

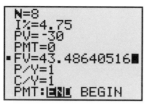

```
N=8
I%=4.75
PV=-30
PMT=0
▪FV=43.48640516█
P/Y=1
C/Y=1
PMT:END BEGIN
```

After 8 years, the amount, or FV, is $43.49.

DISCUSSING THE IDEAS

1. The table in *Investigation 2*, exercise 1 can be easily produced using a spreadsheet. Why is this so?

2. Suppose you repeated exercises 1 to 5 of Investigation 2 for a higher annual rate of interest. How do you think the graph would change? How would it change if the annual rate of interest were lower?

3. Suppose an account is unchanged by withdrawals or deposits over several years. Explain why compounding interest is a fairer way to calculate interest.

EXERCISES

Checking Your Skills

1. Copy and complete the following table.

Investment	Amount of Simple Interest ($)	Principal ($)	Annual Interest Rate (%)	Time (years)
a		500.00	6.75	3
b	42.53		4.50	1
c	102.38	4 500.00	3.25	
d	1 250.00	10 000.00		2.5

2. Make a table to show the growth of a $450 savings deposit invested at 4.5% compounded annually for 5 years.

3. Use the compound interest formula to determine each amount.

   a) $250 invested for 3 years at 4% compounded annually

   b) $100 invested for 10 years at 5.25% compounded annually

   c) $432 invested for 7 years at 3% compounded annually

4. Interest is compounded annually. How much interest does each investment earn?

    a) $1500 invested for 4 years at 6%

    b) $375 invested for 10 years at 5%

    c) $285.95 invested for 3 years at 4%

5. Canada Savings Bonds are offered each November by the federal government. Canada Compound Interest Savings Bonds issued several years ago earned 8% interest compounded annually. Determine the value of a $500 bond when it matured after 7 years.

6. A donation of $100 000 was made to a college. It was to be used to help pay for an expansion to the student centre. Construction was due to start in 5 years' time, so the board of governors invested the money at 8% with interest compounded annually. What amount did the donation provide toward the student centre when building commenced?

7. Suppose $100 is invested for 25 years with interest compounded annually.

    a) Use the list feature of your calculator or a spreadsheet. Copy and complete this table.

Years	Accumulated Amount at 5% Interest ($)	Accumulated Amount at 10% Interest ($)
0	100.00	100.00
5		
10		
15		
20		
25		

    b) Plot the data for 5% and 10% interest rates on the same grid.

    c) Use your graphs to estimate how many years it takes $100 to grow to $300 at each rate.

    d) When the interest rate is doubled, does the amount double? Explain.

Extending Your Thinking

8. Create a spreadsheet to show the growth of a $100 investment, with interest compounded annually, for annual interest rates of 4%, 5%, and so on. A possible spreadsheet is started below.

	A	B	C	D
1	Growing $100 with interest compounded annually			
2	Interest Rate	0.04	=B2+0.01	=C2+0.01
3	Year	Compound Amount at 4%	Compound Amount at 5%	Compound Amount at 6%

Enter appropriate formulas in the next row. Fill Down from row 4 to display year 2 and beyond. Fill Right from column D to display interest rates greater than 6%. Use the spreadsheet to determine how long it takes money to double at different interest rates.

a) Plot a graph of the time (in years) for money to double against the annual interest rate. Place annual interest rate on the horizontal axis.

b) Use your graph.

i) What interest rate compounded annually would double an investment in 10 years?

ii) About how long does it take money to double when invested at 15%? The Rule of 72 states that the number of years it takes money to double in value is approximately

$$\frac{72}{\text{Annual interest rate}}$$

Use your spreadsheet to verify this rule.

PROJECTS

You have learned about simple interest and compound interest. You will use these skills when you return to the Chapter Project and in the following projects in the Project Book.

- The Rule of 72
- Hot Dog Stand
- Buying or Leasing a Car

COMMUNICATING THE IDEAS

Write a short paragraph to explain the difference between simple interest and compound interest.

In the financial world, interest is often charged or credited more than once a year. Interest is commonly compounded semi-annually, quarterly, or monthly. This means that interest is converted to principal 2, 4, or 12 times a year, respectively.

Interest is usually quoted as an annual rate. If compounding occurs more than once a year, the annual interest rate is divided equally among the interest periods.

For example, if the annual rate is 12% and compounding occurs quarterly, the interest is converted to principal 4 times a year. The interest rate to use for each interest period is 3%.

Here are some terms you should know:

Term Deposit: Available from banks and trust companies, a term deposit offers a higher interest rate than a savings account because it involves a larger amount of money than a typical personal account. The rate of interest is guaranteed for a fixed term or period of investment. Customers who withdraw money before the end of the term forfeit all or part of the interest, depending on the type of agreement.

Guaranteed Investment Certificate (GIC): A GIC offers a higher interest rate than a personal savings account but requires a minimum deposit, typically hundreds of dollars. The money must be invested for an agreed-upon length of time and usually cannot be redeemed before the maturity date.

Registered Retirement Savings Plan (RRSP): The major advantage of an RRSP is the tax break it offers. You do not pay income tax on any earned income contributed to an RRSP; nor do you pay tax on any growth in value until you withdraw RRSP funds. An RRSP plan can hold many different types of investments — savings, term deposits, GICs, mutual funds, stocks, and bonds.

Mortgages: Most people who buy a home, store, or office require a mortgage. This is a long-term loan where the house or store is used as *collateral*. This means the property could be sold to recover the money should the borrower not pay.

Most spreadsheets, and some calculators, have financial features built in. In the following activity you will create a spreadsheet that allows you to compare the effects of different compounding periods.

AT THE COMPUTER: Open your spreadsheet program and start a new spreadsheet.

1. Copy the cells below into a new spreadsheet. Save the spreadsheet as INVESTMENT.

	A	B	C	D	E
1	INVESTMENT				
2	Investment	1000	Interest Rate	0.0475	
3					
4	Time (years)	Annually	Semi-annually		Monthly
5	0	=B2	=B2	=B2	=B2
6	=A5+1				

2. Enter the following formulas.

In cell B6: =$B$5*(1+$D$2)^A6

In cell C6: =$C$5*(1+($D$2/2))^(A6*2)

In cell E6: =$E$5*(1+($D$2/12))^(A6*12)

Use Fill Down to extend the formulas to row 15. Where appropriate, change the format in the cells to show currency.

The formulas used to create the spreadsheet are based on the compound interest formula introduced in *Tutorial 5.5*:

$$A = P(1 + i)^n$$

3. Look at the formulas for row 6. Notice which parts of the formulas change and which parts stay the same. The formula in cell E6 contains the number 12 in two places. It is the formula for monthly compound interest. What are the equivalent numbers used in cell C6 for semi-annual compounding? Why?

4. Explain why the annual interest rate is divided by 12 in cell E6.

5. Insert the heading "Quarterly" in cell D4. Enter a formula for quarterly compounding in row 6 of this column. Use Fill Down to extend the formulas to year 10.

6. Compare the amounts in row 15. What is the effect of compounding more than once a year?

The spreadsheet allows you to change the amount of the deposit and the interest rate.

7. Modify the spreadsheet to show the amount for each principal.

   a) $2000   b) $500

   Compare the amounts after 10 years. What is the effect of doubling the principal of $1000? Halving the principal?

8. Modify the spreadsheet to show the amounts for a principal of $1000 for each annual interest rate.

a) 3%   **b)** 6.5%   **c)** 9.5%

What is the effect of increasing the annual rate? Decreasing the annual rate?

You should have found that the number of times interest is converted to principal affects how quickly the amount grows. You can use your spreadsheet to compare different options.

9. Suppose you want to invest $1000. Modify your spreadsheet to determine which interest rate will produce the better return after 1 year, 10% compounded semi-annually or 10.25% compounded annually.

10. Modify the spreadsheet to determine the principal to be invested at 4% compounded semi-annually to accumulate to $500 in 3 years.

The *effective annual interest rate* is the rate that, with annual compounding, has the same effect as the stated rate (with compounding more than once a year).

For example, in exercise 9, you should have found that a rate of 10% compounded semi-annually produces the same amount as 10.25% compounded annually. We say that 10.25% is the effective annual interest rate for 10% compounded semi-annually.

You may be able to use a graphing calculator to perform some of the financial calculations.

Example

Determine the effective annual rate of interest

Calculate the effective annual interest rate for an investment that earns an annual rate of 10% compounded monthly.

SOLUTION

When determining an effective annual interest rate, it is often easiest to consider what happens to a deposit of $1 over 1 year.

Method 1: Use the spreadsheet INVESTMENT.

Enter $1 in cell B2 and 0.1 in cell D2. Format the cells to show at least 4 decimal places. Note the amount at the end of year 1 in cell E6. This is $1.1047. Adjust the interest rate in cell D2 until the entry in cell B6 has this value. This interest rate is approximately 0.105. The effective annual rate of interest for a rate of 10% compounded monthly is approximately 10.5%.

Method 2: Use the graphing calculator. On the TI-83, press [2nd] [x⁻¹] to access the Finance menu. Choose 1 for the TVM Solver.

First calculate the accumulated amount for $1 invested at 10% compounded monthly. Enter the values shown in the display below left. The entry for PV is −1.

To determine the accumulated amount, move the cursor to FV and press [ALPHA] [ENTER]. The display is shown above right.

To determine the effective annual interest rate, we must find the value of I, which will leave PV and FV unchanged, but with annual compounding. Change C/Y as shown below left, then move the cursor to I, and press [ALPHA] [ENTER] to obtain the display shown below right.

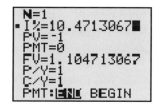

The effective annual interest rate is approximately 10.5%.

DISCUSSING THE IDEAS

1. Why might a bank offer a slightly lower interest rate on savings accounts with more frequent compounding periods?

2. Why do you think banks offer investments at different interest rates?

3. Under what circumstances may an account for which interest is compounded semi-annually be more advantageous than one with interest compounded monthly?

4. In the example, which method of calculating the effective annual interest rate do you think is easier and more accurate? Explain.

Checking Your Skills

1. One bank offers an annual interest rate of 8% compounded annually. Another bank offers an annual interest rate of 8% compounded quarterly. Suppose you deposit $2000 for 10 years. Modify the spreadsheet you saved as INVESTMENT to determine how much more interest you would earn at the second bank.

2. The Rule of 72 says that the number of years for an investment to double is approximately equal to 72 divided by the annual interest rate.

Suppose you invest $100 at 7% compounded semi-annually.

a) What is the effective interest rate?

b) Use mental math and the Rule of 72 to estimate the time for the investment to double.

c) Calculate the number of years taken for the investment to double.

3. Refer to exercise 2. Estimate, using mental math and the Rule of 72, then calculate how long it will take $500 to amount to $2000 if it is invested at 7.5% compounded

a) annually   **b)** semi-annually   **c)** monthly

4. Suppose you invest $2500 for 5 years in one of each of the following pairs of GICs. Which is the better investment of each pair? How much greater are your earnings?

a) i) 12.5% compounded semi-annually
   ii) 11.75% compounded monthly

b) i) 16% compounded monthly
   ii) 17% compounded semi-annually

5. Use the TVM Solver or a spreadsheet. Determine how much money must be invested today, at 6.5% compounded semi-annually, for the investment to amount to $7500 in 3 years.

6. On her 21st birthday, Liz received $5000. This is the accumulated amount of an investment made when she was born. Calculate the principal invested if the annual interest rate was 5% compounded monthly.

7. Use a current annual rate of interest to calculate the amount, after 1 year, of a deposit of $1000 when the interest is compounded

a) annually   **b)** monthly   **c)** daily

Extending Your Thinking

8. Banks use computers to calculate daily interest. They could use the same technology to calculate interest for compounding periods of 1 h, or even 1 s. Use a graphing calculator or a spreadsheet to determine whether there would be any advantage to this. The formulas you can use to calculate interest for 1 d, 1 h, and 1 s, for $100 invested at 6% interest are below.

Y1 = 100(1+0.06/365)^(365*X)

Y2 = 100(1+0.06/(365*24))^(365*24*X)

Y3 = 100(1+0.06/(365*24*3600))^(365*24*3600*X)

X is the number of years.

Select values of X that are multiples of 5. Display the tables of values corresponding to these functions.

a) Compare the amounts after 35 years when interest is calculated by the day, by the hour, and by the second.

b) How do these amounts compare with the amount earned on $100 invested at 6% compounded monthly?

c) Suggest reasons why financial institutions rarely offer interest compounded by the hour or by the minute.

PROJECTS

You have learned to perform calculations involving compound interest. You will use these skills when you return to the Chapter Project and in the following projects in the Project Book.

- The Rule of 72
- Buying or Leasing a Car

COMMUNICATING THE IDEAS

Two different investments can be made for the same length of time at different interest rates. After one year the accumulated amounts are equal. Write a paragraph to explain how this can happen. Provide supporting data.

Computer Lab: Annuities

Most of us borrow money at some time in our lives to finance the purchase of items we wish to have now, but cannot afford to pay in full. When we borrow money from a financial institution we agree to make regular payments over a period of time to pay off the loan.

An agreement that involves equal payments made at regular intervals is called an *annuity*. There are many different kinds of annuities. We will consider a simple annuity where the payment period is the same as the compounding period of the interest.

You can create a spreadsheet to explore options.

Craig wishes to buy a new computer system costing $2507 (including taxes). He cannot pay the full amount, but wants to buy the system today and pay for it over 2 years. He has $500 as a down payment. His bank will lend him the remainder of the money at 10% per annum, compounded monthly, and will require monthly payments from Craig. He has a part-time job, and can afford to pay $80 each month.

 AT THE COMPUTER: Open your spreadsheet program and start a new spreadsheet. Name this spreadsheet LOAN and remember to save your work frequently.

1. The monthly payment the bank will require is not known. Start with the monthly payment of $80.

	A	B	C	D	E
1	Loan				
2		Interest Rate		0.1	
3		Principal		$2007	
4		Monthly Payment		$80	
5					
6	Month	Amount Owing	Interest Charged	Payment	Balance Owing
7	1	=$D$3	=B7*($D$2/12)	=$D$4	=B7+C7-D7
8	=A7+1	=E7	=B8*($D$2/12)	=$D$4	=B8+C8-D8

2. Use Fill Down to extend the spreadsheet from row 8 to display the results for 24 months. Format the appropriate cells to display currency.

3. The $80 payment in cell D4 is what Craig believes he can afford. Change the number in cell D4 to determine, within $1, the monthly payment the bank will require for this loan to be paid off in 2 years.

4. Add an appropriate cell to calculate the total payments on the loan.

5. The *finance charge* is the difference between the cash price of an item and the total payment on the loan, which includes interest charges. What is the finance charge on the bank loan? Save and then close your spreadsheet LOAN.

A regular savings plan is another example of an annuity.

6. Construct a new spreadsheet to explore the result of a regular deposit of $100 at the end of each month into an RRSP account that earns 5% interest, compounded monthly.

7. Use Fill Down to extend the spreadsheet from row 6, to display the results for 2 years. Format the appropriate cells to display currency.

	A	B	C	D	E
1	Regular Savings				
2		Interest Rate		0.05	
3		Payment		$100.00	
4	Month	Account Balance	Interest	Payment	New Balance
5	0	$0.00	=B5*($D$2/12)	=$D$3	=B5+C5+D5
6	1	=E5	=B6*($D$2/12)	=$D$3	=B6+C6+D6
7	2				
8	3				

8. Modify the spreadsheet to determine the total interest earned over the 2 years.

9. Draw a graph of the account balance at the end of each month. Show months on the horizontal axis.

10. Modify the spreadsheet to reflect an interest rate of 10%, compounded monthly. Determine the total interest earned.

11. Compare the amount of interest earned at 5% with that earned at 10%. Write to explain why it is important to obtain the highest rate of interest when investing.

Your graphing calculator also does financial calculations. You can use the TVM Solver of the TI-83 to investigate annuities.

Example 1 **Determine the cost of a loan**

Jenna borrows $2800 from her bank to buy a motorcycle. The terms offered by the bank are an annual interest rate of 4%, compounded monthly, with monthly payments to be made over 3 years.

a) How much will Jenna pay each month?

b) What is the total cost of the loan?

c) What is the finance charge?

SOLUTION

Use the graphing calculator. On the TI-83, access the TVM Solver. The present value is the value of the loan, since the motorcycle must be paid for now. The future value is the amount remaining at the end of the repayments, which will be $0. There will be 12 payments and compounding periods per year. The number of payments is 12×3, or 36. Enter the values shown in the display, below left.

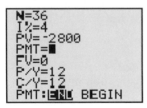
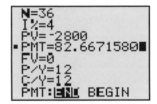

Move the cursor to PMT, and press ALPHA ENTER to obtain the screen on the right.

From the calculator, the payment is $82.67.

Jenna will make a monthly payment of $82.67.

b) The cost of the loan is the total amount paid by Jenna, or $36 \times \$82.67 = \$3066.48$.

c) The finance charge is the difference between the cost of the loan and the loan.

Finance charge = $3066.48 − $2800.00
              = $266.48

Example 2 **Compare amount with principal**

Rick puts $100 a month into an account that pays 6% interest, compounded monthly. Payment is made at the beginning of each month.

a) Draw a graph to illustrate the growth of the amount. On the same grid, draw a graph to illustrate the principal.

b) Explain why it is advantageous to begin investing early.

S O L U T I O N

a) Create a table of values. Use the financial feature of the graphing calculator to calculate the accumulated amounts over a working life span of 30 years.

On the TI-83, access the TVM Solver. The principal in each case is $100 and the interest rate is 6%. The payment is made at the beginning of a payment period, so the word BEGIN should be highlighted.

For the 5-year calculation, for example, there are 5 × 12, or 60 deposits. Enter the values in the display, below left.

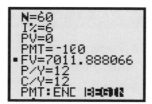

Move the cursor to FV, and press ALPHA ENTER to obtain the screen on the right.

The entries for 5-year intervals are shown below.

Investment Period (years)	Principal ($)	Amount ($)
1	1 200	1 239.72
5	6 000	7 011.89
10	12 000	16 469.87
15	18 000	29 227.28
20	24 000	46 435.11
25	30 000	69 645.89
30	36 000	100 953.76

On the same grid, plot graphs of the principal against the investment period, and the amount against the investment period. The investment period is the independent variable.

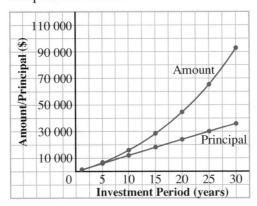

b) Use the graphs from part a. As the number of investment periods increases, so does the difference between the principal and the amount. This difference represents the interest earned. For example, after 15 years the interest earned is $11 227.28, but after 30 years, it is $64 953.76. The longer the saving, the greater the interest earned.

DISCUSSING THE IDEAS

1. Some people choose to use a credit card rather than take out a loan for items they wish to purchase but cannot pay for immediately. Credit card companies often quote the interest rate they charge on overdue accounts per month rather than per year. Why do you think this is so?

2. Suppose you take out a 3-year loan, at 7.5% compounded monthly, to purchase a car. Use your graphing calculator to determine the monthly payment. Explain why the amount of the loan must be used as the present value, not the future value.

3. Banks usually require a car loan to be repaid over 3 or 4 years. Why do you think this is so?

4. By law financial institutions are not permitted to compound interest more frequently than semi-annually for mortgages. Use the example of a 20-year mortgage to explain why monthly compounding is not permitted.

Checking Your Skills

1. Adele takes out a $5000 loan at an interest rate of 9% per year, compounded monthly. She makes a payment of $350 every month. Modify the spreadsheet LOAN to determine how much she still owes after making 12 payments.

2. Calculate the monthly payment for a 2-year loan of $4000 at 12% compounded monthly.

3. Recall the example at the beginning of this Tutorial. You can use the spreadsheet you saved as LOAN to determine the annual interest rate Craig can afford. Set the monthly payment to $100. Leave the loan value at $2007. Change the interest rate in cell D2 until the spreadsheet reflects that the loan is paid off in full, within $1. What annual interest rate can Craig afford?

4. Ravi borrows money to buy a car that costs $12 200. He has $4500 as a down payment. He obtains a 2-year loan at 9.5% compounded monthly. Determine Ravi's monthly payment and the finance charge.

5. Determine the monthly payments and the amount paid for each loan.

   a) a $4000 car loan at 8% compounded monthly for 3 years

   b) a $1200 loan for a stereo system at 6.75% compounded monthly for 18 months

   c) a $2500 loan for a computer system at 7.75% compounded monthly for 2 years

6. Calculate the finance charge for each of the loans in exercise 5.

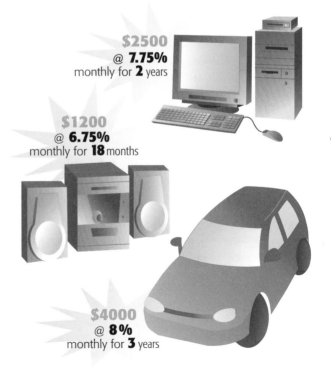

$2500
@ **7.75%**
monthly for **2** years

$1200
@ **6.75%**
monthly for **18** months

$4000
@ **8%**
monthly for **3** years

7. A family borrows $4000 for home renovations. They obtain a 2-year loan at 7.5% compounded monthly. Calculate the monthly payments they must make.

8. Yvonne plans to make regular contributions to her RRSP, starting on January 1. She has two options.

a) She can invest $150 at the beginning of each month in an account that pays 6.25% interest compounded monthly.

b) She can invest $900 on January 1 and July 1 at 6.5% compounded semi-annually.

Which option would you recommend and why?

Extending Your Thinking

9. John applies for a car loan of $16 500. The bank offers financing at 8.5%, compounded monthly, for a term of 3, 4, or 5 years, payable monthly. Modify the spreadsheet LOAN. Determine John's monthly payment for each of the terms. Calculate the total cost of each loan.

PROJECTS

In this Tutorial you studied loans. You will use these skills when you return to the Chapter Project and in the following project in the Project Book.

• Buying or Leasing a Car

COMMUNICATING THE IDEAS

Write a paragraph for an RRSP advertisement to explain why it is better to contribute to an RRSP as early as possible in your working life. Use examples in your explanation.

Goals may be short term, such as a summer vacation, or long term, such as early retirement. When you recognize your goals, you can prepare a budget that works with your income, spending habits, and goals.

You can prepare a budget on paper. A budget worksheet, like the one on page 290, provides a guide. Use a pencil since you may need to change initial estimates. You can also prepare a budget using a computer. The computer will adjust amounts as you revise estimates. The worksheet on page 290 is available as a spreadsheet from *Addison-Wesley Mathematics 11 Technology Kit*.

Governments and businesses typically develop yearly budgets. However, for personal expenses, it is a good idea to plan monthly.

Follow these steps to prepare a budget.

Step 1. Calculate and record your monthly net income. Include all sources of income. Use averages if your hours of work vary from month to month.

Step 2. Record all of your expenses on a budget worksheet.

Step 3. Subtract your expenses from your monthly income. The difference is your discretionary income. A positive amount can go toward your financial goals. A negative amount indicates there is not enough income to cover all of your expenses. Revise your worksheet based on your goals and your income.

When you have prepared a written budget, monitor it. Make appropriate adjustments based on your spending and earning patterns.

A budget is a personal document; it depends on your financial situation and goals. A restrictive budget may be impossible to follow. One that is too lax may delay your financial goals. A good budget should be realistic, comprehensive, and flexible. Although there are no strict rules for developing a budget, this table provides suggested guidelines from the finance industry.

Expense Category	Portion of Monthly Net Income (%)
Housing and utilities	27 – 33
Food and clothing	20 – 26
Health and personal care	3 – 5
Transportation	12 – 14
Recreation and education	6 – 8
Savings	6 – 10
Miscellaneous	12 – 18

Before you prepare personal budgets for yourself or for specific scenarios, review the following examples and complete some of the exercises that follow.

Example 1 **Determine the amount available to spend on housing**

Kelly and Maria will share an apartment while they attend college. Their net monthly income is $2100. According to the guidelines above, approximately how much can they afford for accommodation?

SOLUTION

The guidelines recommend spending 27% to 33% of net income on housing and utilities. This means that Kelly and Maria can probably afford between $567 and $693.

Before they commit to any new expense, Kelly and Maria should check their spending in all categories. They should also check whether monthly rent covers all expenses in the apartment or whether there are additional expenses related to maintenance fees, parking, utilities, and so on.

To create a new budget, or modify a budget to accommodate new goals, requires analysis, reflection, and care. *Example 2* models a process for analyzing and modifying a budget.

Example 2 **Analyze a budget**

This table summarizes Mel's monthly budget. He wants to move into a different apartment and expects to increase his housing and utilities costs to $1000 a month. He still has monthly car payments of $475. Describe the decisions Mel could make to be able to afford the new home.

Expense Category	Amount ($)
Housing and utilities	750
Food and clothing	550
Health and personal care	75
Transportation	700
Recreation and education	200
Savings	75
Miscellaneous	250

SOLUTION

Compare Mel's monthly expenditures to the recommended guidelines.
Add the amounts: $2600 is his monthly net income.

Express each amount as a percent of this sum.

For example,

Housing and utilities $= \frac{750}{2600} \times 100\%$
$= 28.8\%$

Expense Category	Actual (%)	Recommeded (%)
Housing and utilities	28.8	27 to 33
Food and clothing	21.2	20 to 26
Health and personal care	2.9	3 to 5
Transportation	26.9	12 to 14
Recreation and education	7.7	6 to 8
Savings	2.9	6 to 10
Miscellaneous	9.6	12 to 18

Mel is spending twice the recommended amount on transportation. If he moves
into the new apartment, his housing expense will increase to $\frac{1000}{2600} \times 100\%$, or
38.5%, which also exceeds the recommended guideline. Savings and
miscellaneous expenses are significantly lower than recommended. There are
many ways Mel could modify his budget. Here are some possibilities.

• Sell or trade his car for a cheaper model so he can afford to move to a
  different apartment now.

• Delay the move to a new apartment, continue to save and pay off the car
  loan.

There are other solutions Mel may be tempted to
try, but they may not be effective.

• Mel may cut expenses for food, health, and
  recreation. This could lead to problems if he
  loses his job, if he gets sick, or if the car
  requires major repair.

• Mel might investigate options for car insurance
  to see if he can lower his monthly $700
  transportation expense. However, this may not
  work. He needs an additional $250 monthly
  for housing, but there is only $225 per month
  in this category that is not taken up by the
  car payments.

In making his final decision, Mel needs to recognize that the car has put him in debt. He is already over-extended in his transportation expenses. Moving to a new apartment will increase his debt: he will be carrying both a car loan and an increased rental payment. If emergencies arise, it is unlikely that a bank will grant him another loan, which means he may miss payments on the car or the apartment.

Mel may need to acknowledge that he cannot have everything at once. Either he has to defer the move or sell the car and buy something more modest. He will not receive the original value of the car when he sells, due to depreciation, so he may prefer to make the apartment move a long-term goal, working toward it while paying off the loan for the car.

DISCUSSING THE IDEAS

1. Explain the difference between long-term and short-term goals. Give one example of each. Why are goals important?

2. The miscellaneous category might include gifts. What other items do you think would be in this category?

3. Discuss the solutions to *Example 2* with a classmate. Is there a correct solution? Explain.

Practise Your Prior Skills

In the exercises that follow you will work with circle graphs. Try these exercises for preliminary review.

1. Draw a circle graph to represent the following situation.
   Contents of a Garbage Load: Paper 50%; Plastic 10%; Other material 40%

2. The circle graph below represents the world's gold production. In a consignment of 250 kg of gold, approximately how much would you expect to have been produced in Canada?

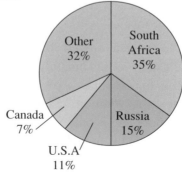

Checking Your Skills

1. Use the information in the table.

   a) What percent of the monthly income is spent in each category?

   b) Compare the spending to the recommended guidelines. In which categories is the person overspending? underspending? spending within the guidelines?

Expense Category	Amount ($)
Housing and utilities	400
Food and clothing	325
Health and personal care	50
Transportation	450
Recreation and education	140
Savings	25
Miscellaneous	150

2. Eric's annual net income is $32 000. Use the suggested spending guidelines. Determine the range of money Eric should budget monthly in each category.

   a) Housing and utilities   **b)** Food and clothing

   c) Transportation   **d)** Savings

3. This circle graph represents Jodi's monthly budget of $1500. Jodi plans to enroll part time at a local business school. She can continue working while she attends school at night and on weekends. The school costs will be approximately $200 a month for 2 years. Construct a new budget for Jodi that allows her to attend school. Explain the decisions you made.

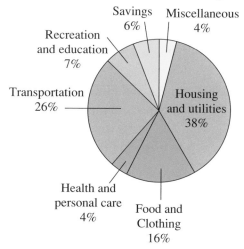

Savings 6% Miscellaneous 4%
Recreation and education 7%
Transportation 26%
Housing and utilities 38%
Health and personal care 4%
Food and Clothing 16%

4. Federal and provincial governments often talk about the deficit and the debt. Investigate the concepts and then write to explain what these words mean and how they relate to budgets.

5. Use the table and the scenario to complete this exercise.

The Zunigas have three children. Both parents work outside the home. The table shows their monthly budget. The Housing category includes the monthly mortgage payment on their home. Because of increased interest rates, their monthly mortgage payment will increase by $200.

Zuniga Family, Monthly Budget	
Expense Category	Amount ($)
Housing and utilities	1200
Food and clothing	800
Health and personal care	150
Transportation	700
Recreation and education	100
Savings	50
Miscellaneous	100

a) Construct a new budget for the Zunigas. Explain your changes.

b) Draw a graph to illustrate your revised budget.

6. Use the table and the scenario to complete this exercise.

Pat and Steve were both working when they created this budget. The transportation expense reflects their purchase of a new car, with monthly loan payments of $750. Steve earns a net income of $1900/month but has just learned that his job is terminated. He will receive 2 months' severance pay. Steve predicts that he can find a new job with a comparable salary within 6 months. Currently, Pat and Steve have $1000 in savings.

Pat and Steve, Monthly Budget	
Expense Category	Amount ($)
Housing and utilities	1500
Food and clothing	700
Health and personal care	150
Transportation	1000
Recreation and education	200
Savings	100
Miscellaneous	100

a) Construct two budgets for Pat and Steve. Base the first budget on the next 2 months, in which monthly net income will not change. Base the second budget on the following 4 months, when only Pat is earning a salary. Explain the decisions you make to get them through the period of projected unemployment.

b) Financial planners recommend people have 3 months' net earnings in their savings. Does this seem reasonable? Explain.

7. If you have access to *Addison-Wesley Mathematics 11 Technology Kit*, use the budget file. Otherwise, use a copy of the budget worksheet on page 290. This exercise is based on the following scenario.

You decide to work for 1 year after high school before you begin post-secondary training. Starting September 1, you work 40 h/week at a grocery store and earn $12.50/h. Your furnished apartment costs $350/month, plus telephone and cable. Your goal is to save $5000 to attend school next year. You purchase a used car and assume payments of $234/month for 1 year. Your parents have paid $425 to license and insure the car for the first year; you will have to meet this cost by August 31 next year. You are paid biweekly and have a net claim code of 1.

a) Estimate your monthly net income.

b) Create a monthly budget. Allow for all of the expenses above. If you prefer to make other choices, note your ideas for a follow-up assignment.

c) Create a table, then draw a graph to summarize your monthly budget.

d) Compare your spending in each category to the recommended guidelines.

e) On November 1, you must spend $500 to winterize your car. Adjust your budget to accommodate this expense, without missing any bills or relinquishing your goal.

Extending Your Thinking

8. Suppose you are a financial planner. Select one of these clients. Describe the client, and determine all the possible expenses that might arise. Estimate the income. Create a monthly budget for your client.

a) a single parent

b) a famous personality

c) a school

d) a non-profit shelter for teen runaways

e) a parks and recreation department for a municipality

PROJECTS

You studied creating a budget in this Tutorial. You will use this when you return to the Chapter Project and in the following projects in the Project Book.

- The Graduation Trip
- Hot Dog Stand
- Buying or Leasing a Car

COMMUNICATING THE IDEAS

Explain what a budget is and why it is important to create a budget. Describe how personal goals relate to budgeting.

Budgeting for Living Independently

On page 278 you described some issues that a person planning to live independently must consider. You have investigated the cost of owning a car. Now you will use your knowledge to prepare a monthly budget for that person.

Steps in preparing a monthly budget will include:

- Calculating and recording the net monthly income; include all sources of income. Use averages if the number of hours is likely to vary from month to month.

- Making a record of all expected expenses on a budget worksheet, on paper, or on a computer.

- Subtracting the total expenses from the total monthly income; a positive amount can go toward financial goals. A negative amount indicates that there is not enough income to cover expenses and the worksheet needs to be revised.

Your teacher can provide you with a worksheet.

Your final project will consist of:

- your initial description of the factors to be considered when planning to live independently

- the details of the cost of running a car

- your final budget worksheet.

Career Skills

People who work as planners must make careful detailed plans, test them to make sure they meet specifications, and revise them as necessary. Planners find employment in the financial, engineering, construction, and design industries.

What Do I Need To Know?

Tutorial	Skills and Concepts	Important Results and Formulas
5.1	• Calculate earnings, including hourly wages, commission, and gratuities	
5.2	• Understand and calculate deductions from payroll	• Estimate EI, CPP, and income tax deductions
5.3	• Understand property taxes; perform foreign exchange calculations; use unit pricing to determine the best value	• 1 Mill $= \frac{1}{1000}$ of \$1 • Property tax $= \frac{\text{Assessed value} \times \text{Mill rate}}{1000}$
5.4	• Reconcile personal and simple business financial statements	
5.5	• Solve investment and credit problems that involve simple interest • Solve investment and credit problems that involve interest compounded annually	• Simple interest: $I = Prt$ • Accumulated amount using compound interest $A = P(1 + i)^n$ • Rule of 72: $\frac{72}{\text{Annual interest rate}}$
5.6	• Use a spreadsheet to investigate compounding periods less than 1 year; use a graphing calculator in finance mode to solve problems related to investments	• Semi-annual compounding: 2 conversions per year • Quarterly compounding: 4 conversions per year • Monthly compounding: 12 conversions per year • $i = \frac{\text{Annual rate}}{\text{Number of compoundings per year}}$ • $n =$ Number of compoundings per year $\times$ Number of years
5.7	• Investigate annuities, loan payments, mortgages, and regular saving plans; use a graphing calculator in finance mode to solve problems related to annuities	• An annuity is a series of equal, regular payments made ove a period of time
5.8	• Understand a budget and how to revise it to meet changing situations	

What Should I Be Able to Do?

When you have completed the work in Chapter 5, you should be able to solve the problems that follow. Part A is investigative.

As you work through the exercises, refer to the *Student Reference*, the *Utilities*, and the *Tutorials* as necessary.

Part A

1. Use a new spreadsheet to compare the following situations.

   I. You pay RRSP contributions annually during the first 10 years of employment, then leave the money invested until retirement age.

   II. You start RRSP contributions after 15 years of employment.

   Assume that employment commences at age 25 and continues until retirement at age 65. Assume an interest rate of 7% with annual compounding. Assume the deposits are made at the beginning of the month.

	A	B	C
1	RRSPs		
2	Fixed Interest Rate		0.07
3	Age	Amount	Amount
4		I	II
5	25	$1000.00	$0.00
6	=A5+1	=$B$5+B5*(1+$C$2)	$0.00

   a) Fill Down to extend the spreadsheet to row 15. Format the appropriate columns to show currency.

   In cell B15, enter = B14*(1+$C$2)

   Use Fill Down to extend the spreadsheet to row 45, when the worker will reach retirement age at 65.

   In cell C20, enter $1000

   In cell C21, enter =$C$20+C20*(1+$C$2)

   Use Fill Down to extend the spreadsheet to row 45, when the worker will reach retirement age at 65.

   b) Compare the final amounts in the two plans. How much has been contributed to each plan? Which plan would you recommend to an employee?

   c) Investigate whether the rate of interest affects the results.

2. Pui Yan is offered two jobs as a chef. The first pays $17/h plus time-and-a-half for overtime. The second pays $15/h and double time for overtime. Assume that overtime is paid after 40 h for both jobs. Which job should Pui Yan accept if he expects to work 45 h each week?

3. Jeremy receives a job offer that pays $12.50/h plus double time for overtime (over 40 h). His boss wants him to work 50 h each week. He pays union dues of $15 a week and a weekly parking fee of $10. Use the information given in *Tutorials 5.1* and *5.2* to estimate Jeremy's weekly net pay.

4. The Smiths' home has a fair market value of $195 000. In that community, the assessed value is 90% of fair market value, and the mill rate is 31.2 mills. What is the Smiths' monthly tax payment?

5. The following transactions were recorded in Ms. Chan's transaction record.

Jan. 1   Balance forward $706.42
Jan. 3   Pay deposit $890
Jan. 4   Cheque #124 to Petty's Meats for $54.67
Jan. 6   Withdrawal of $50 cash
Jan. 8   Cheque #125 to Askew's Foods for $213.56
Jan. 11   Cheque #126 to Braby Motors for $75.57
Jan. 15   Cheque #127 for student fees of $125

Calculate the balance in the account on January 15.

6. If the value of Can $1 is US $0.6615, what is the value of US $1 in Canadian funds?

7. Determine each accumulated amount.

   a) An investment of $2000 at 5.25% interest compounded annually for 10 years.

   b) $1250 invested for 2 years at 7% compounded semi-annually.

8. How long will it take an investment of $500 to accumulate to $1300 if it is invested at 4.5% compounded monthly?

9. How much money must you invest today, at 6.5% compounded quarterly, for the investment to accumulate to $8000 in 3 years?

10. What interest rate would be required to double an investment of $1000 in 10 years if the interest were compounded annually?

11. The Green family plans to renovate their home. They need a loan of $9000. The bank offers to loan them the money at an annual interest rate of 6% compounded monthly to be repaid by monthly payments over 2 years.

   a) Calculate the monthly payment.

   b) Calculate the finance charge for the loan.

Description of Person

- *Name:* Cody
- *Sex:* Male
- *Age:* 22
- *Height:* 6'1"
- *Weight:* 180 lbs.
- *Hair:* Short, blonde
- *Eye Color:* Green
- *Schooling:* University of Winnipeg graduate, 4 years Psychology

Determination of Income

- *Occupation:* Elementary School Child Psychologist
- *Elementary Schools:* Shamrock, Niakwa Place, Van Bellingham, Guyot
- *Office Location:* St. Boniface School Board
- *Employer:* St. Boniface School Division
- *Average Beginning Annual Income for a Child Psychologist:* $ 51,000
- *Personal Annual Income in Manitoba 1999)*
  (High Demand Occupations in Manitoba 1999)
- *Personal Annual Income Without Taxes:* $ 55,000
- *Taxes:*
  EI = 55,000 x .03 = $1,650
  CPP = 55,000 x .03 = $1,650
  Income Tax = 55,000 x .29 = $ 15,950
  Total = 1,650 + 1,650 + 15,950 = $ 19,250
- *Personal Annual Income With Taxes:* 55,000 – 19,250 = $ 35,750

Description of Lifestyle

- *Hobbies:* Playing Soccer, Coaching Soccer, Watching Soccer, Playing Guitar, Listening to Music, Fishing, Camping
- *Work Hours:* 8 a.m. – 4 p.m.
- *Average Day:*
  7:00 a.m.- Wake up, Eat breakfast & Read the paper, Shower, Get dressed
  7:40 a.m.- Leave for work
  7:55 a.m.- Arrive at work
  8:00 a.m.- Paperwork
  8:30 a.m.- Report to school appointments
  11:30 a.m.- Lunch
  12:30 p.m.- Continue with scheduled appointments.
  3:30 p.m.- Record the following days appointments.
  3:45 p.m.- Paperwork
  4:00 p.m.- Leave work
  4:15 p.m.- Arrive at home
  5:00 p.m.- Prepare and eat dinner
  6:30 p.m.- Do some sort of outdoor physical activity
  8:30 p.m.- Watch T.V. and do whatever needs to be done.
  10:00 p.m.- Go to bed.

Part C

Here is a description of the person and lifestyle for whom one student chose to prepare a financial plan. Has he given sufficient information to create a budget?

Here is a sample of the same student's budget. Check his arithmetic. Does he have any errors? Consider his estimates. Do you think they are reasonable for the person and lifestyle he has described?

Monthly Budget Form

				Average Monthly Income
1)	**NET INCOME**	Weekly Amount	Annual Amount	
	Primary Income...........	$687.50	$35,750.00	1) $2,979.17
2)	**SAVINGS (20% of Average Monthly Income)**			
				2) $595.83
3)	**MONTHLY EXPENSES**			
	Mortgage or Rent..............			
	Car Payments..............		$358.00	
	Telephone................		$391.00	
	Groceries...............		$50.00	
	Household Goods...........		196.04	
	Clothing............		$77.75	
	Car Maintenance...........		$200.00	
	Gasoline............		$20.83	
	Entertainmemt............		$59.00	
	Vacation........		$300.00	
	Drivers License...........		$250.00	
	Car Insurance............		$5.00	MONTHLY TOTAL
			$75.00	

TOTAL MONTHLY PAYMENTS   3) $1,907.62

SUMMARY

Average Monthly Income............			1) $2,979.17
Savings.........	2)	$595.83	
Total Monthly Expenses...........	3)	$1,907.62	
Total Amount 2 + 3.........			
Amount Available for Other Savings...........		$2,503.45	
	5)	$475.72	

Here is the student's calculation of the cost of buying a car. Do you agree with him?

Calculation of Cost of Buying a Car

- Car Purchased: 1996 Sunfire SE Coupe
  (Auto Trader Magazine)
- Description of Car: Red, 2.2L Engine, 5 Speed Transmission, Air Conditioning, Cruise Control, AM/FM Cassette Player, Rear Spoiler, 47 Liter Gas Tank
  (Auto Trader Magazine)

- Cost To Purchase: $12,800
  (Auto Trader Magazine)
- Cost To Purchase w/ Tax: 12, 800 x .14 = $14, 592
- Drivers License: $60 per year
  (Manitoba Driver Licensing Department)
- Car Insurance: $ 900 per year
  (Manitoba Public Insurance Department)

- Down Payment: $500
- Method of Payment: Car- (14, 592 - 500) ÷ 3 years ÷ 12 months = $391 per mo. , 3 yrs
  Car Insurance- 900 ÷ 12 months = $75 per mo.
  Drivers License- 60 ÷ 12 months = $5 per mo.
  Total- 391 + 75 + 5 = $471 per mo.

Canada Pension Plan Contributions
Biweekly (26 pay periods a year)

Cotisations au Régime de pensions du Canada
Aux deux semaines (26 périodes de paie par année)

Pay Rémunération From - De	To - À	CPP RPC	Pay Rémunération From - De	To - À	CPP RPC	Pay Rémunération From - De	To - À	CPP RPC	Pay Rémunération From - De	To - À	CPP RPC
1121.90	1122.18	34.56	1142.47	1142.75	35.28	1163.04	1163.32	36.00	1183.61	1183.89	36.72
1122.19	1122.46	34.57	1142.76	1143.03	35.29	1163.33	1163.60	36.01	1183.90	1184.18	36.73
1122.47	1122.75	34.58	1143.04	1143.32	35.30	1163.61	1163.89	36.02	1184.19	1184.46	36.74
1122.76	1123.03	34.59	1143.33	1143.60	35.31	1163.90	1164.18	36.03	1184.47	1184.75	36.75
1123.04	1123.32	34.60	1143.61	1143.89	35.32	1164.19	1164.46	36.04	1184.76	1185.03	36.76
1123.33	1123.60	34.61	1143.90	1144.18	35.33	1164.47	1164.75	36.05	1185.04	1185.32	36.77
1123.61	1123.89	34.62	1144.19	1144.46	35.34	1164.76	1165.03	36.06	1185.33	1185.60	36.78
1123.90	1124.18	34.63	1144.47	1144.75	35.35	1165.04	1165.32	36.07	1185.61	1185.89	36.79
1124.19	1124.46	34.64	1144.76	1145.03	35.36	1165.33	1165.60	36.08	1185.90	1186.18	36.80
1124.47	1124.75	34.65	1145.04	1145.32	35.37	1165.61	1165.89	36.09	1186.19	1186.46	36.81
1124.76	1125.03	34.66	1145.33	1145.60	35.38	1165.90	1166.18	36.10	1186.47	1186.75	36.82
1125.04	1125.32	34.67	1145.61	1145.89	35.39	1166.19	1166.46	36.11	1186.76	1187.03	36.83
1125.33	1125.60	34.68	1145.90	1146.18	35.40	1166.47	1166.75	36.12	1187.04	1187.32	36.84
1125.61	1125.89	34.69	1146.19	1146.46	35.41	1166.76	1167.03	36.13	1187.33	1187.60	36.85
1125.90	1126.18	34.70	1146.47	1146.75	35.42	1167.04	1167.32	36.14	1187.61	1187.89	36.86
1126.19	1126.46	34.71	1146.76	1147.03	35.43	1167.33	1167.60	36.15	1187.90	1188.18	36.87
1126.47	1126.75	34.72	1147.04	1147.32	35.44	1167.61	1167.89	36.16	1188.19	1188.46	36.88
1126.76	1127.03	34.73	1147.33	1147.60	35.45	1167.90	1168.18	36.17	1188.47	1188.75	36.89
1127.04	1127.32	34.74	1147.61	1147.89	35.46	1168.19	1168.46	36.18	1188.76	1189.03	36.90
1127.33	1127.60	34.75	1147.90	1148.18	35.47	1168.47	1168.75	36.19	1189.04	1189.32	36.91
1127.61	1127.89	34.76	1148.19	1148.46	35.48	1168.76	1169.03	36.20	1189.33	1189.60	36.92
1127.90	1128.18	34.77	1148.47	1148.75	35.49	1169.04	1169.32	36.21	1189.61	1189.89	36.93
1128.19	1128.46	34.78	1148.76	1149.03	35.50	1169.33	1169.60	36.22	1189.90	1190.18	36.94
1128.47	1128.75	34.79	1149.04	1149.32	35.51	1169.61	1169.89	36.23	1190.19	1190.46	36.95
1128.76	1129.03	34.80	1149.33	1149.60	35.52	1169.90	1170.18	36.24	1190.47	1190.75	36.96
1129.04	1129.32	34.81	1149.61	1149.89	35.53	1170.19	1170.46	36.25	1190.76	1191.03	36.97
1129.33	1129.60	34.82	1149.90	1150.18	35.54	1170.47	1170.75	36.26	1191.04	1191.32	36.98
1129.61	1129.89	34.83	1150.19	1150.46	35.55	1170.76	1171.03	36.27	1191.33	1191.60	36.99
1129.90	1130.18	34.84	1150.47	1150.75	35.56	1171.04	1171.32	36.28	1191.61	1191.89	37.00
1130.19	1130.46	34.85	1150.76	1151.03	35.57	1171.33	1171.60	36.29	1191.90	1192.18	37.01
1130.47	1130.75	34.86	1151.04	1151.32	35.58	1171.61	1171.89	36.30	1192.19	1192.46	37.02
1130.76	1131.03	34.87	1151.33	1151.60	35.59	1171.90	1172.18	36.31	1192.47	1192.75	37.03
1131.04	1131.32	34.88	1151.61	1151.89	35.60	1172.19	1172.46	36.32	1192.76	1193.03	37.04
1131.33	1131.60	34.89	1151.90	1152.18	35.61	1172.47	1172.75	36.33	1193.04	1193.32	37.05
1131.61	1131.89	34.90	1152.19	1152.46	35.62	1172.76	1173.03	36.34	1193.33	1193.60	37.06
1131.90	1132.18	34.91	1152.47	1152.75	35.63	1173.04	1173.32	36.35	1193.61	1193.89	37.07
1132.19	1132.46	34.92	1152.76	1153.03	35.64	1173.33	1173.60	36.36	1193.90	1194.18	37.08
1132.47	1132.75	34.93	1153.04	1153.32	35.65	1173.61	1173.89	36.37	1194.19	1194.46	37.09
1132.76	1133.03	34.94	1153.33	1153.60	35.66	1173.90	1174.18	36.38	1194.47	1194.75	37.10
1133.04	1133.32	34.95	1153.61	1153.89	35.67	1174.19	1174.46	36.39	1194.76	1195.03	37.11
1133.33	1133.60	34.96	1153.90	1154.18	35.68	1174.47	1174.75	36.40	1195.04	1195.32	37.12
1133.61	1133.89	34.97	1154.19	1154.46	35.69	1174.76	1175.03	36.41	1195.33	1195.60	37.13
1133.90	1134.18	34.98	1154.47	1154.75	35.70	1175.04	1175.32	36.42	1195.61	1195.89	37.14
1134.19	1134.46	34.99	1154.76	1155.03	35.71	1175.33	1175.60	36.43	1195.90	1196.18	37.15
1134.47	1134.75	35.00	1155.04	1155.32	35.72	1175.61	1175.89	36.44	1196.19	1196.46	37.16
1134.76	1135.03	35.01	1155.33	1155.60	35.73	1175.90	1176.18	36.45	1196.47	1196.75	37.17
1135.04	1135.32	35.02	1155.61	1155.89	35.74	1176.19	1176.46	36.46	1196.76	1197.03	37.18
1135.33	1135.60	35.03	1155.90	1156.18	35.75	1176.47	1176.75	36.47	1197.04	1197.32	37.19
1135.61	1135.89	35.04	1156.19	1156.46	35.76	1176.76	1177.03	36.48	1197.33	1197.60	37.20
1135.90	1136.18	35.05	1156.47	1156.75	35.77	1177.04	1177.32	36.49	1197.61	1197.89	37.21
1136.19	1136.46	35.06	1156.76	1157.03	35.78	1177.33	1177.60	36.50	1197.90	1198.18	37.22
1136.47	1136.75	35.07	1157.04	1157.32	35.79	1177.61	1177.89	36.51	1198.19	1198.46	37.23
1136.76	1137.03	35.08	1157.33	1157.60	35.80	1177.90	1178.18	36.52	1198.47	1198.75	37.24
1137.04	1137.32	35.09	1157.61	1157.89	35.81	1178.19	1178.46	36.53	1198.76	1199.03	37.25
1137.33	1137.60	35.10	1157.90	1158.18	35.82	1178.47	1178.75	36.54	1199.04	1199.32	37.26
1137.61	1137.89	35.11	1158.19	1158.46	35.83	1178.76	1179.03	36.55	1199.33	1199.60	37.27
1137.90	1138.18	35.12	1158.47	1158.75	35.84	1179.04	1179.32	36.56	1199.61	1199.89	37.28
1138.19	1138.46	35.13	1158.76	1159.03	35.85	1179.33	1179.60	36.57	1199.90	1200.18	37.29
1138.47	1138.75	35.14	1159.04	1159.32	35.86	1179.61	1179.89	36.58	1200.19	1200.46	37.30
1138.76	1139.03	35.15	1159.33	1159.60	35.87	1179.90	1180.18	36.59	1200.47	1200.75	37.31
1139.04	1139.32	35.16	1159.61	1159.89	35.88	1180.19	1180.46	36.60	1200.76	1201.03	37.32
1139.33	1139.60	35.17	1159.90	1160.18	35.89	1180.47	1180.75	36.61	1201.04	1201.32	37.33
1139.61	1139.89	35.18	1160.19	1160.46	35.90	1180.76	1181.03	36.62	1201.33	1201.60	37.34
1139.90	1140.18	35.19	1160.47	1160.75	35.91	1181.04	1181.32	36.63	1201.61	1201.89	37.35
1140.19	1140.46	35.20	1160.76	1161.03	35.92	1181.33	1181.60	36.64	1201.90	1202.18	37.36
1140.47	1140.75	35.21	1161.04	1161.32	35.93	1181.61	1181.89	36.65	1202.19	1202.46	37.37
1140.76	1141.03	35.22	1161.33	1161.60	35.94	1181.90	1182.18	36.66	1202.47	1202.75	37.38
1141.04	1141.32	35.23	1161.61	1161.89	35.95	1182.19	1182.46	36.67	1202.76	1203.03	37.39
1141.33	1141.60	35.24	1161.90	1162.18	35.96	1182.47	1182.75	36.68	1203.04	1203.32	37.40
1141.61	1141.89	35.25	1162.19	1162.46	35.97	1182.76	1183.03	36.69	1203.33	1203.60	37.41
1141.90	1142.18	35.26	1162.47	1162.75	35.98	1183.04	1183.32	36.70	1203.61	1203.89	37.42
1142.19	1142.46	35.27	1162.76	1163.03	35.99	1183.33	1183.60	36.71	1203.90	1204.18	37.43

B-22   Employee's maximum CPP contribution for the year 1999 is $1186.50   La cotisation maximale de l'employé au RPC pour l'année 1999 est de 1186,50 $

Pay Rémunération From - De	To - À	CPP RPC	Pay Rémunération From - De	To - À	CPP RPC	Pay Rémunération From - De	To - À	CPP RPC	Pay Rémunération From - De	To - À	CPP RPC
1114.38	1114.65	28.80	1134.95	1135.23	29.52	1155.52	1155.80	30.24	1176.09	1176.37	30.96
1114.66	1114.94	28.81	1135.24	1135.51	29.53	1155.81	1156.08	30.25	1176.38	1176.65	30.97
1114.95	1115.23	28.82	1135.52	1135.80	29.54	1156.09	1156.37	30.26	1176.66	1176.94	30.98
1115.24	1115.51	28.83	1135.81	1136.08	29.55	1156.38	1156.65	30.27	1176.95	1177.23	30.99
1115.52	1115.80	28.84	1136.09	1136.37	29.56	1156.66	1156.94	30.28	1177.24	1177.51	31.00
1115.81	1116.08	28.85	1136.38	1136.65	29.57	1156.95	1157.23	30.29	1177.52	1177.80	31.01
1116.09	1116.37	28.86	1136.66	1136.94	29.58	1157.24	1157.51	30.30	1177.81	1178.08	31.02
1116.38	1116.65	28.87	1136.95	1137.23	29.59	1157.52	1157.80	30.31	1178.09	1178.37	31.03
1116.66	1116.94	28.88	1137.24	1137.51	29.60	1157.81	1158.08	30.32	1178.38	1178.65	31.04
1116.95	1117.23	28.89	1137.52	1137.80	29.61	1158.09	1158.37	30.33	1178.66	1178.94	31.05
1117.24	1117.51	28.90	1137.81	1138.08	29.62	1158.38	1158.65	30.34	1178.95	1179.23	31.06
1117.52	1117.80	28.91	1138.09	1138.37	29.63	1158.66	1158.94	30.35	1179.24	1179.51	31.07
1117.81	1118.08	28.92	1138.38	1138.65	29.64	1158.95	1159.23	30.36	1179.52	1179.80	31.08
1118.09	1118.37	28.93	1138.66	1138.94	29.65	1159.24	1159.51	30.37	1179.81	1180.08	31.09
1118.38	1118.65	28.94	1138.95	1139.23	29.66	1159.52	1159.80	30.38	1180.09	1180.37	31.10
1118.66	1118.94	28.95	1139.24	1139.51	29.67	1159.81	1160.08	30.39	1180.38	1180.65	31.11
1118.95	1119.23	28.96	1139.52	1139.80	29.68	1160.09	1160.37	30.40	1180.66	1180.94	31.12
1119.24	1119.51	28.97	1139.81	1140.08	29.69	1160.38	1160.65	30.41	1180.95	1181.23	31.13
1119.52	1119.80	28.98	1140.09	1140.37	29.70	1160.66	1160.94	30.42	1181.24	1181.51	31.14
1119.81	1120.08	28.99	1140.38	1140.65	29.71	1160.95	1161.23	30.43	1181.52	1181.80	31.15
1120.09	1120.37	29.00	1140.66	1140.94	29.72	1161.24	1161.51	30.44	1181.81	1182.08	31.16
1120.38	1120.65	29.01	1140.95	1141.23	29.73	1161.52	1161.80	30.45	1182.09	1182.37	31.17
1120.66	1120.94	29.02	1141.24	1141.51	29.74	1161.81	1162.08	30.46	1182.38	1182.65	31.18
1120.95	1121.23	29.03	1141.52	1141.80	29.75	1162.09	1162.37	30.47	1182.66	1182.94	31.19
1121.24	1121.51	29.04	1141.81	1142.08	29.76	1162.38	1162.65	30.48	1182.95	1183.23	31.20
1121.52	1121.80	29.05	1142.09	1142.37	29.77	1162.66	1162.94	30.49	1183.24	1183.51	31.21
1121.81	1122.08	29.06	1142.38	1142.65	29.78	1162.95	1163.23	30.50	1183.52	1183.80	31.22
1122.09	1122.37	29.07	1142.66	1142.94	29.79	1163.24	1163.51	30.51	1183.81	1184.08	31.23
1122.38	1122.65	29.08	1142.95	1143.23	29.80	1163.52	1163.80	30.52	1184.09	1184.37	31.24
1122.66	1122.94	29.09	1143.24	1143.51	29.81	1163.81	1164.08	30.53	1184.38	1184.65	31.25
1122.95	1123.23	29.10	1143.52	1143.80	29.82	1164.09	1164.37	30.54	1184.66	1184.94	31.26
1123.24	1123.51	29.11	1143.81	1144.08	29.83	1164.38	1164.65	30.55	1184.95	1185.23	31.27
1123.52	1123.80	29.12	1144.09	1144.37	29.84	1164.66	1164.94	30.56	1185.24	1185.51	31.28
1123.81	1124.08	29.13	1144.38	1144.65	29.85	1164.95	1165.23	30.57	1185.52	1185.80	31.29
1124.09	1124.37	29.14	1144.66	1144.94	29.86	1165.24	1165.51	30.58	1185.81	1186.08	31.30
1124.38	1124.65	29.15	1144.95	1145.23	29.87	1165.52	1165.80	30.59	1186.09	1186.37	31.31
1124.66	1124.94	29.16	1145.24	1145.51	29.88	1165.81	1166.08	30.60	1186.38	1186.65	31.32
1124.95	1125.23	29.17	1145.52	1145.80	29.89	1166.09	1166.37	30.61	1186.66	1186.94	31.33
1125.24	1125.51	29.18	1145.81	1146.08	29.90	1166.38	1166.65	30.62	1186.95	1187.23	31.34
1125.52	1125.80	29.19	1146.09	1146.37	29.91	1166.66	1166.94	30.63	1187.24	1187.51	31.35
1125.81	1126.08	29.20	1146.38	1146.65	29.92	1166.95	1167.23	30.64	1187.52	1187.80	31.36
1126.09	1126.37	29.21	1146.66	1146.94	29.93	1167.24	1167.51	30.65	1187.81	1188.08	31.37
1126.38	1126.65	29.22	1146.95	1147.23	29.94	1167.52	1167.80	30.66	1188.09	1188.37	31.38
1126.66	1126.94	29.23	1147.24	1147.51	29.95	1167.81	1168.08	30.67	1188.38	1188.65	31.39
1126.95	1127.23	29.24	1147.52	1147.80	29.96	1168.09	1168.37	30.68	1188.66	1188.94	31.40
1127.24	1127.51	29.25	1147.81	1148.08	29.97	1168.38	1168.65	30.69	1188.95	1189.23	31.41
1127.52	1127.80	29.26	1148.09	1148.37	29.98	1168.66	1168.94	30.70	1189.24	1189.51	31.42
1127.81	1128.08	29.27	1148.38	1148.65	29.99	1168.95	1169.23	30.71	1189.52	1189.80	31.43
1128.09	1128.37	29.28	1148.66	1148.94	30.00	1169.24	1169.51	30.72	1189.81	1190.08	31.44
1128.38	1128.65	29.29	1148.95	1149.23	30.01	1169.52	1169.80	30.73	1190.09	1190.37	31.45
1128.66	1128.94	29.30	1149.24	1149.51	30.02	1169.81	1170.08	30.74	1190.38	1190.65	31.46
1128.95	1129.23	29.31	1149.52	1149.80	30.03	1170.09	1170.37	30.75	1190.66	1190.94	31.47
1129.24	1129.51	29.32	1149.81	1150.08	30.04	1170.38	1170.65	30.76	1190.95	1191.23	31.48
1129.52	1129.80	29.33	1150.09	1150.37	30.05	1170.66	1170.94	30.77	1191.24	1191.51	31.49
1129.81	1130.08	29.34	1150.38	1150.65	30.06	1170.95	1171.23	30.78	1191.52	1191.80	31.50
1130.09	1130.37	29.35	1150.66	1150.94	30.07	1171.24	1171.51	30.79	1191.81	1192.08	31.51
1130.38	1130.65	29.36	1150.95	1151.23	30.08	1171.52	1171.80	30.80	1192.09	1192.37	31.52
1130.66	1130.94	29.37	1151.24	1151.51	30.09	1171.81	1172.08	30.81	1192.38	1192.65	31.53
1130.95	1131.23	29.38	1151.52	1151.80	30.10	1172.09	1172.37	30.82	1192.66	1192.94	31.54
1131.24	1131.51	29.39	1151.81	1152.08	30.11	1172.38	1172.65	30.83	1192.95	1193.23	31.55
1131.52	1131.80	29.40	1152.09	1152.37	30.12	1172.66	1172.94	30.84	1193.24	1193.51	31.56
1131.81	1132.08	29.41	1152.38	1152.65	30.13	1172.95	1173.23	30.85	1193.52	1193.80	31.57
1132.09	1132.37	29.42	1152.66	1152.94	30.14	1173.24	1173.51	30.86	1193.81	1194.08	31.58
1132.38	1132.65	29.43	1152.95	1153.23	30.15	1173.52	1173.80	30.87	1194.09	1194.37	31.59
1132.66	1132.94	29.44	1153.24	1153.51	30.16	1173.81	1174.08	30.88	1194.38	1194.65	31.60
1132.95	1133.23	29.45	1153.52	1153.80	30.17	1174.09	1174.37	30.89	1194.66	1194.94	31.61
1133.24	1133.51	29.46	1153.81	1154.08	30.18	1174.38	1174.65	30.90	1194.95	1195.23	31.62
1133.52	1133.80	29.47	1154.09	1154.37	30.19	1174.66	1174.94	30.91	1195.24	1195.51	31.63
1133.81	1134.08	29.48	1154.38	1154.65	30.20	1174.95	1175.23	30.92	1195.52	1195.80	31.64
1134.09	1134.37	29.49	1154.66	1154.94	30.21	1175.24	1175.51	30.93	1195.81	1196.08	31.65
1134.38	1134.65	29.50	1154.95	1155.23	30.22	1175.52	1175.80	30.94	1196.09	1196.37	31.66
1134.66	1134.94	29.51	1155.24	1155.51	30.23	1175.81	1176.08	30.95	1196.38	1196.65	31.67

B-56 Employee's maximum CPP contribution for the year 1999 is $1186.50   La cotisation maximale de l'employé au RPC pour l'année 1999 est de 1186,50 $

Employment Insurance Premiums / Cotisations à l'assurance-emploi

Insurable Earnings Rémunération assurable		EI premium Cotisation d'AE	Insurable Earnings Rémunération assurable		EI premium Cotisation d'AE	Insurable Earnings Rémunération assurable		EI premium Cotisation d'AE	Insurable Earnings Rémunération assurable		EI premium Cotisation d'AE
From - De	To - À		From - De	To - À		From - De	To - À		From - De	To - À	
1129.61	1129.99	28.81	1157.85	1158.23	29.53	1186.08	1186.47	30.25	1214.32	1214.70	30.97
1130.00	1130.39	28.82	1158.24	1158.62	29.54	1186.48	1186.86	30.26	1214.71	1215.09	30.98
1130.40	1130.78	28.83	1158.63	1159.01	29.55	1186.87	1187.25	30.27	1215.10	1215.49	30.99
1130.79	1131.17	28.84	1159.02	1159.41	29.56	1187.26	1187.64	30.28	1215.50	1215.88	31.00
1131.18	1131.56	28.85	1159.42	1159.80	29.57	1187.65	1188.03	30.29	1215.89	1216.27	31.01
1131.57	1131.96	28.86	1159.81	1160.19	29.58	1188.04	1188.43	30.30	1216.28	1216.66	31.02
1131.97	1132.35	28.87	1160.20	1160.58	29.59	1188.44	1188.82	30.31	1216.67	1217.05	31.03
1132.36	1132.74	28.88	1160.59	1160.98	29.60	1188.83	1189.21	30.32	1217.06	1217.45	31.04
1132.75	1133.13	28.89	1160.99	1161.37	29.61	1189.22	1189.60	30.33	1217.46	1217.84	31.05
1133.14	1133.52	28.90	1161.38	1161.76	29.62	1189.61	1189.99	30.34	1217.85	1218.23	31.06
1133.53	1133.92	28.91	1161.77	1162.15	29.63	1190.00	1190.39	30.35	1218.24	1218.62	31.07
1133.93	1134.31	28.92	1162.16	1162.54	29.64	1190.40	1190.78	30.36	1218.63	1219.01	31.08
1134.32	1134.70	28.93	1162.55	1162.94	29.65	1190.79	1191.17	30.37	1219.02	1219.41	31.09
1134.71	1135.09	28.94	1162.95	1163.33	29.66	1191.18	1191.56	30.38	1219.42	1219.80	31.10
1135.10	1135.49	28.95	1163.34	1163.72	29.67	1191.57	1191.96	30.39	1219.81	1220.19	31.11
1135.50	1135.88	28.96	1163.73	1164.11	29.68	1191.97	1192.35	30.40	1220.20	1220.58	31.12
1135.89	1136.27	28.97	1164.12	1164.50	29.69	1192.36	1192.74	30.41	1220.59	1220.98	31.13
1136.28	1136.66	28.98	1164.51	1164.90	29.70	1192.75	1193.13	30.42	1220.99	1221.37	31.14
1136.67	1137.05	28.99	1164.91	1165.29	29.71	1193.14	1193.52	30.43	1221.38	1221.76	31.15
1137.06	1137.45	29.00	1165.30	1165.68	29.72	1193.53	1193.92	30.44	1221.77	1222.15	31.16
1137.46	1137.84	29.01	1165.69	1166.07	29.73	1193.93	1194.31	30.45	1222.16	1222.54	31.17
1137.85	1138.23	29.02	1166.08	1166.47	29.74	1194.32	1194.70	30.46	1222.55	1222.94	31.18
1138.24	1138.62	29.03	1166.48	1166.86	29.75	1194.71	1195.09	30.47	1222.95	1223.33	31.19
1138.63	1139.01	29.04	1166.87	1167.25	29.76	1195.10	1195.49	30.48	1223.34	1223.72	31.20
1139.02	1139.41	29.05	1167.26	1167.64	29.77	1195.50	1195.88	30.49	1223.73	1224.11	31.21
1139.42	1139.80	29.06	1167.65	1168.03	29.78	1195.89	1196.27	30.50	1224.12	1224.50	31.22
1139.81	1140.19	29.07	1168.04	1168.43	29.79	1196.28	1196.66	30.51	1224.51	1224.90	31.23
1140.20	1140.58	29.08	1168.44	1168.82	29.80	1196.67	1197.05	30.52	1224.91	1225.29	31.24
1140.59	1140.98	29.09	1168.83	1169.21	29.81	1197.06	1197.45	30.53	1225.30	1225.68	31.25
1140.99	1141.37	29.10	1169.22	1169.60	29.82	1197.46	1197.84	30.54	1225.69	1226.07	31.26
1141.38	1141.76	29.11	1169.61	1169.99	29.83	1197.85	1198.23	30.55	1226.08	1226.47	31.27
1141.77	1142.15	29.12	1170.00	1170.39	29.84	1198.24	1198.62	30.56	1226.48	1226.86	31.28
1142.16	1142.54	29.13	1170.40	1170.78	29.85	1198.63	1199.01	30.57	1226.87	1227.25	31.29
1142.55	1142.94	29.14	1170.79	1171.17	29.86	1199.02	1199.41	30.58	1227.26	1227.64	31.30
1142.95	1143.33	29.15	1171.18	1171.56	29.87	1199.42	1199.80	30.59	1227.65	1228.03	31.31
1143.34	1143.72	29.16	1171.57	1171.96	29.88	1199.81	1200.19	30.60	1228.04	1228.43	31.32
1143.73	1144.11	29.17	1171.97	1172.35	29.89	1200.20	1200.58	30.61	1228.44	1228.82	31.33
1144.12	1144.50	29.18	1172.36	1172.74	29.90	1200.59	1200.98	30.62	1228.83	1229.21	31.34
1144.51	1144.90	29.19	1172.75	1173.13	29.91	1200.99	1201.37	30.63	1229.22	1229.60	31.35
1144.91	1145.29	29.20	1173.14	1173.52	29.92	1201.38	1201.76	30.64	1229.61	1229.99	31.36
1145.30	1145.68	29.21	1173.53	1173.92	29.93	1201.77	1202.15	30.65	1230.00	1230.39	31.37
1145.69	1146.07	29.22	1173.93	1174.31	29.94	1202.16	1202.54	30.66	1230.40	1230.78	31.38
1146.08	1146.47	29.23	1174.32	1174.70	29.95	1202.55	1202.94	30.67	1230.79	1231.17	31.39
1146.48	1146.86	29.24	1174.71	1175.09	29.96	1202.95	1203.33	30.68	1231.18	1231.56	31.40
1146.87	1147.25	29.25	1175.10	1175.49	29.97	1203.34	1203.72	30.69	1231.57	1231.96	31.41
1147.26	1147.64	29.26	1175.50	1175.88	29.98	1203.73	1204.11	30.70	1231.97	1232.35	31.42
1147.65	1148.03	29.27	1175.89	1176.27	29.99	1204.12	1204.50	30.71	1232.36	1232.74	31.43
1148.04	1148.43	29.28	1176.28	1176.66	30.00	1204.51	1204.90	30.72	1232.75	1233.13	31.44
1148.44	1148.82	29.29	1176.67	1177.05	30.01	1204.91	1205.29	30.73	1233.14	1233.52	31.45
1148.83	1149.21	29.30	1177.06	1177.45	30.02	1205.30	1205.68	30.74	1233.53	1233.92	31.46
1149.22	1149.60	29.31	1177.46	1177.84	30.03	1205.69	1206.07	30.75	1233.93	1234.31	31.47
1149.61	1149.99	29.32	1177.85	1178.23	30.04	1206.08	1206.47	30.76	1234.32	1234.70	31.48
1150.00	1150.39	29.33	1178.24	1178.62	30.05	1206.48	1206.86	30.77	1234.71	1235.09	31.49
1150.40	1150.78	29.34	1178.63	1179.01	30.06	1206.87	1207.25	30.78	1235.10	1235.49	31.50
1150.79	1151.17	29.35	1179.02	1179.41	30.07	1207.26	1207.64	30.79	1235.50	1235.88	31.51
1151.18	1151.56	29.36	1179.42	1179.80	30.08	1207.65	1208.03	30.80	1235.89	1236.27	31.52
1151.57	1151.96	29.37	1179.81	1180.19	30.09	1208.04	1208.43	30.81	1236.28	1236.66	31.53
1151.97	1152.35	29.38	1180.20	1180.58	30.10	1208.44	1208.82	30.82	1236.67	1237.05	31.54
1152.36	1152.74	29.39	1180.59	1180.98	30.11	1208.83	1209.21	30.83	1237.06	1237.45	31.55
1152.75	1153.13	29.40	1180.99	1181.37	30.12	1209.22	1209.60	30.84	1237.46	1237.84	31.56
1153.14	1153.52	29.41	1181.38	1181.76	30.13	1209.61	1209.99	30.85	1237.85	1238.23	31.57
1153.53	1153.92	29.42	1181.77	1182.15	30.14	1210.00	1210.39	30.86	1238.24	1238.62	31.58
1153.93	1154.31	29.43	1182.16	1182.54	30.15	1210.40	1210.78	30.87	1238.63	1239.01	31.59
1154.32	1154.70	29.44	1182.55	1182.94	30.16	1210.79	1211.17	30.88	1239.02	1239.41	31.60
1154.71	1155.09	29.45	1182.95	1183.33	30.17	1211.18	1211.56	30.89	1239.42	1239.80	31.61
1155.10	1155.49	29.46	1183.34	1183.72	30.18	1211.57	1211.96	30.90	1239.81	1240.19	31.62
1155.50	1155.88	29.47	1183.73	1184.11	30.19	1211.97	1212.35	30.91	1240.20	1240.58	31.63
1155.89	1156.27	29.48	1184.12	1184.50	30.20	1212.36	1212.74	30.92	1240.59	1240.98	31.64
1156.28	1156.66	29.49	1184.51	1184.90	30.21	1212.75	1213.13	30.93	1240.99	1241.37	31.65
1156.67	1157.05	29.50	1184.91	1185.29	30.22	1213.14	1213.52	30.94	1241.38	1241.76	31.66
1157.06	1157.45	29.51	1185.30	1185.68	30.23	1213.53	1213.92	30.95	1241.77	1242.15	31.67
1157.46	1157.84	29.52	1185.69	1186.07	30.24	1213.93	1214.31	30.96	1242.16	1242.54	31.68

Yearly maximum insurable earnings are $39,000
Yearly maximum employee premiums are $994.50

Le maximum annuel de la rémunération assurable est de 39 000 $
Le cotisation maximal annuelle de l'employé est de 994,50 $ C-11

Saskatchewan
Federal and Provincial Tax Deductions
Biweekly (26 pay periods a year)

Saskatchewan
Retenues d'impôt fédéral et provincial
Aux deux semaines (26 périodes de paie par année)

Pay Rémunération		If the employee's claim code from the TD1(E) form is Si le code de demande de l'employé selon le formulaire TD1(F) est										
From De	Less than Moins de	0	1	2	3	4	5	6	7	8	9	10
						Deduct from each pay Retenez sur chaque paie						
915. -	931.	241.00	176.50	168.60	152.80	137.10	121.75	104.55	89.25	73.95	58.65	43.30
931. -	947.	245.25	180.75	172.85	157.05	141.25	125.85	109.45	94.15	78.85	63.55	48.20
947. -	963.	249.55	185.05	177.15	161.35	145.50	130.00	114.35	99.05	83.75	68.45	53.10
963. -	979.	253.80	189.30	181.40	165.60	149.75	134.10	118.80	103.45	88.15	72.85	57.55
979. -	995.	258.05	193.55	185.65	169.85	154.05	138.25	122.90	107.60	92.25	76.95	61.65
995. -	1011.	262.30	197.80	189.90	174.10	158.30	142.50	127.00	111.70	96.35	81.05	65.75
1011. -	1027.	266.55	202.05	194.15	178.35	162.55	146.75	131.10	115.80	100.50	85.15	69.85
1027. -	1043.	270.80	206.30	198.40	182.60	166.80	151.00	135.20	119.90	104.60	89.25	73.95
1043. -	1059.	275.05	210.55	202.65	186.85	171.05	155.25	139.45	124.00	108.70	93.40	78.05
1059. -	1075.	279.30	214.80	206.90	191.15	175.30	159.50	143.70	128.10	112.80	97.50	82.15
1075. -	1091.	283.60	219.10	211.20	195.40	179.55	163.75	147.95	132.20	116.90	101.60	86.25
1091. -	1107.	287.85	223.35	215.45	199.65	183.85	168.00	152.25	136.45	121.00	105.70	90.35
1107. -	1123.	292.10	227.60	219.70	203.90	188.10	172.30	156.50	140.70	125.10	109.80	94.45
1123. -	1139.	296.35	231.85	223.95	208.15	192.35	176.55	160.75	144.95	129.20	113.90	98.55
1139. -	1155.	301.85	237.35	229.45	213.65	197.85	182.05	166.25	150.45	134.65	119.20	103.85
1155. -	1171.	308.30	243.80	235.90	220.10	204.30	188.50	172.70	156.90	141.10	125.40	110.10
1171. -	1187.	314.75	250.25	242.35	226.55	210.75	194.95	179.15	163.35	147.55	131.75	116.35
1187. -	1203.	321.20	256.70	248.80	233.00	217.20	201.40	185.60	169.80	154.00	138.20	122.55
1203. -	1219.	327.65	263.15	255.25	239.45	223.65	207.85	192.05	176.25	160.45	144.65	128.85
1219. -	1235.	334.15	269.65	261.70	245.95	230.10	214.30	198.50	182.70	166.90	151.10	135.30
1235. -	1251.	340.60	276.10	268.20	252.40	236.55	220.75	204.95	189.15	173.35	157.55	141.75
1251. -	1267.	347.05	282.55	274.65	258.85	243.05	227.25	211.45	195.65	179.85	164.05	148.20
1267. -	1283.	353.50	289.00	281.10	265.30	249.50	233.70	217.90	202.10	186.30	170.50	154.65
1283. -	1299.	359.95	295.45	287.55	271.75	255.95	240.15	224.35	208.55	192.75	176.95	161.15
1299. -	1315.	366.40	301.90	294.00	278.20	262.40	246.60	230.80	215.00	199.20	183.40	167.60
1315. -	1331.	372.85	308.35	300.45	284.65	268.85	253.05	237.25	221.45	205.65	189.85	174.05
1331. -	1347.	379.35	314.80	306.90	291.15	275.30	259.50	243.70	227.90	212.10	196.30	180.50
1347. -	1363.	385.80	321.30	313.40	297.60	281.75	265.95	250.15	234.35	218.55	202.75	186.95
1363. -	1379.	392.25	327.75	319.85	304.05	288.25	272.45	256.65	240.85	225.05	209.25	193.40
1379. -	1395.	398.70	334.20	326.30	310.50	294.70	278.90	263.10	247.30	231.50	215.70	199.85
1395. -	1411.	405.15	340.65	332.75	316.95	301.15	285.35	269.55	253.75	237.95	222.15	206.35
1411. -	1427.	411.60	347.10	339.20	323.40	307.60	291.80	276.00	260.20	244.40	228.60	212.80
1427. -	1443.	418.05	353.55	345.65	329.85	314.05	298.25	282.45	266.65	250.85	235.05	219.25
1443. -	1459.	424.70	360.15	352.25	336.45	320.65	304.80	289.05	273.25	257.45	241.65	225.80
1459. -	1475.	431.65	366.75	358.85	343.05	327.25	311.45	295.65	279.85	264.05	248.25	232.40
1475. -	1491.	438.60	373.35	365.45	349.65	333.85	318.05	302.25	286.45	270.65	254.85	239.00
1491. -	1507.	445.55	379.95	372.05	356.25	340.45	324.65	308.85	293.05	277.25	261.45	245.60
1507. -	1523.	452.60	386.65	378.75	362.95	347.15	331.35	315.55	299.75	283.95	268.15	252.30
1523. -	1539.	459.65	393.35	385.45	369.65	353.85	338.05	322.25	306.45	290.65	274.85	259.05
1539. -	1555.	466.70	400.05	392.15	376.35	360.55	344.75	328.95	313.15	297.35	281.55	265.75
1555. -	1571.	473.75	406.75	398.85	383.05	367.25	351.45	335.65	319.85	304.05	288.25	272.45
1571. -	1587.	480.80	413.50	405.60	389.80	373.95	358.15	342.35	326.55	310.75	294.95	279.15
1587. -	1603.	487.85	420.30	412.30	396.50	380.70	364.90	349.10	333.30	317.50	301.70	285.85
1603. -	1619.	494.90	427.35	419.10	403.20	387.40	371.60	355.80	340.00	324.20	308.40	292.55
1619. -	1635.	501.95	434.45	426.15	409.90	394.10	378.30	362.50	346.70	330.90	315.10	299.30
1635. -	1651.	509.00	441.50	433.20	416.65	400.80	385.00	369.20	353.40	337.60	321.80	306.00
1651. -	1667.	516.10	448.55	440.25	423.70	407.50	391.70	375.90	360.10	344.30	328.50	312.70
1667. -	1683.	523.15	455.60	447.30	430.80	414.25	398.40	382.60	366.80	351.00	335.20	319.40
1683. -	1699.	530.40	462.65	454.40	437.85	421.30	405.15	389.35	373.55	357.75	341.95	326.10
1699. -	1715.	537.85	469.70	461.45	444.90	428.35	411.85	396.05	380.25	364.45	348.65	332.80
1715. -	1731.	545.25	476.75	468.50	451.95	435.40	418.85	402.75	386.95	371.15	355.35	339.55
1731. -	1747.	552.70	483.80	475.55	459.00	442.45	425.90	409.45	393.65	377.85	362.05	346.25
1747. -	1763.	560.15	490.90	482.60	466.05	449.50	432.95	416.40	400.35	384.55	368.75	352.95
1763. -	1779.	567.55	497.95	489.65	473.10	456.55	440.00	423.45	407.05	391.25	375.45	359.65
1779. -	1795.	575.00	505.00	496.70	480.15	463.60	447.05	430.55	414.00	398.00	382.20	366.35

This table is available on diskette (TOD).   Vous pouvez obtenir cette table sur disquette (TSD).   D-9

Monthly Budget Worksheet for _____

Average Monthly Net Income _____

Projected Expenses

1. HOUSING and UTILITIES

Rent or Mortgage

Utilities _____

Cable _____

Insurance _____

Taxes _____

Repairs _____

_____

TOTAL _____

% of Net Income _____

2. FOOD and CLOTHING

Groceries

Eating Out _____

Clothing _____

Footwear _____

_____

TOTAL _____

% of Net Income _____

3. HEALTH and PERSONAL CARE

Prescriptions

Dental _____

Other Medical _____

Skin and Hair Care _____

_____

TOTAL _____

% of Net Income _____

4. TRANSPORTATION

Public Transit

Taxis _____

Car Payments _____

Car Licence _____

Car Insurance _____

Gas, Oil, etc. _____

Repairs _____

_____

TOTAL _____

% of Net Income _____

5. RECREATION and EDUCATION

Entertainment

Hobbbies _____

Vacations _____

Lessons _____

School Expenses _____

_____

TOTAL _____

% of Net Income _____

6. SAVINGS

Short Term

Long Term _____

_____

TOTAL _____

% of Net Income _____

7. MISCELLANEOUS

Gifts

Donations _____

_____

TOTAL _____

% of Net Income _____

Summary

Net Income

1. Housing and Utilities

2. Food and Clothing _____

3. Health and Personal Care _____

4. Transportation _____

5. Recreation and Education _____

6. Savings _____

7. Miscellaneous _____

Total Monthly Expenses

Discretionary Income _____

6

Circles

Overview

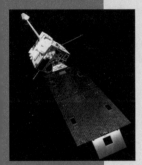

You should do at least one project that uses the skills you develop in this chapter. The recommended projects in the Project Book are:

- The Math Quilt
- Boxer Shorts
- Designing a Newsletter
- Crystallography

Circle Design

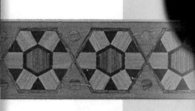

CHAPTER PROJECT

To complete this Chapter Project, you need to understand the properties of circles. Complete *Tutorials 6.1* to *6.3* to develop an understanding of some of these properties. You will revisit the Chapter Project on page 322 of this chapter.

Have you ever noticed how many designs use circles? For this Chapter Project, you will use the properties of circles to create a design. You will first research different designs, then choose one of these designs for your project and research its history. Next, you will practise making a circle design by creating the Yin and Yang symbol. Finally, after learning more properties of circles, you will complete your design. Here are some initial questions to consider.

- How will your design be used?

- What is the history of the form of design you plan to use?

- What medium will you use for your design (for example, fabric, paint, or wood)?

- Will you use colour?

- What is the scale of your design?

- What tools will you use?

Research designs. Sources of information include the Internet, and books on art, crafts, and the history of design. Your finished project will include the "work of art," a photocopy of the "work of art" indicating the properties of circles you used on the copy, and a brief history of the design with examples.

FYI Visit: www.awl.com/canada/school/connections

You can start your research from our Internet site: Click on <u>MATHLINKS</u>
followed by the *Applied Mathematics 11* logo. Then select a topic under
Circle Designs.

TUTORIAL 6.1   Using *The Geometer's Sketchpad*

Dynamic software, such as *The Geometer's Sketchpad*, allows us to explore geometry in a new way. We can investigate theorems or explore new ideas by observing how measurements and relationships change as a diagram is manipulated.

This Tutorial will help you become familiar with the software before you attempt the Investigations in the following Tutorials.

Investigation 1   The Toolbox

From the **File** menu choose **New Sketch**.

1. On the left of the screen is a column called the Toolbox. Before you work with *The Geometer's Sketchpad*, you must select one of these tools.

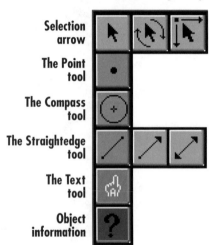

Selection arrow
The Point tool
The Compass tool
The Straightedge tool
The Text tool
Object information

There are 3 Selection arrows. To see them, click on the Selection arrow, hold down the mouse button and drag to the right. Beside the Translation arrow is a Rotation arrow and a Dilatation arrow. To choose either of these, drag to highlight the tool you want, then release the mouse button.

There are 3 Straightedge tools. To see them, click on the Straightedge tool, hold down the mouse button and drag to the right. Beside the Segment tool, there is a Ray tool and a Line tool.

2. Follow the instructions below to explore some features of the Toolbox.

Click on this tool …   … and do this:

a) To draw 4 points click 4 times in different locations on the screen. Notice that a point has a dark, black outline when first drawn. The outline disappears when the second point is drawn.

b) Click on one point. Hold down the mouse button and drag to an adjacent point. Click on this point. Hold down the mouse button and drag to the next point. Repeat until a quadrilateral is drawn.

Notice the little black squares on each segment as it is completed. These show when a segment is *selected*.

c) Click on one vertex. Notice that the black outline reappears. This shows that the point is selected. Hold down the mouse button and drag the vertex. By dragging different vertices, you can make the figure a square, a parallelogram, or even a straight line.

d) As you move closer to a point or line, the hand turns black. Click, and the object will be labelled. Click again and the label disappears.

e) Labels can be changed to other letters or even words. Use the Text tool to double-click on the label, not on the object. A dialog box will appear and a new label can be typed.

f) Use the Compass tool to draw a circle. Hold down the mouse button anywhere on the screen. Move the mouse. A circle is drawn. Notice the four little black squares. These appear when the circle is selected.

g) The circle has a point on it called the control point. Drag this point or the centre point to make the circle larger or smaller.

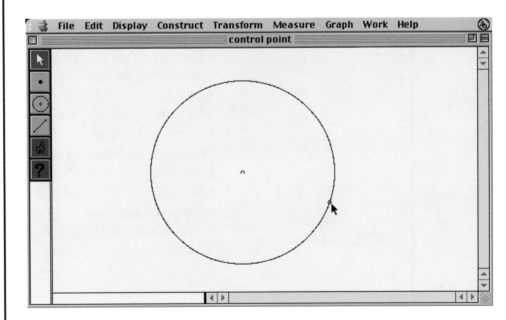

The Measure Menu

In this Investigation, you will explore the **Measure** menu and learn some special geometry features of *The Geometer's Sketchpad.*

From the **File** menu choose **New Sketch**.

There are nine menus at the top of the screen. Click on each menu to display its contents.

Many of the options are grey. They cannot be chosen unless the correct objects have been selected.

1. Measuring Circles

Click on this tool …

… and do this:

a) Draw a circle. Go to the **Measure** menu. Several items are now black. Choose **Radius**. The radius will be measured and the measure displayed on the screen. (If the measurement is not in centimetres, you can change it. From the **Display** menu choose **Preferences**. Under **Distance Unit** select **cm**, then click **OK**).

b) Check that the circle is still selected. From the **Measure** menu choose **Area**. The area measure is displayed. From the **Measure** menu choose **Circumference**. Its measure is displayed.

c) Drag the control point of the circle. Observe how the measurements change.

d) To move a measurement, click on it, hold down the mouse button, then drag the measurement to a new location.

2. Measuring Length

Click on this tool...   *.... and do this:*

a) Draw a segment. Two black squares show that the segment is selected.

b) From the **Measure** menu choose **Length**. The length of the segment will appear on the screen.

c) Click on an endpoint of the segment. Drag by holding down the mouse button. Notice that the measurement changes.

3. Measuring Area and Perimeter

Click on this tool...   *...and do this:*

Draw five points on the screen. Do not connect them. We will use a different technique to complete a pentagon.

a) Hold down the shift key, then click on each point. From the **Construct** menu choose **Segment**. A pentagon is constructed.

b) Click anywhere on the screen to deselect everything.

c) Hold down the shift key, then click on each side of the pentagon. Go to the **Measure** menu. Notice that it is not possible to select **Perimeter** and **Area** because they are grey.

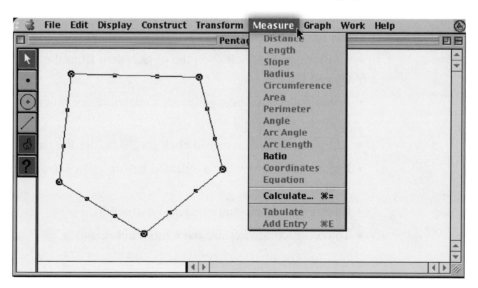

d) Click anywhere on the screen to deselect everything.

e) Hold down the shift key, then click on each vertex of the pentagon.

f) From the **Construct** menu choose **Polygon Interior**. The pentagon interior is now striped. This shows that it is selected.

g) From the **Measure** menu choose **Area**.

h) Drag a vertex of the pentagon. Watch the area measurement change as the figure changes.

i) Select the pentagon interior. From the **Display** menu choose **Color**, then pick your favourite colour. Click anywhere on the screen.

Sketchpad Tips

- When a segment or circle has black squares on it, or when a point is outlined in black, the object is selected. You may not be able to carry out a procedure if the wrong objects are selected. To *deselect* an object click on the **Selection** tool, then click anywhere on the screen.

- To select multiple objects: hold down the shift key while clicking on each object.

- To construct segment AB: select A and B, then from the **Construct** menu choose **Segment**.

- To label: choose the 🖐 tool. Click on the object to display its label. To change a label: double-click on the label and type a new letter.

- To hide an object: click on the object, then from the **Display** menu choose **Hide**.

- If you make a mistake and want to delete a construction, click on it, then from the **Edit** menu select **Undo**.

- After labelling, ensure you click on ▶ before the next construction.

- Ensure you know what is selected before you choose from the **Construct** menu.

- Ensure you deselect after each construction.

- To construct: always use the **Construct** menu.

1. How do you select all the points on the screen at once?

2. Explain how to deselect an object.

3. How can you change the shape of a triangle?

4. How can you change the size of a circle?

PROJECT

You have learned to use dynamic software. You will use these skills when you return to the Chapter Project and in the following projects in the Project Book.

- The Math Quilt
- Boxer Shorts
- Designing a Newsletter
- Crystallography

COMMUNICATING THE IDEAS

In your journal, list some advantages and disadvantages of using computer software such as *The Geometer's Sketchpad*.

Properties of Chords in Circles

Sometimes the setting sun looks like a large orange ball that drops below the horizon. Visualize the sun doing this as you look at the pictures. The centre of the sun moves straight down. The line segment formed by the horizon and the sun is horizontal. A line segment that has both endpoints on the circle is called a *chord* of the circle. In this Tutorial you will investigate the properties of chords.

STUDENT REFERENCE

Some of the terms used in the Tutorials in this chapter may be new to you. For definitions of terms, and accompanying diagrams, look in the Student Reference.

Practise Your Prior Skills

You will use some properties of line segments and symmetry properties of a circle in the work that follows. Try these exercises to review the terms.

1. Draw a line segment AB in your notebook. Use a ruler and protractor to draw the *perpendicular bisector* of AB. Label any angles and congruent line segments.

2. Draw a circle in your notebook. Draw at least two chords that are lines of symmetry for the circle. What are these chords called?

STUDENT REFERENCE

If you need more instruction on the "perpendicular bisector" of a line segment or a "line of symmetry of a circle," look in the Student Reference.

In the following Investigations, you will use dynamic software to explore some properties of chords of a circle. The Investigations use *The Geometer's Sketchpad*. If you are using different dynamic software, consult the manual for the appropriate commands and keystrokes.

Chord Property 1

You will investigate the line that passes through the centre of a circle and intersects a chord at a 90° angle.

Step 1: Construct a circle.

   1. Open *The Geometer's Sketchpad* and choose **New Sketch** from the **File** menu.

   2. Draw a circle. Label the centre A and the control point B.

Step 2: Construct a chord of the circle.

   3. The circle is still selected from exercise 2. From the **Construct** menu choose **Point On Object**. Label the point C. Select the circle. From the **Construct** menu choose **Point On Object**. Label the point D.

   4. Select points C and D. From the **Construct** menu choose **Segment**. This chord, CD, must not be a diameter.

Step 3: Construct a line through the centre of the circle that is perpendicular to the chord.

   5. Select the centre of the circle, A, and chord CD.

   6. From the **Construct** menu choose **Perpendicular Line**. This constructs a line from A perpendicular to CD. Through which special point of the chord does this perpendicular line appear to pass?

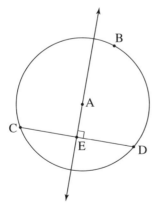

Step 4: Measure the line segments.

   7. Select the chord CD and the line you have just constructed.

   8. From the **Construct** menu choose **Point at Intersection**. Label it E.

   9. Select points E and C, one endpoint of the chord.

   10. From the **Measure** menu choose **Distance**. The length of EC is displayed.

11. Select points E and D, the other endpoint of the chord.

12. From the **Measure** menu choose **Distance**. The length of ED is displayed.

13. Compare the lengths in exercises 10 and 12. What do you notice?

14. Visualize the same construction for other chords, and for chords in other circles. What do you expect to observe about the distances from the point of intersection of the perpendicular to the endpoints of the chord? What name do we give this point of intersection?

Step 5: Check your prediction.

15. Check your prediction for other chords of this circle. Select one endpoint of the chord. Move it around the circle.

16. Check your prediction for other circles. Select the centre of the circle. Move it around the screen.

A *conjecture* is a conclusion based on examples.

17. Write a conjecture about the line that passes through the centre of the circle and is perpendicular to a chord.

Investigation 2 **Chord Property 2**

You will investigate the perpendicular bisector of a chord.

Step 1: Construct a circle.

1. From the **File** menu choose **New Sketch**.

2. Draw a circle. Label its centre A and the control point B.

Step 2: Construct a chord of the circle.

3. From the **Construct** menu choose **Point On Object**. Do this twice. Label the points C and D.

4. Select points C and D. From the **Construct** menu, choose **Segment**. This constructs chord CD. This particular segment must not be a diameter.

Step 3: Construct the perpendicular bisector of the chord.

5. The chord CD is still selected from exercise 4. From the **Construct** menu choose **Point at Midpoint**. This marks the midpoint of the chord. Label the midpoint E.

6. Select point E and chord CD. From the **Construct** menu choose **Perpendicular Line**. This draws the perpendicular bisector of the chord.

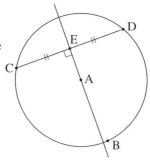

7. Through what other point does the perpendicular bisector of this chord pass?

8. Visualize repeating this construction for other chords, and for chords in other circles. Predict through which point the perpendicular bisector of a chord will pass.

Step 4: Check your prediction.

9. Check your prediction for other chords of this circle. Select one endpoint of the chord. Move it around the circle.

10. Check your prediction for other circles. Select the centre of the circle. Move it around the screen.

11. Write a conjecture about the perpendicular bisector of a chord in a circle.

In the Investigations you confirmed the following properties of chords.

> ### *Properties of Chords*
>
> The perpendicular from the centre of the circle to a chord bisects the chord.
>
> The perpendicular bisector of any chord passes through the centre of the circle.

Practise Your Prior Skills

In the exercises that follow, you will use the Pythagorean Theorem to solve problems. Try these exercises as preliminary review.

1. Calculate the length of the indicated side in each of the following triangles. Round the lengths to 2 decimal places.

a)
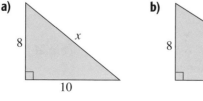

b)

c)
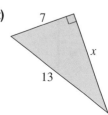

To examine a completed example using the Pythagorean Theorem, look in the Student Reference.

Example 1 — Determine the distance from the centre of a circle to a chord

In the diagram below, O is the centre of a circle with radius 9 cm. OB is perpendicular to CD, and CD = 12 cm. Determine the value of x, rounded to 2 decimal places.

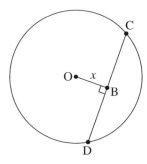

SOLUTION

Use the chord property from *Investigation 1*. OB intersects the chord at its midpoint.

Chord CD = 12 cm, so DB = BC = 6 cm

Radius = 9 cm, so OD = 9 cm

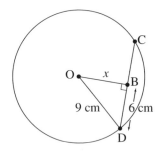

Triangle OBD is a right triangle, so use the Pythagorean Theorem.

$$OB^2 + BD^2 = OD^2$$

Substitute BD = 6, OB = x, and OD = 9:

$$x^2 + 6^2 = 9^2$$

Solve for x.
$$x^2 = 9^2 - 6^2$$
$$x = \sqrt{9^2 - 6^2}$$

Use a calculator. $x = 6.71$, rounded to 2 decimal places

Thus, the length of OB is 6.71 cm.

Example 2 **Determine the length of a line segment in a circle**

This diagram (not drawn to scale) represents a cross section of a fuel line on an F-18 aircraft.

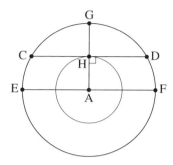

A is the centre of the circle, and GA is perpendicular to CD. Some measurements are taken with a vernier caliper: diameter EF = 0.358 cm and chord CD = 0.140 cm. If the segment GH is longer than 0.010 cm, the fuel line is not within safety specifications and must be replaced. Determine whether the fuel line will have to be replaced. Explain.

SOLUTION

Since GA is perpendicular to CD, H is the midpoint of CD.

Chord CD = 0.140 cm

So CH = DH = 0.070 cm

Diameter EF = 0.358 cm

Since EA and AF are radii, EA = AF = 0.179 cm

Transfer the information to a diagram. For the sake of clarity, the smaller circle has not been included in the diagram below.

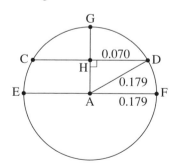

Construct AD to form right △ADH. Since AD is a radius, AD = 0.179 cm.

Use the Pythagorean Theorem in △ADH:

$$HD^2 + HA^2 = AD^2$$

Substitute the known measures.

$$(0.07)^2 + HA^2 = (0.179)^2$$

Solve for HA. $\quad HA^2 = (0.179)^2 - (0.07)^2$

$$HA = \sqrt{(0.179)^2 - (0.07)^2}$$

$$HA \doteq 0.164\ 745$$

Since GA is a radius, GA = 0.179 cm. We also know that
GH + HA = GA.

Substitute the known measures. $\quad GH + 0.164\ 745 = 0.179$

$$GH \doteq 0.014\ 255$$

GH is approximately 0.014 cm. This is longer than the permitted 0.010 cm, so the fuel line must be replaced.

DISCUSSING THE IDEAS

1. In the Investigations, why were you asked to draw a chord that was not a diameter?

2. In the diagram below left, O is the centre of the circle. What conclusion can be reached?

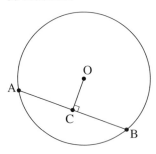 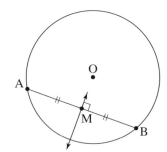

3. In the diagram above right, O is the centre of the circle. What conclusion can be reached?

4. A line segment is marked on a page.

   a) How many different circles pass through the endpoints of this line segment?

   b) What is true of a line that intersects the segment and contains the centre of the circle?

   c) What is the special name for a line segment whose endpoints are on a circle?

5. Draw a circle and one chord of the circle. Connect the centre of the circle to the midpoint of the chord with a line segment. Draw the radius from one endpoint of the chord. Describe the triangle that is formed. If you know the lengths of two sides of this triangle, how can you calculate the length of the third side?

EXERCISES

Checking Your Skills

1. Determine each value of x. Point O is the centre of each circle.

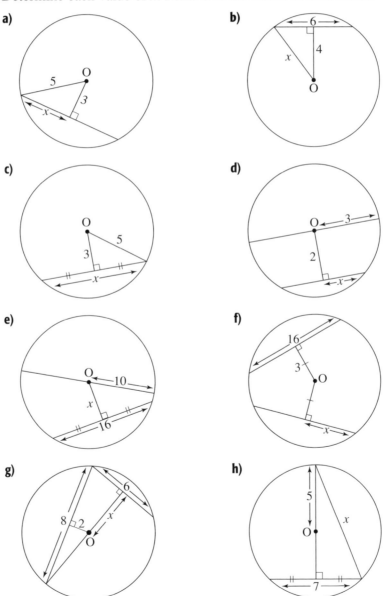

a)

b)

c)

d)

e)

f)

g)

h)

2. A pathway is constructed under a roadway using a cylindrical concrete pipe, shown below left. The pipe has a diameter of 3.6 m. The engineer wishes to pave the pathway. The headroom at the centre of the pathway is to be 3 m. How wide will the pathway be? Round your answers to the nearest hundredth of a metre.

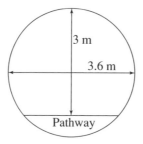

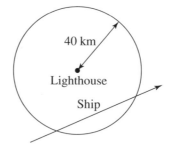

3. From a lighthouse, the range of visibility on a clear day is 40 km (above right). A ship passes through this area travelling in a straight line; it is visible as it travels a distance of 35.8 km. How far was the ship from the lighthouse at its closest point? Round your answer to the nearest hundredth of a kilometre.

4. An archaeologist studies the material remains of past human life and activities. She often has to fit together pieces like a jigsaw puzzle. Sometimes when pieces of the puzzle are missing, the archaeologist makes an educated guess as to what is lost.

The archaeologist has found a fragment of a plate and wishes to sketch the remainder. Assume the plate is circular. What would the sketch look like? Trace this fragment into your notebook. Use the properties of chords in circles to complete the sketch as accurately as possible.

5. A homeowner is installing a circular swimming pool. He wants a small shallow area at one side of the pool and he wants the pool to be 12 m in diameter. If the rope dividing the shallow and deep areas is to be 8 m long, how wide will the shallow area be at its widest point?

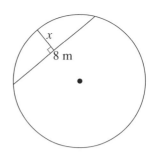

6. A meteorite is a mass of stone or metal that enters Earth's atmosphere from space and strikes Earth's surface, creating a crater. Many of the world's largest meteorite craters have been found in Canada.

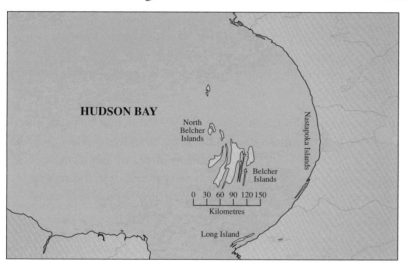

Some people believe that the circular outline of part of the eastern shore of Hudson Bay was created when a meteorite struck Earth millions of years ago. Trace the map into your notebook. If these people are correct, how far from the shoreline was the centre of impact?

7. A quiltmaker is designing a new quilt. He bases his design on circles and squares. A square of side 15 cm is inscribed in a circle (below left). What is the distance between the midpoints of the sides of the square and the centre of the circle?

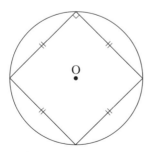

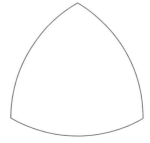

8. A circle has constant width (diameter). This is why it has been popular as the shape for utility hole covers. However, there are other figures that have constant width. The most famous figure is the Reuleaux triangle (above right).

When a drill bit has the shape of a Reuleaux triangle, a square (or almost square) hole can be drilled. The shape of the rotor in a rotary combustion engine is a Reuleaux triangle.

a) To construct a Reuleaux triangle:
  - Draw an equilateral triangle ABC. Place the compass point on A and the pencil point on B.
  - Draw an arc to connect vertices B and C.
  - Move the compass point to vertex B and draw an arc to connect A and C.
  - Move the compass point to C and draw an arc to connect A and B. These arcs form a Reuleaux triangle.

b) Assume the sides of △ABC represent chords in a circle. Construct the circle.

c) Look at your construction. What would be an advantage and a disadvantage of constructing utility hole covers in the shape of a Reuleaux triangle?

9. You know that the centre of a circle lies on the perpendicular bisector of a chord of the circle. Use this property and the problem-solving strategy of working backward to draw a circle through the vertices of any triangle. Use *The Geometer's Sketchpad*. Begin by drawing any triangle on the screen. Then construct the circumcircle, that is, the circle through the vertices of the triangle.

Extending Your Thinking

10. The ancient Greeks regarded certain shapes as more pleasing than others. One of these shapes was the golden rectangle. In the golden rectangle,

the ratio of the longer side to the shorter side is: $\dfrac{1 + \sqrt{5}}{2} : 1$.

Rewrite this ratio using decimals rounded to the nearest hundredth.

To construct a golden rectangle:

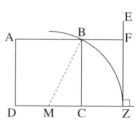

  - Construct a square ABCD.
  - Construct the midpoint M of CD.
  - Draw a circle with centre at M and radius MB.
  - Extend DC to intersect the circle at Z.
  - Construct a line ZE perpendicular to DZ.
  - Extend AB to intersect ZE at F.
  - Rectangle AFZD is a golden rectangle. If the original square ABCD is removed, the remaining rectangle BFZC is also a golden rectangle.
  - What is the ratio of DZ to AD? How does this compare to the ratio you wrote?

11. In homebuilding, arched windows are popular. To build these windows, templates must be created. An architect has drawn four sketches of arched windows for her client. Each arch is an arc of a circle.

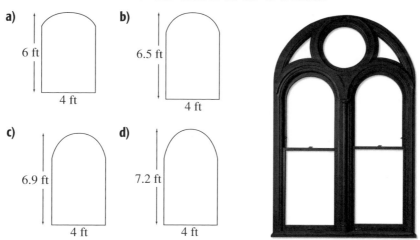

a) 6 ft — 4 ft

b) 6.5 ft — 4 ft

c) 6.9 ft — 4 ft

d) 7.2 ft — 4 ft

Which of the four designs is most pleasing to your eye? The homeowner chooses design b. The architect is pleased because this window is based on the properties of the golden rectangle. The width of the window is 4 feet, the height is 6.5 feet, and the height of the arch is 1.5 feet. To draw the arch accurately, you must find the centre of the circle on which the arch is drawn.

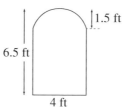

1.5 ft

6.5 ft

4 ft

Make a scale drawing of the window. Using the three measurements shown, determine the location of the centre of the circle to the nearest tenth of a foot.

PROJECT

In this Tutorial you discovered the properties of chords in a circle. You will need these skills for the Chapter Project and the following project in the Project Book.

• The Math Quilt

COMMUNICATING THE IDEAS

Create a display of the chord properties you discovered in this Tutorial. Include diagrams in your summary.

Properties of Angles in Circles

Photographers often view an object from many different positions before they take a photograph of the particular object. Below are five photographs of the same building taken from different positions. The front of the building takes up the entire width of each photograph.

To determine where the photographer stood to take these photographs, you need to use properties of angles in circles.

Point O is the centre of a circle, and A, B, and C are points on the circle. ∠ABC shown below is the *inscribed angle* subtended by arc AC. ∠AOC is the *central angle* subtended by arc AC.

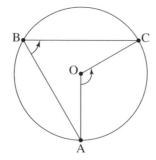

**STUDENT
REFERENCE**

For the terms "inscribed angle" and "central angle" look in the Student Reference.

The following Investigations use *The Geometer's Sketchpad*. If you use different dynamic geometry software, consult the manual for the appropriate commands and keystrokes.

Central Angle and Inscribed Angle

You will investigate the relationship between an inscribed angle and the central angle subtended by the same arc of a circle.

Step 1: Construct a circle and two points on it.

1. From the **File** menu choose **New Sketch**.

2. Draw a circle. Label its centre A and a control point B.

3. The circle is still selected from exercise 2. From the **Construct** menu choose **Point On Object**. Label the point C.

The points B and C divide the circle into two arcs. The longer arc is called the *major arc* BC, and the shorter arc is the *minor arc* BC.

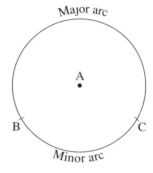

Step 2: Draw an inscribed angle subtended by minor arc BC.

4. Select the circle. Construct a third point and label it D. You have three points on the circle labelled B, C, and D. If D is not on the major arc BC, select D and move it around the circle until it is on the major arc.

5. Select points B and D. From the **Construct** menu choose **Segment** to construct chord BD.

6. Select points C and D. From the **Construct** menu choose **Segment** to construct chord CD. ∠BDC is an inscribed angle subtended by minor arc BC.

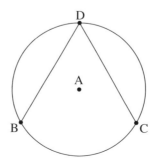

Step 3: Draw the central angle subtended by minor arc BC.

7. Select points A and B. Choose **Segment** from the **Construct** menu.

8. Select points A and C. Choose **Segment** from the **Construct** menu. ∠BAC is the central angle subtended by minor arc BC.

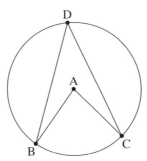

Step 4: Measure the inscribed and central angles subtended by the minor arc BC.

9. Select points B, A, and C (in that order). From the **Measure** menu choose **Angle**. The measure of ∠BAC is displayed. The angle measure should be given to the nearest tenth. If it is not, from the **Display** menu choose **Preferences**. Under **Angle Unit** select **degrees**, under **Precision** select **tenths**, then click **OK**.

10. Select points B, D, and C (in that order). From the **Measure** menu choose **Angle**. The measure of ∠BDC is displayed.

11. Compare the measures of ∠BAC and ∠BDC. What do you notice?

12. Visualize repeating this construction for other positions of B and C and other circles. What do you expect to observe about the measures of ∠BAC and ∠BDC?

Step 5: Check your prediction.

13. Select one point on the circle and move it around the circle. To check for other circles select the centre of the circle and move it around the screen.

14. Write a conjecture about the central angle and inscribed angle subtended by the same arc of a circle.

Investigation 2 **Angle in a Semicircle**

You will investigate the inscribed angle subtended by a diameter of a circle.

Step 1: Construct a circle with line segment AB as diameter.

1. From the **File** menu choose **New Sketch**.

2. Draw and label line segment AB.

3. Select the line segment. From the **Construct** menu choose **Point at Midpoint**. Label the midpoint C.

4. To draw a circle with diameter AB: select A and the midpoint, C. From the **Construct** menu choose **Circle by Centre and Point**.

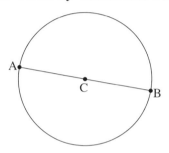

Step 2: Draw the inscribed angle subtended by a diameter.

5. The circle is still selected from exercise 4. From the **Construct** menu choose **Point On Object**. Label the point D.

6. To construct ∠ADB inscribed in the semicircle:
Select A and D. From the **Construct** menu choose **Segment**.
Select B and D. From the **Construct** menu choose **Segment**.

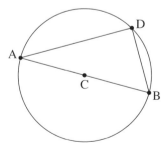

Step 3: Measure the inscribed angle.

7. Select points A, D, and B (in that order).

8. From the **Measure** menu choose **Angle**. The measure of ∠ADB is displayed.

9. Select point D and move it around the circle. What do you notice?

10. Visualize repeating this construction for the other semicircles. What do you expect to observe about the measure of ∠ADB?

Step 4: Check your prediction.

11. To check your prediction for other circles, select the point A and move it around the screen to make the circle larger, then smaller.

12. Make a conjecture about the measure of the inscribed angle subtended by a diameter.

Investigation 3 | **Inscribed Angles**

You will investigate the relationship between the measures of inscribed angles subtended by the same arc of a circle.

Step 1: Construct a circle and four points on it.

1. From the **File** menu choose **New Sketch**.

2. Draw a circle. Label the centre A and the control point B.

3. Construct and label 3 more points C, D, and E on the circle.

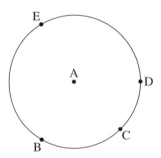

Step 2: Draw inscribed angles subtended by an arc.

4. To draw the inscribed angle ∠BDC subtended by minor arc BC:
Select points B and D. From the **Construct** menu choose **Segment**.
Select points C and D. From the **Construct** menu choose **Segment**.

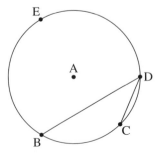

5. To draw the inscribed angle ∠BEC subtended by minor arc BC:
Select points B and E. From the **Construct** menu choose **Segment**.
Select points C and E. From the **Construct** menu choose **Segment**.

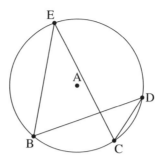

Step 3: Measure the inscribed angles.

6. Select B, D, and C (in that order). From the **Measure** menu choose **Angle**. The measure of ∠BDC is displayed.

7. Select B, E, and C (in that order). From the **Measure** menu choose **Angle**. What do you notice?

8. Visualize repeating this construction for other positions of D and E, for other positions of B and C, and for other circles. What do you expect to observe about the measures of the inscribed angles?

Step 4: Check your prediction.

9. Select point C and move it around the circle. Select the centre A and move it around the screen.

10. Write a conjecture about the measures of inscribed angles subtended by the same arc.

In the Investigations you confirmed the following properties of angles in a circle.

Angle Properties of a Circle

The measure of a central angle is twice the measure of an inscribed angle subtended by the same arc.

An angle inscribed in a semicircle is a right angle.

Inscribed angles subtended by the same arc of a circle are equal.

Use properties of angles in circles to find an angle

The design for a circular panel is shown. O is the centre of the circle.

∠ACB = 30°. Determine the measure of the angle subtended by major arc AB at E.

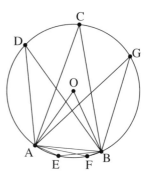

SOLUTION

Draw in central angle AOB and use the angle property from *Investigation 1*.

∠AOB = 2∠ACB
      = 2(30°)
      = 60°

Reflex ∠AOB = 360° − ∠AOB
            = 300°

Reflex ∠AOB is subtended by major arc AB. This major arc subtends inscribed ∠AEB.

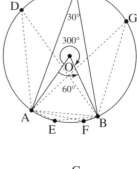

Use the angle property from *Investigation 1*.

Reflex ∠AOB = 2∠AEB
    so, 300° = 2∠AEB
        150° = ∠AEB

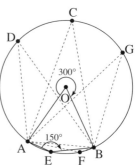

DISCUSSING THE IDEAS

1. Explain why the conjecture in *Investigation 2* is a special case of the conjecture in *Investigation 1*.

2. Explain why the conjecture of *Investigation 3* can be justified using the conjecture of *Investigation 1*.

3. Where did the photographer stand to take the photographs shown at the beginning of this Tutorial?

Checking Your Skills

1. Determine each value of *x*. Point O is the centre of each circle.

a)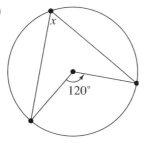

b)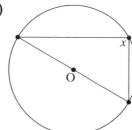

c)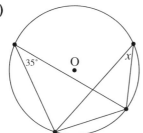

d)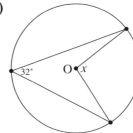

e)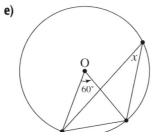

f)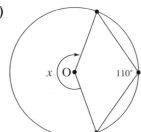

2. Determine each value of *x* and *y*. Point O is the centre of the circle.

a)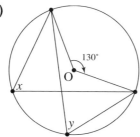

b)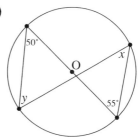

c)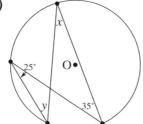

d)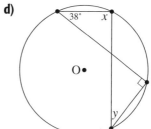

e)

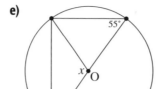

f)

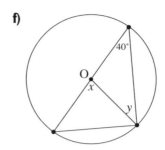

3. One warm-up activity for a hockey goalie is to have the players line up at the blue line and take turns shooting at the goal.

a) Explain why it is easier for some players to score than others.

b) How could the players be arranged so the shooting angle is the same for each player?

4. Carpenters use an instrument called a square (sometimes called a carpenter's, or framing, square) to lay out and check right angles. Describe how a carpenter can find the centre of a circle using this instrument (right).

5. Use a tube from a roll of paper towels. Place a pen on a shelf at eye level and view it through the tube. Adjust your distance from the pen until it fits exactly across the opening (right). Keep the pen sighted so that it fits exactly across the opening, move to another position, and note the location by placing pennies or markers.

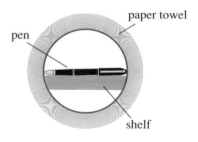

Repeat this several times. Visualize the points on the floor where you were standing when you saw the pen framed by the tube. What geometric figure do these points form? Explain why the points form this figure.

6. Lori photographs homes for real estate advertisements. She is taking a photograph of a house with a camera that has a 50° angle of view. Since the neighbouring houses need repair, she wants the house she is photographing to take up the entire field of view.

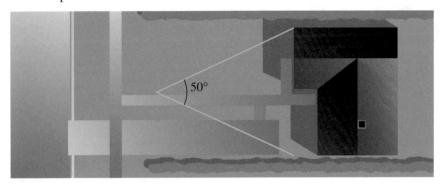

a) Draw a diagram to show the possible places Lori could stand to take the photograph.

b) Gita's camera has a wide-angle lens with a 70° field of view. Draw another diagram to show the possible places she could stand to take a picture of the same house.

c) Compare and contrast the two diagrams.

Extending Your Thinking

7. Construct a figure similar to the one shown. Measure ∠ACB and ∠ADB. How do their measures relate? Explain this relationship.

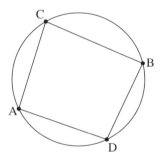

PROJECT

In this Tutorial you discovered the properties of angles in circles. You will need these skills for the Chapter Project and in the following project in the Project Book.

• The Math Quilt

COMMUNICATING THE IDEAS

Draw three labelled diagrams that could be enlarged and mounted on a poster to demonstrate the angle properties you investigated in this Tutorial.

Yin and Yang

This symbol represents the Chinese Yin and Yang. Yin and Yang are opposite, yet complementary, forces that are equally strong; like dark and light, or dry and wet. The white and black dots indicate that the qualities of Yin cannot exist without Yang, and vice versa.

In the following exercises, you will duplicate the Yin and Yang symbol. The symbol comprises three sizes of circles or parts of these circles. You will need a compass and a ruler. If you wish, you can use *The Geometer's Sketchpad* to construct this symbol.

1. Draw a circle. Mark a point at the centre of the circle.

2. Lightly draw a diameter.

3. Measure and mark the midpoint of each radius that forms the diameter. These midpoints represent the centres of two smaller circles.

4. Place the compass point on one midpoint and the pencil point at the centre of the large circle. Draw a semicircle on one side of the diameter. Repeat this construction for the other midpoint; draw a semicircle on the other side of the diameter.

5. Erase the diameter.

6. Draw a small circle around each midpoint.

7. Colour in your Yin and Yang symbol to match the one above.

At the beginning of this Chapter Project you began making plans for a design. Your design may be in one of the following forms:

postage stamp; brass rubbing; wood banding on a box; sign for a shop; poster for an art show; quilt sample; sundial; greetings card; or some other idea (approved by your teacher)

CHAPTER PROJECT

To complete this Chapter Project, you need to understand more properties of circles and polygons inscribed in circles. Complete *Tutorials 6.4* to *6.5* to develop an understanding of these properties. The last stage of the Chapter Project is on page 346 of this chapter.

Your finished project will include: the "work of art," a photocopy of the "work of art" indicating the properties of circles you used, and a brief history of the form you used along with some examples. For brass rubbings, for example, you would include a discussion of the origins of brass rubbings, and some sketches. Research your chosen form and consider how you will incorporate the properties of chords and angles into your design. Make a rough sketch of your design and enhance it with the use of colour.

Career Skills

People who work in design usually make initial sketches, then construct accurate drawings. Colour is an important part of their designs. Designers work in many different fields from fashion design to engineering. They pay great attention to detail.

Properties of Tangents to a Circle

Circle designs, such as the one shown below, have been used to decorate buildings for centuries. This Yemeni design was made in the late 3rd or early 4th century. Even today in certain areas of the world, craftsmen who make geometric patterns on wood, marble, metal, and ceramics use the traditional tools of compass and ruler.

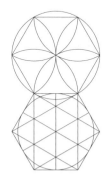

The design in the picture above shows a hexagon with an *inscribed* circle. Each side of the hexagon is a *tangent* to the inscribed circle because it touches the circle in exactly one point. The point where the tangent touches the circle is called *the point of tangency*.

In this Tutorial, you will investigate some of the properties of tangents to a circle.

These Investigations use *The Geometer's Sketchpad*. If you use different dynamic geometry software, consult the manual for the appropriate commands and keystrokes.

Investigation 1 **Angle Between a Tangent Line and Radius**

You will investigate the angle between the tangent and the radius of the circle at the point of tangency.

Step 1: Construct a circle.

1. From the **File** menu choose **New Sketch**.

2. Draw a circle. Label its centre A and the control point B.

Step 2: Draw a secant.

3. The circle is still selected from exercise 2. From the **Construct** menu choose **Point On Object**. Label the point C.

4. Select points B and C. From the **Toolbox** (at the left of the screen) select the **Line** tool (to select the **Line** tool, click on the **Straightedge** tool, hold the mouse button down and drag over to the **Line** tool). From the **Construct** menu choose **Line**.

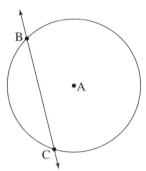

The line drawn intersects the circle at two points and is called a *secant*.

Step 3: Move the secant line until it becomes a tangent to the circle.

5. Select point C and move it until it coincides with point B.

The secant now intersects the circle in only one point, B, and is therefore a *tangent*. The tangent intersects the circle at the point of tangency.

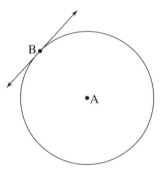

Step 4: Construct the radius of the circle at the point of tangency.

6. Select the centre of the circle A, and the point of tangency, B. From the **Toolbox** select the **Segment** tool. From the **Construct** menu choose **Segment**.

7. Select the tangent. From the **Construct** menu choose **Point On Object**. This program tends to plot the point at the point of tangency, so, if necessary, select the new point and move it to another place on the tangent line. Label the point D.

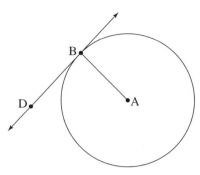

Step 5: Measure the angle between the tangent and the radius at the point of tangency.

8. Select, in this order, the points A, B, and D.

9. From the **Measure** menu choose **Angle**. The measure of ∠ABD is displayed. (Since B and C coincide, this angle may be displayed as ∠ACD.)

10. Select points B and D and move them together around the circle. What do you notice?

11. Visualize repeating this construction for other circles. What do you expect to observe about the angle between the tangent and the radius at the point of tangency?

Step 5: Check your prediction.

12. Move the centre of the circle A around the screen. Ensure that B and C always coincide.

13. Make a conjecture about the measure of the angle between the radius drawn to a point of tangency and the tangent at that point.

Investigation 2 **The Lengths of Tangent Segments from an External Point**

You will investigate the lengths of the tangent segments that can be drawn to a circle from a point outside the circle.

Step 1: Draw a circle and mark two points on it.

1. From the **File** menu choose **New Sketch**.

2. Draw a circle. Label its centre A and the control point on the circle B.

3. The circle is still selected from exercise 2. From the **Construct** menu choose **Point On Object**. Label the point C. Select the circle, choose another point on it and label it D.

Step 2: Construct two tangents.

4. Select points A and C. From the **Construct** menu choose **Segment**. Select points A and D. From the **Construct** menu choose **Segment**.

5. Construct the tangent at C by constructing the perpendicular to radius AC at C. Select segment AC and point C. From the **Construct** menu choose **Perpendicular Line**.

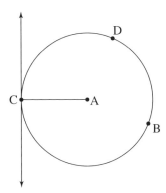

6. Construct the tangent at D by constructing the perpendicular to radius AD at D. Select segment AD and point D. From the **Construct** menu choose **Perpendicular Line**.

7. Select the control point, B, and move it around the screen until the tangents intersect. Select the two tangents, then from the **Construct** menu choose **Point at Intersection**. Label the point E.

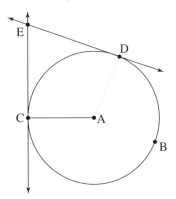

Step 3: Measure the lengths of the tangent segments from the external point to the points of tangency.

8. Select points C and E. From the **Measure** menu choose **Distance**. Similarly, measure the distance ED. What do you notice?

9. Select point C or D and move it around the circle. What do you notice?

10. Visualize repeating the construction for other external points and tangents, and for other circles. What do you expect to observe about the lengths of the tangent segments?

Step 4: Check your prediction.

11. Check your prediction for other circles by moving A around the screen.

12. Make a conjecture about the lengths of the tangent segments to a circle from an external point.

Investigation 3: The Angle Between a Tangent and a Chord and the Inscribed Angle on the Opposite Side of the Chord

You will investigate the relationship between the angle formed by a tangent and a chord and the inscribed angle opposite the chord.

Step 1: Construct a circle.

1. From the **File** menu choose **New Sketch**.

2. Draw a circle. Label its centre A and the control point B.

Step 2: Draw a secant.

3. The circle is still selected from exercise 2. From the **Construct** menu choose **Point On Object**. Label the point C.

4. Select points B and C. From the **Toolbox** (at the left of the screen) select the **Line** tool. From the **Construct** menu choose **Line**.

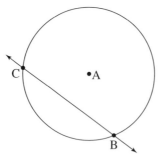

The line drawn intersects the circle at two points and is called a secant.

Step 3: Move the secant until it becomes a tangent to the circle.

5. Select point C and move it until it coincides with point B.

The secant now intersects the circle in only one point, B, and is therefore a tangent. The tangent intersects the circle at the point of tangency.

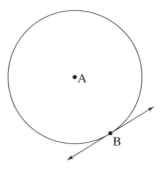

Step 4: Draw an inscribed angle that is subtended by a chord that has one endpoint at the point of tangency.

6. Construct and label two more points D and E on the circle.

7. To draw the chord EB with one endpoint at the point of tangency:
Select points E and B. From the **Construct** menu choose **Segment**.

8. To draw the inscribed angle ∠EDB subtended by EB:
Select points D and E. From the **Construct** menu choose **Segment**.
Select points D and B. From the **Construct** menu choose **Segment**.

9. Select the tangent. From the **Construct** menu choose **Point On Object**. Label the point F. The point should be in a position on the tangent line to form an acute angle ∠EBF. If necessary, move point F.

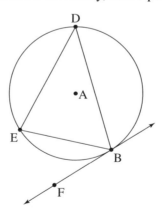

Step 5: Measure the angle between the tangent and the chord and the inscribed angle.

10. Select E, D, and B (in that order). From the **Measure** menu choose **Angle**. The measure of ∠EDB is displayed. (Since B and C coincide, this angle may be displayed as ∠EDC.)

11. Select E, B, and F (in that order). From the **Measure** menu choose **Angle**. The measure of ∠EBF is displayed. What do you notice?

12. Visualize repeating this construction for other circles. What do you expect to observe about the angle between the chord and the tangent and the inscribed angle that is opposite the tangent?

Step 6: Check your predictions.

13. To check your prediction for other angles move E and D, and for other circles move A around the screen.

14. Make a conjecture about the measures of the angle between a tangent and a chord and the inscribed angle that is opposite the chord.

Tangent Properties

A tangent to a circle is perpendicular to the radius at the point of tangency.

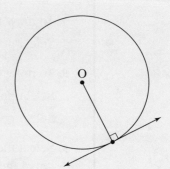

The tangent segments to a circle from an external point are equal.

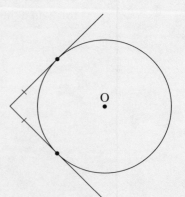

The angle between a tangent and a chord is equal to the inscribed angle on the opposite side of the chord.

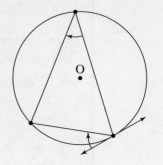

Example 1 Determine the distance from an external point to the centre of a circle

In the diagram, O is the centre of the circle, and AB and AC are tangent segments. Determine the lengths of AC and AO.

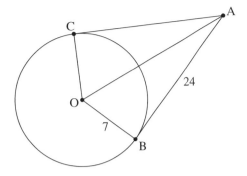

SOLUTION

From *Investigation 2*, AC = AB
Hence, AC = 24

From *Investigation 1*, ∠ACO = 90°

Use the Pythagorean Theorem in △ACO.

$$AO^2 = AC^2 + OC^2$$
$$= 24^2 + 7^2$$
$$AO = \sqrt{24^2 + 7^2}$$
$$= 25$$

Hence, AO = 25

Example 2 Calculate the length of a tangent segment

The diagram shows a satellite in orbit. The lines represent the limit of the paths of radio signals transmitted between Earth and the satellite. Points A and B represent places on Earth that are on the edge of the satellite's area of coverage. Each line is a tangent to the circle because it touches the circle in exactly one point.

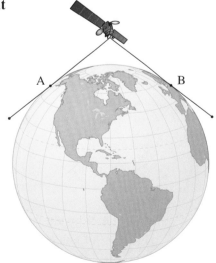

At its closest point, the satellite is 980 km from Earth. The radius of Earth is approximately 6606 km. What is the distance from the satellite to A?

SOLUTION

Start by drawing a diagram to illustrate the problem.
The diagram is not to scale.

From *Investigation 1*, the tangent is perpendicular to
the radius at the point of tangency. Use the
Pythagorean Theorem in right △SOA.

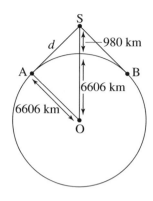

$$d^2 + 6606^2 = (6606 + 980)^2$$
$$d^2 + 6606^2 = 7586^2$$
$$d = \sqrt{7856^2 - 6606^2}$$
$$d \doteq 3729.36$$

The distance from the satellite to A is approximately 3729 km.

DISCUSSING THE IDEAS

1. In *Chapter 1*, you drew parabolas. Visualize a parabola. Could a tangent to a
   parabola be described as a line that intersects the parabola in exactly one
   point? Draw a diagram to demonstrate your answer to other members of
   your class or group.

2. Explain how you can find the centre of a circle if you are given two tangents
   to the circle from an external point. Use a diagram in your explanation.

3. In *Tutorial 6.3*, you confirmed that an inscribed angle in a semicircle is
   always a right angle. In the diagram below, visualize a circle passing
   through the points A, B, C, and D. Where is the centre of this circle?

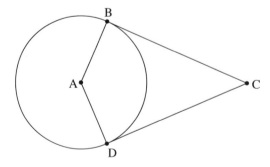

4. Why are you able to use the Pythagorean Theorem to calculate the lengths
   of tangent segments?

Practise Your Prior Skills

In the exercises that follow you will work with triangles and congruent figures.
Try these exercises for preliminary review.

1. Determine each value of *x*.

a)

b)

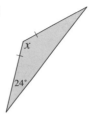

c)

d)

2. In each diagram, are the triangles congruent? If they are, explain why.

a)

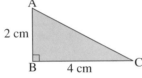

b)

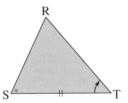

E X E R C I S E S

Checking Your Skills

1. Determine each value of *x* and *y*. Point O is the centre of each circle.

a)

b)

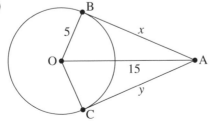

c)

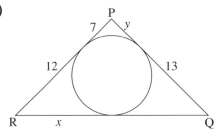

d)

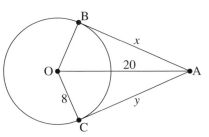

e)

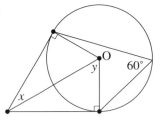

f)

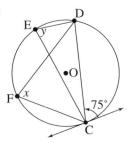

2. Determine each value of x and y. O is the centre of the circle.

a)

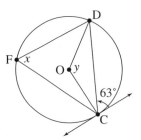

b)

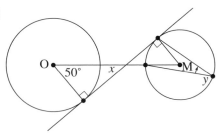

3. Determine each value of x and y. O is the centre of the circle.

a)

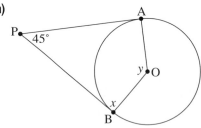

b)

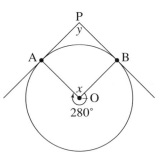

c)

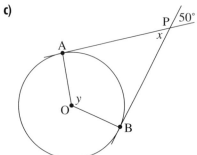

d)

e)

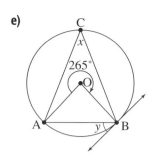

f)

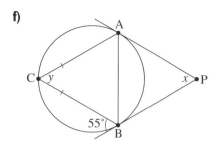

4. Recall from page 310, that the ancient Greeks regarded certain shapes as more pleasing than others. One such example is the golden rectangle. From the golden rectangle, a golden spiral can be formed. Complete part a to construct a golden spiral.

a) Draw rectangle ABCD where the width-to-length ratio is 1:1.6. A width of 15 cm and a length of 24 cm are suitable.

Mark points E and F on rectangle ABCD so that AEFD is a square.
With the compass point at F, and radius FE, draw minor arc ED.
AD and AE are tangents to the circle at D and E.
Mark points G and H so that EBGH is a square.
With the compass point at H, draw minor arc EG. BE and BG are tangents to the circle.
Continue this procedure of constructing squares and minor arcs until you are unable to draw any further.

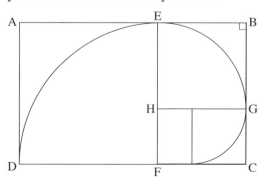

b) Where in nature have you seen this shape?

5. Eratosthenes (c. 276–192 B.C.) estimated the circumference of Earth as 37 680 km and used this value to calculate its radius. With modern day measurement tools and techniques, a more accurate value of Earth's radius can be determined.

An observer in an airplane at an altitude of 4300 m notes that the angle between her line of sight to the horizon and the vertical is 87.933 333 33°. What is Earth's radius to the nearest tenth of a kilometre? What assumptions are you making?

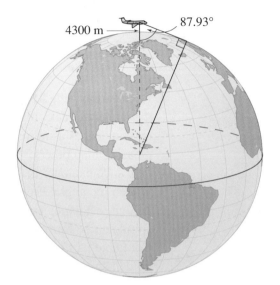

4300 m   87.93°

6. What length of strapping is needed to wrap once around three logs each with diameter 1.2 m? Would you cut the strapping to exactly this length? Explain.

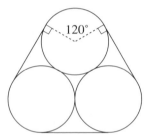

120°

7. a) We can use an angle property and a tangent property to construct a tangent from an external point to a circle. Draw a circle and mark an external point P. Join P to the centre, O, of the circle. Use OP as a diameter of another circle. Draw this new circle. Use the angle in a semicircle property and the angle between radius and tangent property. Complete the construction of a tangent from P to the circle centre O.

b) Recall the carpenter's square from page 320. Explain how you can use the results of part a, along with the carpenter's square, to draw a tangent to the circle, centre O, from an external point.

Extending Your Thinking

8. A pipe is supported by a brace at 45° to the horizontal and vertical. The pipe has an external diameter of 20 cm. Calculate the length of the brace AB. Express the answer to one decimal place.

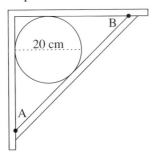

9. A belt on the crankshaft of a car transfers the motion of the engine to another component, such as the water pump, by encircling two wheels. The length of the belt depends on the diameter of the wheels and the distance between their centres.

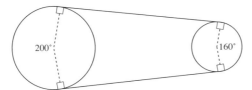

Two wheels, of radii 2 inches and 4 inches, are placed with their centres 12 inches apart. What is the length of the belt that encircles these wheels?

PROJECT

In this Tutorial you discovered the properties of tangents to a circle. You will need these skills when you return to the Chapter Project and in the following project in the Project Book.

• The Math Quilt

COMMUNICATING THE IDEAS

Draw labelled diagrams to summarize the tangent properties you investigated in this Tutorial.

Art and architectural features such as mosaics and tiled floors depend on repeating patterns of various shapes. The unit of the pattern may be a triangle, a rectangle, or a many-sided *polygon*. In this Tutorial, you will investigate some of the properties of polygons.

Investigation 1

Interior Angles in a Polygon

You will investigate the angles in a polygon.

1. Choose *convex polygons*. In a convex polygon each interior angle is less than 180°.

   a) Copy the following table into your notebook. Complete the table.
   In the second column, draw a sketch of a polygon with the number of sides given in column 1. Connect one vertex of this polygon to all of the other vertices. Note the number of triangles formed in column 3.
   We know that the sum of the interior angles in a triangle is 180°.
   We can find the sum of the interior angles of a polygon by multiplying:

   sum of interior angles = number of triangles formed × 180°

Number of Sides in a Polygon	Sketch	Number of Triangles Formed	Sum of the Interior Angles of the Polygon
3		1	(1)(180°) = 180°
4		2	(2)(180°) = 360°
5		3	(3)(180°) = 540°
6			
7			
8			
9			
10			
11			
12			

   b) Use your table to predict the number of triangles formed and the sum of the angles of a 17-sided convex polygon.

c) Write a formula for the sum of the interior angles of an *n*-sided convex polygon. Check the formula with your teacher.

2. The formula you wrote in exercise 1 can be rearranged and written in different ways.

a) Change your formula so that it contains 90° instead of 180°.

b) If you expressed your formula using brackets or parentheses, use the distributive property and simplify.

c) How many different arrangements of this formula can you find?

3. A *concave polygon* has at least one angle greater than 180°.

a) Draw a concave quadrilateral. By joining vertices, divide the quadrilateral into triangles that do not overlap. Determine the sum of the interior angles.

b) Use the formula you wrote in exercise 1c. Calculate the sum of the angles in a concave quadrilateral.

c) Repeat parts a and b for concave polygons with 5 sides, 6 sides, …, 12 sides.

d) For each polygon you drew, how do your answers for parts a and b compare?

e) Does the formula you wrote in exercise 1c for convex polygons apply to concave polygons? Explain.

In an earlier Tutorial, you discovered that a circle can always be drawn through the vertices of a triangle. If a circle can be drawn through the vertices of a quadrilateral, it is called a *cyclic quadrilateral*.

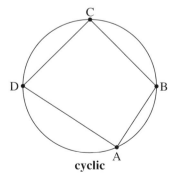

cyclic

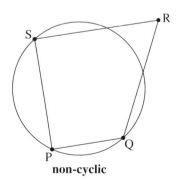

non-cyclic

This Investigation uses *The Geometer's Sketchpad*. If you use different dynamic geometry software, consult the manual for the appropriate commands and keystrokes.

Cyclic Quadrilaterals

You will investigate the opposite angles of a cyclic quadrilateral.

Step 1: Draw a circle and mark 4 points on it.

1. Open *The Geometer's Sketchpad*. From the **File** menu choose **New Sketch**.

2. Draw a circle. Label its centre A and the control point B.

3. From the **Construct** menu choose **Point On Object**. Label the point C. Select the circle and choose **Point On Object** twice. Label the points D and E.

Step 2: Construct a cyclic quadrilateral.

4. Select points B, C, D, E in the order they appear on the circle. From the **Construct** menu choose **Segment**.

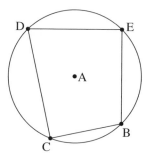

Step 3: Find the sum of opposite angles of a cyclic quadrilateral.

5. Find the measures of the two opposite angles in the quadrilateral.

Select C, D, E (in that order), then choose **Angle** from the **Measure** menu.

Select C, B, E (in that order), then choose **Angle** from the **Measure** menu. Add these angle measures.

6. Find the measures of the other two opposite angles, ∠DCB and ∠DEB. Add these angle measures. What do you notice?

7. Visualize repeating this construction for different sets of points and for different circles. What do you expect to observe about the sum of the measures of opposite angles of a cyclic quadrilateral?

Step 4: Check your prediction.

8. To check your prediction for different cyclic quadrilaterals, select one vertex of the quadrilateral and move it around the circle. To check your prediction for other circles select the centre A and move it around the screen.

9. Write a conjecture about the opposite angles in a cyclic quadrilateral.

In the Investigations, you confirmed the following properties of polygons.

Polygon Properties

In any polygon with n sides, the sum of the angles is $(2n - 4)$ right angles, or $180°(n - 2)$.

The opposite angles of a cyclic quadrilateral are supplementary, that is, the sum of the two angles is $180°$.

Example

Sum of the Interior Angles of a Polygon

A field of study in mathematics that is fairly new (about 94 years old) is called *fractals*. One well-known fractal is the Koch snowflake curve, believed by many to be the first fractal. One aspect of fractals that fascinates mathematicians is that the perimeters are infinite yet the areas are finite! The first four steps in the construction of the Koch snowflake curve are shown below. The first polygon is an equilateral triangle. Visualize these steps continuing indefinitely. After each step, the polygon comes closer and closer to the snowflake curve.

a) How was each polygon formed from the previous polygon?

b) How many sides does each polygon have? How do the measures of the sides compare?

c) Predict the number of sides the 5th polygon will have.

d) What are the measures of the angles in each polygon?

e) What is the sum of the angles in each polygon?

S O L U T I O N

a) Each side of the polygon is trisected and an equilateral triangle is drawn on the middle trisected segment. This middle segment is then erased.

b) Each side of one polygon transforms into 4 sides. The numbers of sides are 3, 12, 48, 192. Each side in the new polygon is one-third the size of each side in the preceding polygon.

c) The number of sides increases by a factor of 4 each time. In the fifth polygon, there are 4×192 sides $= 768$ sides.

d) The first polygon is an equilateral triangle, so each angle is 60°.
The second polygon has 6 angles that are each 60°, and 6 angles that are each 360° − 120°, or 240°.
The third and fourth polygons comprise angles that have the same measures as the second polygon: 60° and 240°.

e) Use the formula for the sum of the angles in a polygon with n sides: $180°(n − 2)$.
For the first polygon $n = 3$: $180°(3 − 2) = 180°$
For the second polygon $n = 12$: $180°(12 − 2) = 1800°$
For the third polygon $n = 48$: $180°(48 − 2) = 8280°$
For the fourth polygon $n = 192$: $180°(192 − 2) = 34\,200°$

DISCUSSING THE IDEAS

1. A certain cyclic quadrilateral has diagonals that are diameters of the circle. What is this special kind of quadrilateral? What other special kind of quadrilateral might it be?

2. You can always construct a circle that passes through three non-collinear points in a plane. Is it possible to draw a circle through four non-collinear points in a plane? Explain.

3. Show with illustrations that not all quadrilaterals are cyclic.

4. In the Example:

a) Explain how we know that some angles in the second polygon measure 240°.

b) Explain how we know that the angles in the third and fourth polygons have the same measures as those in the second polygon.

Practise Your Prior Skills

In the exercises that follow, you will work with supplementary angles. Try these exercises for preliminary review.

1. Determine the value of x.

a)

b)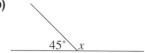

If you need to review "supplementary angles" look in the Student Reference.

STUDENT REFERENCE

Checking Your Skills

1. What is the sum of the angles in each polygon?

a)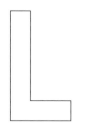

b)

c)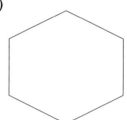

d)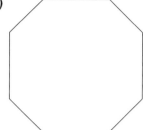

2. Determine each value of *x* and *y*. Point O is the centre of the circle.

a)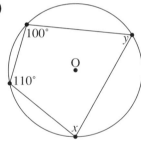

b)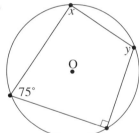

c)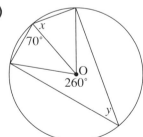

d)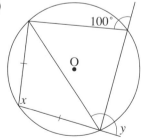

3. Engineers often need to know angles before they can make calculations of a force. The diagram below shows a cross-section of a dam. Use the information in the diagram to calculate $\angle DEF$.

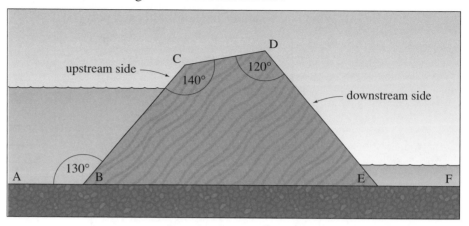

A *tessellation* is a tiling pattern in which the same figure is repeated over and over to cover a plane with no gaps or overlaps. An example is shown below.

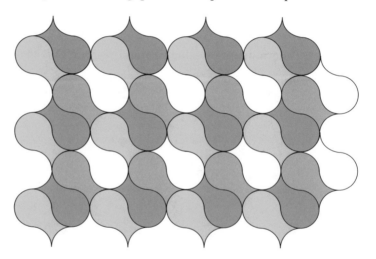

4. A *regular polygon* has all sides equal and all angles equal. To tessellate a plane with regular polygons, the sum of the angles around a vertex cannot be more than 360°. Which combinations of regular polygons would tessellate around a vertex? Create a tessellation that uses regular polygons.

5. In a benzene molecule, C_6H_6, all 12 atoms lie in the same plane with the 6 carbon nuclei as vertices of a regular hexagon. What is the angle formed by the two segments that join 3 consecutive carbon nuclei?

6. When tessellating a plane with regular polygons, you need to know the measure of the interior angle of the polygon. What is the formula for determining the measure of the interior angle in any regular polygon?

Extending Your Thinking

7. Design your own tessellation. You can use either a computer graphics program or the drawing package of a word processing program.

   a) Draw a polygon with an even number of sides, such as a rectangle, a parallelogram, or a hexagon.

   b) Draw a simple shape on one side of your polygon.

   c) Copy the shape onto the opposite side.

   d) Draw a simple shape along another side of the polygon and copy it onto the opposite side.

   e) Erase or delete the original polygon. Add details to your design.

   f) Copy the design and tessellate.

PROJECT

In this Tutorial you discovered some properties of polygons. You will need these skills when you do the Chapter Project and the following projects in the Project Book.

- The Math Quilt
- Boxer Shorts
- Designing a Newsletter
- Crystallography

COMMUNICATING THE IDEAS

Draw labelled diagrams of two special types of quadrilateral that are always cyclic. Write to explain why they are always cyclic.

The Details

You will now create your design using the properties of chords, angles, tangents, and polygons that you learned in *Tutorials 6.2* to *6.5*. Use your sketches. You may wish to add more details or change your design.

You may use a computer graphics program or the drawing package of a word processing program, or you may prefer to draw your design accurately by hand.

Use colour to enhance the design.

Make a copy of your design and indicate on it the properties of circles and polygons used.

Your finished project will include:

- the "work of art"
- a photocopy of the "work of art" with the properties used indicated on the photocopy
- a brief history of the form you used along with some examples

Career Skills

Technicians with skills in Computer Aided Design (CAD) find employment with architectural, engineering, and design companies. An understanding of the properties of geometric figures and the ability to use colour effectively are important in design-related occupations.

What Do I Need to Know?

Tutorial	Skills and Concepts	Important Results and Formulas
6.1	• Practise geometry constructions using dynamic software	
6.2	• Discover the properties of chords in a circle	• The perpendicular from the centre of a circle to a chord bisects the chord • The perpendicular bisector of any chord passes through the centre of a circle
6.3	• Discover the properties of angles in a circle	• The measure of the central angle in a circle is twice the measure of the inscribed angle subtended by the same arc • An angle inscribed in a semicircle is a right angle • Inscribed angles subtended by the same arc are equal
6.4	• Discover the properties of tangent lines to a circle	• A tangent to a circle is perpendicular to the radius at the point of tangency • From an external point, the tangents to a circle are equal • The angle between a tangent and a chord of a circle is equal to the inscribed angle on the opposite side of the chord
6.5	• Discover the properties of polygons in a circle	• The sum of the interior angles in a polygon is $(2n - 4)$ right angles, or $180°(n - 2)$ • The opposite angles of a cyclic quadrilateral are supplementary (their sum is 180°)

What Should I Be Able To Do?

When you have completed the work in Chapter 6, you should be able to solve the problems that follow. Part A is investigative.

As you work through the exercises, refer to the *Student Reference*, the *Utilities*, and the *Tutorials* as necessary.

Part A

1. There are many properties of circles that have not been explored in this chapter. You will investigate one of these properties, using *The Geometer's Sketchpad* or similar software.

   a) Draw a circle. Label the centre of the circle.

   b) Draw two different chords (not diameters) that have the same length.

   c) Connect the midpoint of each chord with the centre of the circle.

   d) Measure the lengths of these line segments. What do you notice?

   e) Visualize repeating the construction for different circles and line segments. What do you expect to observe?

   f) Check your prediction with other examples.

   g) Make a conjecture about equal chords in a circle.

Part B

2. Determine each value of *x* to the nearest tenth of a unit. Point O is the centre of the circle.

   a) 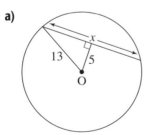   **b)** 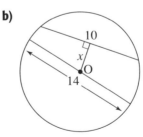   **c)**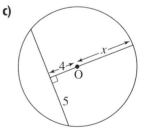

3. An archaeologist has found a fragment that looks as if it was part of a circular object.

   Trace this picture into your notebook. This picture has been drawn accurately. What is the radius of the object?

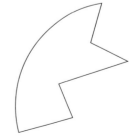

4. A light bulb is at the centre of the ceiling of a room that is 8 feet wide. This is illustrated in the following cross-sectional diagram. The light bulb is at P and QR represents the floor.

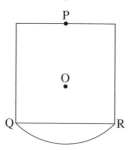

O is the centre of the circle drawn through P, Q, and R. The line through P is a tangent to the circle. The radius of the circle is 5 feet.

a) Calculate the distance from O to RQ.

b) Calculate the height of the room.

5. Determine each value of *x*. Point O is the centre of each circle.

a)
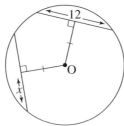

b)
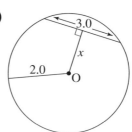

c)
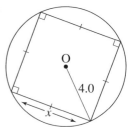

6. Determine each value of *x* and *y*. Point O is the centre of each circle.

a)
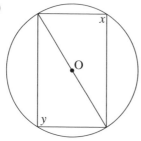

b)
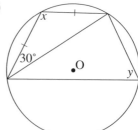

c)
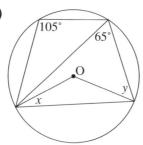

d)
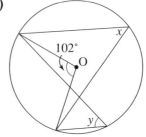

7. Determine each value of x and y. Point O is the centre of each circle.

a)
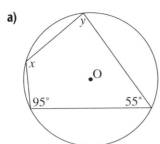

b)
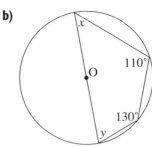

c)

d)
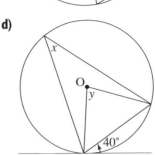

8. The radius of Earth is approximately 6606 km. A satellite is in orbit around Earth. Its distance to point A is 3600 km. What is the distance (to the nearest kilometre) from the satellite to a point directly below it on Earth?

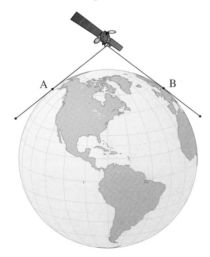

9. A circular plate is packaged in a box with a square base with sides 15 cm. The sides of the plate touch the sides of the box. How far is the centre of the plate from a corner of the box?

10. a) Write a formula for the sum of the interior angles in a polygon with n sides.

b) Write the steps to change this formula into one that uses 90°.

c) What is the sum of the interior angles of a nonagon (9 sides)?

11. Determine each value of *x* and *y*. Point O is the centre of each circle.

a)

x

115°

O

y

b)

110°

O

50°

x

y

12. A circular disk has diameter 12 cm. The disk is packed in a box with a square base so that the disk touches the sides of the box. What is the length of the side of the square base?

Part C

The Chapter Project combines many skills and concepts in a single problem. Here are samples of student work. Review these samples to gain insights into your own project work.

1. Is the design appropriate for its intended use? Has colour been used effectively?

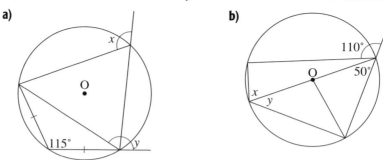

2. Have the appropriate properties of circles and polygons been indicated on the photocopy of the design? Is the student's work accurate? Examine the student's report on the history of the design medium. Write a summary of this student's work.

Properties:

$\overline{CB} = 5.5cm$

$\overline{AB} = \overline{AB} = 7.4cm$

$\angle COB = 88°$

$\angle CAB = 44°$

$\overline{ED} = \overline{FD} = 12.5cm$

$\overline{DG} = 9cm$

$\overline{AG} = 8cm$ (diameter)

$\overline{OA} = \overline{OG} = \overline{OC} = \overline{OB} = 4cm$ (radius)

$\overline{AC}, \overline{AB},$ and $\overline{CB}$ are chords

$\angle COB = 2\angle CAB$

$\overline{ED} = \overline{FD}$ are tangents

$\overline{AD}$ is a perpindicular bisector of chord $\overline{CB}$

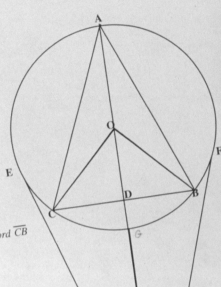

Neon Signs

Neon is a chemical that makes up part of the earth's atmosphere. The chemical was discovered in 1898 by Sir William Raleigh and Morris Travis in Britain. Neon lighting was first introduced in 1910 by Georges Claude in Paris.

Neon lighting and advertising became commonplace since its discovery because they are easier to read from farther away. It has also been used by airports as it cuts through the fog better. Neon signs were first introduced as an alternative to incandescent light.

The methods used today to make the signs is very similar to the methods used fifty years ago. A glass bender joins and bends sections of tubing together to create the desired pattern. A neon signs contains neon, and also some levels of argon, mercury, and phosphors are used to create the variety of colours. Once the tube is sealed, electricity is used to create a discharge in the gas which lights it up.

Although the signs seem expensive at first, they can be repaired for little cost, and can last up to 20 years. This why it is popular "Art" form in use today.

7 Measurement

Overview

You should do at least one project that uses the skills you learn in this chapter. **To cover the curriculum, you should complete Estimating the Volume of Timber in a Woodlot in the Project Book.** Other recommended projects in the Project Book are:

- Barn Design
- Indoor Climbing Walls

Giant Set Design

Several movies, such as *Honey I Shrunk the Kids*, and *Gulliver's Travels* are based on the idea that the characters are much smaller than their surroundings. One way to make people appear much smaller than they actually are is to surround them with everyday objects that are much larger than usual. Set designers and stage carpenters must design and build models of everyday objects to an appropriate scale that fits the stage. Careful measurements of the original objects must be taken. Small errors in the original measurements will result in large errors in the giant replica.

In this project, you will design and construct a giant replica of a common object as part of a set for a theatrical production. You will use scale, orthographic diagrams, and maximum and minimum values of measurements. Here are some initial points to consider.

- Describe other forms of entertainment where giant replicas of everyday objects could be used.

- When do you think it might be appropriate to reduce all the objects on a theatrical set?

- Other methods can be used in movies or on television to enlarge a person or reduce the surroundings. Describe other methods you know.

- Suppose you wish to recreate a giant's kitchen. List the things that you must consider before you decide on an appropriate scale for the models.

- Describe the processes that you think should precede the construction of a giant replica.

- Suppose you have to create a giant replica of a match. What properties should the material have?

CHAPTER PROJECT

To complete this Chapter Project, you will measure an object and draw an accurate orthographic diagram of it. Complete *Tutorials 7.1* to *7.3* to develop an understanding of the related skills. You will return to this Chapter Project on page 380.

FYI Visit: www.awl.com/canada/school/connections

You can start your research on our Internet site: Click on <u>MATHLINKS</u> then the *Applied Mathematics 11* logo. Select a topic under "Giant Set Design."

Enlarging and Reducing in Two Dimensions

Have you ever used a photocopier to reduce or enlarge a diagram? The result is a *scale drawing*. These are used frequently in industry. A scale drawing is a reproduction of a diagram. It is either larger or smaller than the original, but has the same shape. Each dimension of the original figure is multiplied by the same *scale factor*. In order to visualize the actual figure, you need to know the scale of the scale drawing.

Practise Your Prior Skills

You will use ratios and convert measurement units. Try these exercises as preliminary review.

1. Write each ratio in lowest terms.

   a) 76 : 100   **b)** 30 : 24   **c)** 1.5 : 0.5

2. The ratio of the mass of an elephant's brain to its body mass is 1 : 600. Estimate the brain mass of a 1650-kg elephant.

3. The ratio of boys to girls in a class is 7 : 25. What fraction of the class represents girls?

4. Convert 3.5 km to centimetres.

5. A beetle is 13.4 mm long. What is its length in metres?

STUDENT REFERENCE

If you need to review "ratio," the "metric system," or the "imperial system" for the relationship between imperial and metric units of length, look in the Student Reference.

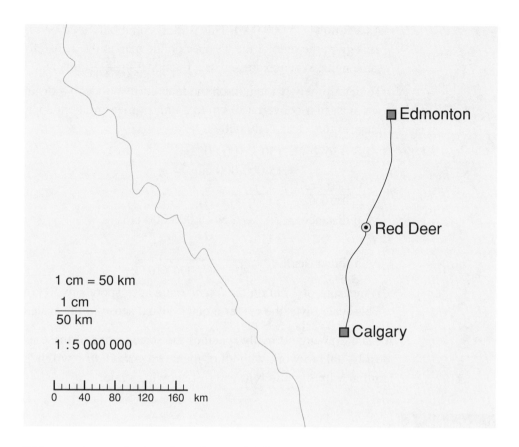

1 cm = 50 km

$\dfrac{1 \text{ cm}}{50 \text{ km}}$

1 : 5 000 000

This map is a scale drawing of part of Alberta. The scale of any map can be specified in four equivalent ways:

- As a **statement** (1 cm = 50 km). This indicates that 1 cm on the map corresponds to an actual distance of 50 km on the ground. The first number always refers to the distance on the map, the second to the actual distance.

   On the map, the straight-line distance between Calgary and Edmonton is about 5.8 cm. Thus, the actual straight-line distance between the two cities is 5.8 × 50 km = 290 km.

- As a **rate** $\dfrac{1 \text{ cm}}{50 \text{ km}}$. The numerator gives the distance on the map and the denominator shows the actual distance.

   To calculate the scale factor, you need to change the units so they are the same in the numerator and the denominator. You can use the CONVERT program for the TI-83 or the conversion table in the Student Reference.

$$\begin{aligned}
1 \text{ km} &= 100\ 000 \text{ cm} \\
50 \text{ km} &= 50 \times 100\ 000 \text{ cm} \\
&= 5\ 000\ 000 \text{ cm}
\end{aligned}$$

   The scale factor is $\dfrac{1}{5\ 000\ 000}$. This can also be expressed as a decimal (0.000 000 2) or in scientific notation (2.0×10^{-7}).

- As a **ratio** (1 : 5 000 000). This is most commonly used on scale drawings. This gives the ratio of the distance on the map to the actual distance in the same units. When expressed as a fraction, $\frac{1}{5\,000\,000}$, this ratio is the scale factor.

To determine what length on the map corresponds to a distance of 150 km, we must first convert 150 km to a unit of measurement appropriate to the map, in this case, centimetres:

$$150 \text{ km} = 150 \times 100\,000 \text{ cm}$$
$$= 15\,000\,000 \text{ cm}$$
$$\frac{\text{Map distance}}{15\,000\,000} = \frac{1}{5\,000\,000}$$
$$\text{Map distance} = \frac{1}{5\,000\,000} \times 15\,000\,000 \text{ cm}$$
$$= 3 \text{ cm}$$

- As a **linear scale** ⊢┼┼┼┼┼┼┼┼┼┼┼┼┼⊢
  0   40   80   120   160 km.

A measure of 1 cm on the *linear scale* corresponds to 50 km on the ground. This scale gives the reader a quick visual sense of the scale of the map.

A scale drawing normally specifies the scale in one of these four ways. You must be able to work with all of them. *Investigation 1* will help you to become familiar with the different ways of showing scale.

Investigation 1   **Using a Map Scale**

Surveyors use a measuring device called a "tight-chain" to determine boundaries of plots of land. Two surveyors determine that a proposed building site is rectangular, measuring 175 m by 50 m. To make a scale drawing of the site, they use a scale of 1 : 2500.

1. What are the dimensions of the building site in centimetres?

2. What is the scale factor of the scale drawing?

3. Use the scale to calculate the length and width of the rectangle in the scale drawing.

4. Use a metric ruler to draw the rectangle to scale.

5. Below the scale drawing, display the scale in the following 3 forms: statement, ratio, and linear scale.

6. Predict what happens to the dimensions of the rectangle in the scale drawing if the scale is changed to

  a) 1 : 5000   **b)** 1 : 1250

7. Check your predictions from 6a and 6b by drawing the rectangle using the new scale.

Creating a Floor Plan

You will work in groups of 3 or 4 to create a scale drawing using an appropriate scale.

You will need an imperial tape measure.

Choose a room that has a shape more complicated than a simple rectangle. This could be your math classroom, lunchroom, gymnasium, or some other room.

1. Make a working sketch of the floor plan to show the shape of the room.

2. Measure the dimensions of the room to the nearest inch. Record the measurements in the appropriate places on your sketch.

3. Your scale drawing is to be prepared on an $8\frac{1}{2}$- by 11-inch piece of paper. Decide on an appropriate scale for the floor plan.

4. What is the scale factor for your plan?

5. Use this scale factor to convert each measured dimension to its scale dimension.

6. To draw your accurate floor plan, use these scale measurements.

7. Choose one of the four forms to indicate the scale you used.

Example

Reduce an object according to a given scale

A table tennis table measures 2.7 m by 1.5 m. Use a scale of 1 : 50 to create a scale drawing of a table tennis table.

SOLUTION

A table tennis table is rectangular in shape.

The scale is 1 : 50, so the scale factor is $\frac{1}{50}$.

Thus, $\frac{\text{Drawing length}}{\text{Actual length}} = \frac{1}{50}$

The length is 2.7 m, or 270 cm.

$$\frac{\text{Drawing length}}{270 \text{ cm}} = \frac{1}{50}$$

Drawing length $= \frac{1}{50} \times 270$ cm

$$= 5.4 \text{ cm}$$

The width is 1.5 m, or 150 cm.

$$\frac{\text{Drawing width}}{150 \text{ cm}} = \frac{1}{50}$$

Drawing width $= \frac{1}{50} \times 150$ cm

$$= 3 \text{ cm}$$

The scale drawing of the table tennis table is shown below. The court and net placement markings are also indicated.

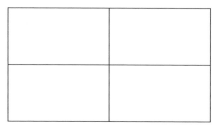

Scale 1 : 50

DISCUSSING THE IDEAS

1. A car's odometer shows that the distance from Edmonton to Calgary is 299 km. In the introduction to this Tutorial we determined the distance to be 290 km. Why do you think these numbers are not the same?

2. Give an example of an appropriate use of each format for stating scale.

3. Explain how you determined the dimensions of the scale drawing in *Investigation 1*.

4. In *Investigation 2*, explain how you arrived at an appropriate scale for your floor plan.

5. A map is a reduction of reality. Suppose a map has a scale of 1 : 50 000. You could reverse your viewpoint and think of reality as an enlargement of the map. What would be the scale of the enlargement?

6. The scale of a scale drawing is given in ratio form. How can you tell, just by looking at the numbers in the ratio, whether the scale drawing is a reduction or an enlargement of reality?

Checking Your Skills

1. A rectangular classroom measures 9 m by 8 m.

   a) Make a scale drawing of the classroom using a scale of 1 : 50.

   b) Make a scale drawing of the classroom using a scale of 1 : 100.

2. A volleyball court measures 18 m by 9 m. Make a scale drawing of the court using a scale of 1 cm = 2 m.

3. The top view of the car shown below is not drawn to scale.

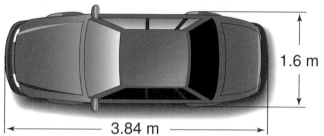

1.6 m

3.84 m

   a) Assume that the car is 3.84 m long and 1.6 m wide. Make a scale drawing of the car using a scale of 1 : 32.

   b) The front and back wheels on the car are 2.88 m apart. How far apart should they be on the scale drawing?

4. Make an accurate scale drawing of the L-shaped living room shown in the sketch below. Use a scale factor of 3.5.

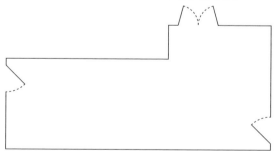

5. Obtain a paper clip. Measure its dimensions. Suppose you make a scale drawing of the paper clip using a scale of 5 : 1.

   a) Will the drawing be a reduction or an enlargement?

   b) Calculate the dimensions of the scale drawing of the paper clip.

   c) Make the scale drawing of the paper clip on grid paper.

6. The blueprint for a specialized tool is shown.

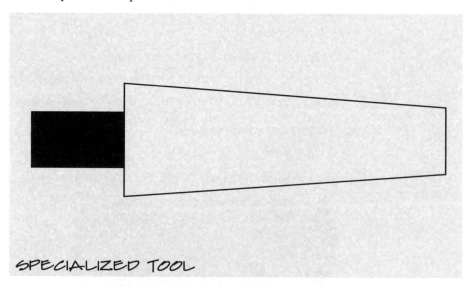

SPECIALIZED TOOL

The scale of this blueprint is 1 : 2. Make an actual-sized drawing of the tool.

7. A clothing company designed this logo for its jeans.

The marketing team decided to use this logo for sweatshirts. Each dimension of the logo was increased by a scale factor of 1.5. Draw the new version of the logo.

8. Use surveyor's chains, measuring tapes, or other linear measuring devices to measure a chosen plot of land. Make a scale drawing of the plot.

9. Use a national, provincial, or territorial road map.

   a) Plan a trip to visit five towns located on the map, then return home.

   b) Using roads and highways, trace your route on a separate sheet of paper.

   c) Use the scale of the map to estimate the actual distance of your trip as accurately as possible.

   d) The phrase "as the crow flies" refers to the straight-line distance between two places. Estimate the total distance of your trip "as the crow flies." How does this compare with your answer to part c?

Extending Your Thinking

10. Draw an outline of your hand on an $8\frac{1}{2}$- by 11-inch piece of paper and give it to your teacher to reduce or enlarge on a photocopier. Determine the scale of the enlargement or reduction by completing the following steps.

   a) Copy and complete the table.

	Measure on photocopy (to nearest tenth cm)	Measure on original (to nearest tenth cm)	Measure on photocopy / Measure on original in lowest terms
Width of wrist at its narrowist point			
Width of index finger at its widest point			
Length of ring finger (4th finger)			

   b) Are the three ratios significantly different? Explain.

   c) Write each ratio so that its smaller term is 1. That is, divide both terms in the ratio by the smaller term.

   e) Determine the mean of the three ratios to one decimal place. Compare this result for the scale of the photocopy to the scale factor set on the photocopy machine. If the results do not agree, explain why.

PROJECT

In this Tutorial, you have worked with scales and made scale drawings. You will use these skills when you return to the Chapter Project and in the following projects in the Project Book.

• Barn Design

• Indoor Climbing Walls

COMMUNICATING THE IDEAS

List at least three different uses for scale drawings or scale factors. What are the typical scale factors used in each situation?

Plans and diagrams are used frequently in industry. Construction workers use them to build homes; engineering technicians use them in the design studio and workshop; and scientists use them to represent structures.

A good diagram is essential for good planning. It may save time and money by exposing potential flaws or trouble spots. Before anything is built, diagrams are often produced to give instructions, to provide a visual representation, and to guide the construction process. These initial diagrams are called *blueprints,* because in the past, they showed white lines on a blue background.

A *pictorial diagram* represents the shape of a three-dimensional object in two dimensions, as viewed from one particular position. A pictorial diagram gives the impression of three dimensions. Features are drawn as they appear, so the features often appear distorted. A round hole may be drawn as an oval, or perpendicular edges may not appear to meet at 90°. A pictorial diagram does not show holes or other features inside an object, no matter which perspective is used.

The pictorial diagram to the right represents a three-dimensional object.

To remedy these shortcomings, orthographic diagrams are used in industry to provide more detailed information.

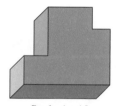

Scale 1 : 10

An *orthographic diagram* shows up to six views of the object. Usually three views are sufficient: the top, front, and side views. It also shows internal features. The views of an orthographic diagram are shown in positions relative to each other. Each view is drawn as you would see it if you looked directly at it. None of the views attempts to give the illusion of three-dimensions.

The orthographic diagram (right) represents the object in the pictorial diagram shown above.

Notice that all the outside edges, including those that indicate changes in level, are shown in the orthographic diagram by solid lines. The broken lines show how the different views are aligned. The internal features of an object, such as holes, are shown as broken lines in orthographic diagrams.

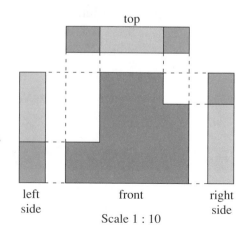

top

left side   front   right side

Scale 1 : 10

Example 1

Draw an orthographic diagram of an object with holes through it.

Draw an orthographic diagram of this object. Show the square and circular holes through it.

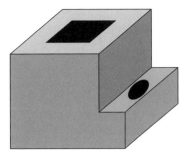

SOLUTION

Broken lines show internal holes or indentations in objects. They also show how the holes extend through the object. Solid lines indicate the external features of the object.

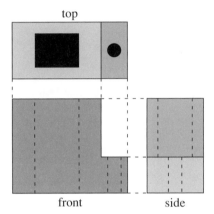

top

front   side

Example 2 **Draw an orthographic diagram of an object with a circular cross-section.**

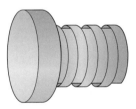

a) Draw an orthographic diagram of this screw.

b) Circular objects, like this screw, usually require only two views in an orthographic diagram. Why?

c) Suppose you use this screw to attach one arm on a pair of sunglasses. Estimate the scale of the diagram.

SOLUTION

a)

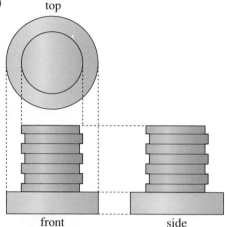

b) The front and side views are identical, so only one view needs to be shown.

c) A typical eyeglass screw is about 2 mm across its head. The same distance on the scale drawing is 2 cm. The scale is 2 cm = 2 mm, or 20 mm : 2 mm, which reduces to 10 : 1.

Example 3 **Decreasing the size of a machine part**

Below is an orthographic diagram of a U-shaped joint. A mechanical engineer determines that the joint is too large and must be reduced in size. She calculates that 0.8 is the scale factor for the reduction.

a) On the diagram, measure lengths a and b to the nearest centimetre.

b) Use the scale in the diagram. What are the lengths of a and b on the joint?

c) Use the new scale factor. What are the lengths of a and b on the smaller joint?

d) Suppose you used the same orthographic diagram for the new joint. What would the scale of the diagram be?

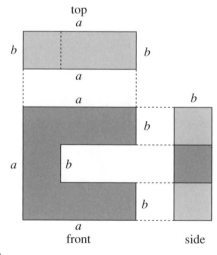

Scale 2 : 1

a) To the nearest centimetre, a is 3 cm and b is 1 cm.

b) For the scale 2 : 1, the scale factor is $\frac{2}{1}$, or 2.

$$\text{Scale factor} = \frac{\text{Drawing length}}{\text{Actual length}}$$

For length a, $\frac{2}{1} = \frac{3 \text{ cm}}{\text{Actual length}}$

Actual length = 1.5 cm

For length b, $\frac{2}{1} = \frac{1 \text{ cm}}{\text{Actual length}}$

Actual length = 0.5 cm

c) The scale factor is 0.8.

The length a on the smaller joint is

1.5 cm $\times$ 0.8 = 1.2 cm.

The length b on the smaller joint is

$0.5 \times 0.8 = 0.4$ cm.

d) The new scale is:

Length on drawing : Length on object

= 3 cm : 1.2 cm

Multiply by 10 and remove units.

= 30 : 12

Divide by 6.

The scale is 5 : 2.

DISCUSSING THE IDEAS

1. Describe the advantages and disadvantages of orthographic and pictorial diagrams.

2. Which types of orthographic diagrams require only two points of view? Do you think any type of orthographic diagram would require more than three points of view? Can you think of any that may need five, or even six points of view?

3. Suppose a scale drawing of an object is available. The object is to be enlarged or reduced. How can the scale of the drawing be adjusted so that it still represents the object? Use the solution to *Example 3* to help with your explanation.

Checking Your Skills

1. Use the same scale to draw orthographic diagrams for each object.

a)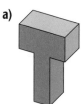

b)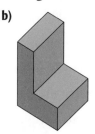

2. Use the same scale to draw a pictorial diagram of each object.

a)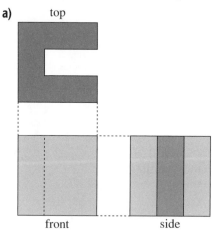

b)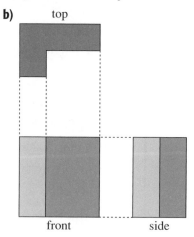

3. Your city wishes you to construct its new swimming pool. The pool's surface will have the shape of two overlapping circles, as shown.

The bottom of the swimming pool in the main pool slopes gradually down from a depth of 1 m in the shallow end to 2 m at the neck. The bottom of the pool in the diving tank has a depth of 2 m all around the edge and gradually slopes to 4 m at the centre.

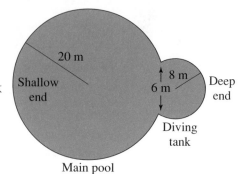

a) Sketch a rough pictorial diagram of the swimming pool.

b) Choose an appropriate scale and draw an accurate orthographic diagram to this scale. Label the diagram with the actual dimensions of the pool.

4. A sphere has a spherical cavity inside it. The diameter of the cavity is much smaller than the diameter of the sphere. Draw an orthographic diagram of the sphere in each of the following situations.

a) The centre of the cavity is at the centre of the sphere.

b) The centre of the cavity is not at the centre of the sphere.

5. From the scale drawing below, construct an actual-size model of the box.

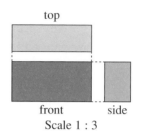

top

front   side

Scale 1 : 3

6. Architects, engineers, and designers often build a clay model to visualize an object. Use modelling clay to build a model of the object shown in the plan below.

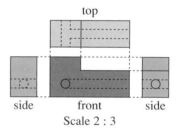

top

side   front   side

Scale 2 : 3

7. Choose an object in your classroom or an object from home. Measure the object. Choose a suitable scale, then make an orthographic diagram of the object.

Extending Your Thinking

8. Design and create an object for which the orthographic diagram requires more than three views. First draw the orthographic diagram and then relevant pictorial diagrams. Finally, build a model of the object.

PROJECT

In this Tutorial, you enlarged and reduced three-dimensional objects and drew orthographic diagrams. You will use these skills in the Chapter Project and in the following project in the Project Book.

• Indoor Climbing Walls

COMMUNICATING THE IDEAS

Design your own object that will show as many of the conventions relating to orthographic diagrams as possible. Draw both pictorial and orthographic diagrams of the object. Write a paragraph to explain how each diagram represents the key features of the object.

The Uncertainty of a Measurement

International trade is important in our society. Suppose that a computer part is manufactured in Asia for use in a computer built in Canada. The Canadian manufacturer will specify the dimensions of the computer part, and the Asian manufacturer will try to meet those specifications. How can we be sure that measurements in Canada are the same as those in Asia?

Since 1889, an international organization, the General Conference on Weights and Measures, has set *measurement standards*. In 1889, the metre was defined as the distance between two very fine marks on a bar made of platinum-iridium — an alloy that resists rusting and other changes. Thirty copies of this standard bar were made and sent to laboratories in various parts of the world. These standard bars were kept in carefully controlled conditions. They were then used to ensure that all devices for measuring length had the same length, no matter where they were made in the world. Other standards were set for mass, time, temperature, and other basic physical quantities.

Today the standard for the metre is the distance travelled by light in a vacuum in a certain fraction of a second. This standard is considered more accurate, constant, and easily reproducible around the world than the old one.

All measurements are approximate. For example, if you measure the length of this rectangle, you will find that it is approximately 2.3 cm. This means that it is closer to 2.3 cm than to either 2.2 cm or 2.4 cm. We say that the length is 2.3 cm *to the nearest tenth of a centimetre*. This means that the actual length is between 2.25 cm and 2.35 cm. One way to specify the uncertainty of a measurement is to use a range of values. You could quote the measurement as (2.3 ± 0.05) cm. This shows that you are sure that the greatest possible measurement is

$(2.30 + 0.05)$ cm = 2.35 cm,

and the least possible measurement is

$(2.30 - 0.05)$ cm = 2.25 cm.

Measurement error is the difference between a measure and its true value. We do not know the true value of a measure, so we cannot know the true measurement error. We use the *uncertainty of measurement* to approximate the measurement error. If the uncertainty is not stated, we assume that it is one-half of the precision of the instrument used to make the measure. The *precision* is equal to the smallest scale division of the measuring instrument. So a measurement of 104.2°C has a precision of 0.1°C and an uncertainty of 0.05°C.

Consider the following situation, where the length of a bolt is measured using a ruler.

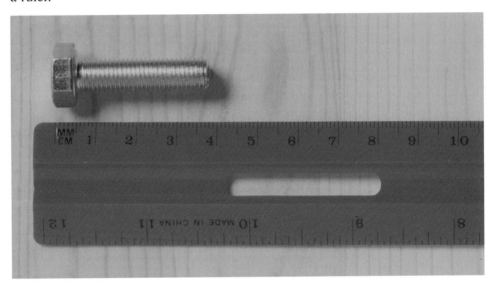

The precision of the ruler is 0.1 cm. Based on this precision, we state that the bolt is 3.8 cm long. The length could be a minimum of 3.75 cm or a maximum of 3.85 cm. The uncertainty is 0.05 cm.

> If the uncertainty of measurement is not stated, we assume that it is one-half the precision of the instrument.

It is accepted practice to quote the same number of decimal places for the measurement and the uncertainty, so we should quote 3.80 cm instead of 3.8 cm for the measurement.

The length of the bolt is quoted as (3.80 ± 0.05) cm.

If you need a more precise measurement, you must use a measuring instrument with smaller scale divisions.

Adding and Subtracting Measurements with the Same Precision

You will investigate the effect of adding or subtracting measurements on the uncertainty of the result. You need a metric ruler with a precision of 1 mm.

1. Use a metric ruler to measure the length and width of your textbook. Record the measurements in your notebook.

2. Based on the precision of your ruler, what is the uncertainty for each measurement? Write your measurements using the ± notation.

3. Determine the limits for the length and width of your textbook.

4. The semi-perimeter of your textbook is the sum of the length and width of the book. Use your results from exercise 3 to find the maximum and minimum lengths of the semi-perimeter of your textbook.

5. What is the average length of the semi-perimeter?

6. Find the difference between the average and minimum lengths of the semi-perimeter. This is the uncertainty for the semi-perimeter. Write the semi-perimeter using the ± notation.

7. What are the limits of the difference between the length and width of your textbook? Write the difference between the length and width of your textbook using the ± notation.

8. How is the uncertainty of the sum of the length and width related to the individual uncertainties of the original measurements of length and width?

9. How is the uncertainty of the difference between the length and width related to the individual uncertainties of the original measurements of length and width?

10. Based on your observations in exercises 8 and 9, make a statement about how the uncertainty of a sum or difference of measurements is related to the individual uncertainties of the measurements.

In *Investigation 1*, you used the same ruler to take measurements, so the measurements had the same precision. Next you will investigate what happens to uncertainties if the instruments used to make individual measurements have different precisions.

Investigation 2 **Adding and Subtracting Measurements with Different Precision**

You will need a metric ruler with a precision of 1 mm, and a metric tape or metre stick with a precision of 1 cm.

  1. Repeat *Investigation 1* using one device to measure the length and the other device to measure the width. Use only the precision indicated by the device. For simplicity, give both measurements in centimetres.

  2. Are your conclusions the same as those of exercise 10 of *Investigation 1*?

  3. Predict what will happen to the uncertainty of the result when you add or subtract two measurements.

  4. Check your predictions by adding, then subtracting, measurements of (0.3070 ± 0.0005) m and (4.120 ± 0.005) m.

The conclusion of these Investigations is worth remembering:

> The uncertainty in a sum or difference of measurements is the sum of the uncertainties of the individual measurements.

We need a rule that will help us report answers in a meaningful way when adding or subtracting measurements with different precisions.

Consider the measurements (0.3070 ± 0.0005) m and (4.120 ± 0.005) m from exercise 4 in *Investigation 2*. The sum of these measurements is (4.4270 ± 0.0055) m. The limits of the sum are 4.4325 m and 4.4215 m, so the digit 2 in the sum is uncertain. This is caused by the precision of the second measurement. We should not retain any digits after an uncertain digit, so we round the measure and state the uncertainty of the least precise measure. We would report the sum as (4.430 ± 0.005) cm. This has the same precision and uncertainty as the least precise individual measurement, (4.120 ± 0.005) m.

> When adding or subtracting measurements, the precision and uncertainty of the final measurement are equal to the precision and uncertainty of the least precise individual measurement.

Example 1 **Adding measurements**

A bus company plans to purchase two new buses for its fleet. The two buses must fit end-to-end in a new garage built especially to house them. The length of the garage space available is (11.320 ± 0.005) m. The manufacturer's specifications state that the buses will have lengths of (6.860 ± 0.005) m and (4.450 ± 0.005) m. Will both buses fit into the garage?

S O L U T I O N

If the buses are parked end-to-end, with no space between them, they will take up a distance of

(6.860 + 4.450) ± (0.005 + 0.005) m = (11.310 ± 0.010) m

The buses will take up between 11.30 m and 11.32 m.

The length of the garage may be as much as

(11.320 + 0.005) m, or 11.325 m, or a little as

(11.320 − 0.005) m, or 11.315 m.

The amount of space available in the garage might be as much as 11.325 m, so there is a chance that the buses will fit, but they will have to be parked very carefully! There is also a chance that the buses will not fit.

Example 2 **Subtracting measurements**

A zoo is to acquire a new animal. In the animal's natural environment, the difference between the highest and lowest temperatures does not exceed 10°C. The zoo wants the animal to prosper in its new home. Several existing animal houses have space for the animal. Are any of the animal houses in the table below suitable for the new animal?

Animal House	Highest recorded temperature (°C)	Lowest recorded temperature (°C)
A	25.0 ± 0.5	15.0 ± 0.5
B	29.0 ± 0.5	24.0 ± 0.5
C	32.0 ± 0.5	25.0 ± 0.5
D	33.0 ± 0.5	22.0 ± 0.5

SOLUTION

The difference between the average warmest temperature and the average coolest temperature is:

House A: Difference $= (25 - 15) \pm (0.5 + 0.5)$
$$= (10 \pm 1)°C$$

House B: Difference $= (29 - 24) \pm (0.5 + 0.5)$
$$= (5 \pm 1)°C$$

House C: Difference $= (32 - 25) \pm (0.5 + 0.5)$
$$= (7 \pm 1)°C$$

House D: Difference $= (33 - 22) \pm (0.5 + 0.5)$
$$= (11 \pm 1)°C$$

Animal houses B and C seem to be suitable. The temperature difference is not more than 8°C for each house. Animal houses A and D are more risky, since the temperature differences for each may exceed 10°C.

DISCUSSING THE IDEAS

1. For simplicity, we have assumed that the uncertainty is one-half the smallest scale division on a measuring instrument. Discuss some other factors that would affect the uncertainty of a measurement.

2. Describe how you would determine the uncertainty of a measurement that is made using a ruler.

3. Suppose two measurements are made. Explain why the uncertainty of the sum of the measurements is the same as the uncertainty of their difference.

4. Explain why the precision of the sum or difference of two measurements is equal to the precision of the least precise measurement.

5. The terms *measurement error* and *uncertainty of measurement* are closely related. Explain how they are similar and how they are different.

Checking Your Skills

1. Determine the uncertainty for each of the following measurements. State any assumptions you make.

	Measurement tool	Measurement	Uncertainty
a)	metric ruler	24.7 cm	
b)	graduated cylinder	81 mL	
c)	micrometer	9.23 mm	
d)	yardstick	13.2 inches	
e)	Imperial scale	2.4 pounds	
f)	thermometer	101.8°C	

2. For each pair of measurements, determine the sum and difference. Round each result to the appropriate decimal places, and quote the appropriate uncertainty.

a) (26.230 ± 0.005) mm, (11.170 ± 0.005) mm

b) (517.0 ± 0.5) m, (403.0 ± 0.5) m

c) (11.0 ± 0.5) km/h, (11.0 ± 0.5) km/h

d) (5.30 ± 0.05) g, (3.240 ± 0.005) g

e) (7.2160 ± 0.0005) s, (13.40 ± 0.05) s

f) $(280\,000 \pm 20\,000)$, $(115\,000 \pm 2500)$

3. Find the limits for the perimeter of each figure. Assume uncertainties of one-half the precision.

a) A triangle with sides of lengths 3 cm, 4 cm, and 5 cm

b) A square with sides of length 12 mm

c) A rectangle with a length of 12 m and a width of 8 m

4. In a month of 30 d, the average rainfall per day was 3.0 mm to the nearest 0.5 mm. Determine limits of the total amount of rainfall for the month.

5. A skeleton model of an object uses wires for the edges of the object. What is the minimum length of wire required to make a skeleton model of each object? Assume the uncertainties are half the precision.

a) A cube of edge length 4 cm

b) A rectangular box of length 5.2 cm, width 3.1 cm, and height 6.5 cm

c) A square pyramid whose base has sides of length 3 inches and whose slanting edges have lengths of 5 inches

6. The lengths of two pieces of plastic tubing are measured as 11.3 cm and 5.9 cm.

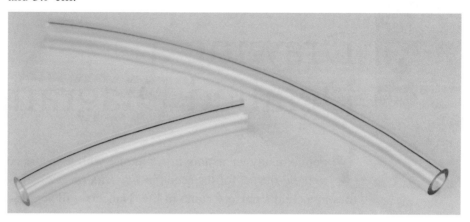

   a) Determine the uncertainty for each measurement.

   b) When the two pieces of tubing are joined, they overlap by
   (0.50 ± 0.05) cm. Determine the total length of the two pieces of
   tubing when they are joined. What is the uncertainty of the total length?

7. A bottle of acid states on its label that it contains (1000 ± 5) mL.
   A technician removes 10 volumes each of 25 mL, measured to the nearest
   1 mL. What is the greatest and least volume of acid remaining in the bottle?

Extending Your Thinking

8. A railroad track is made from pieces of track. Each piece of track has
   a length of (12.00 ± 0.05) m. When the pieces of track are joined, there
   is a gap between them of (1.0 ± 0.2) cm. If 3000 pieces of track are
   laid, estimate the length of the entire track. What is the uncertainty in
   your estimate?

PROJECT

In this Tutorial, you have added and subtracted measurements. You will use these
skills when you return to the Chapter Project and in the following projects in the
Project Book.

- Barn Design
- Indoor Climbing Walls

COMMUNICATING THE IDEAS

Why are measurement standards so important? In your explanation, describe
several serious problems that could occur if there were no accurate, universal
measurement standards.

Drawing a Detailed Diagram

Your company wants to win a contract with a theatre company to build the set for the scene in *The Nutcracker* ballet when the toys in a child's nursery come to life. Dancers will act the parts of dolls and other toys, so the surrounding objects must be enlarged. You must submit an enlarged replica of one of the everyday objects.

- Choose the object you will replicate.
- Make a sketch of the object.
- Make accurate measurements of the dimensions of the object and record these on the sketch. Indicate the uncertainty of measurement for each measurement.
- Draw orthographic diagrams of the object showing as many views as necessary to accurately depict the object. Record the measurements on the diagrams using the ± notation.

Save your sketch and orthographic diagrams. You will use them again when you return to the Chapter Project.

CHAPTER PROJECT

To complete this Chapter Project, you must calculate the volume of material that is needed to build a model. Complete *Tutorials 7.4* to *7.6*, then return to the Chapter Project on page 400.

Career Skills

The ability to create an accurate scale drawing is useful in careers that involve design. Interior decorators, stage designers, exhibition designers, architects, and engineers all use scale drawings for planning and executing complex projects. Machinists, carpenters, and technicians require skill in reading scale drawings and orthographic diagrams. Many computer programs, called CAD or computer-assisted design programs, are available to assist in creating these designs.

In an earlier grade, you learned that accuracy is an indication of how close a measure is to its true value. In this Tutorial, you will calculate the percentage error of measurements. The percentage error allows us to compare the accuracy of different measures.

Practise Your Prior Skills

You will use the concept of accuracy, and work with fractions and percents. Try these examples as preliminary review.

1. The following diagrams represent shots at a target. Which diagram best represents

   a) good precision but poor accuracy?

   b) good accuracy and good precision?

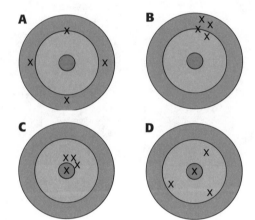

2. Express $2\frac{7}{8}$ as a decimal.

3. What percent of 6000 is 3?

4. A coat regularly priced at $195 is on sale for $156. What percent of the original price is the discount?

STUDENT REFERENCE

If you wish to review "accuracy" or "percent", look in the Student Reference.

Accuracy is important in industry. Defective products often cause machinery breakdown, and so reduce profitability. For this reason they are often discarded.

Example 1 **Comparing accuracy**

Two new machines are being considered to replace an aging machine that is part of a production line in a factory. In a test, machine A produced 152 parts, of which 4 were defective. Machine B produced 195 parts of which 5 were defective. Which machine should the factory purchase?

SOLUTION

Machine B produced more defective parts, but the comparison is not fair, since it also produced more good parts than machine A.

The comparison of the machines should be based on how many of their parts are defective when they each produce the same number of parts.

To do this, determine the percent of defective parts produced by each machine.

Percent of defective parts produced by machine A is $\frac{4}{152} \times 100\% \doteq 2.63\%$

Percent of defective parts produced by machine B is $\frac{5}{195} \times 100\% \doteq 2.56\%$

Thus, machine B is better since it is more accurate and produces a smaller percent of defective parts.

We can use a similar process to compare the accuracy of different measurements.

No measurement is ever exact. The accuracy of a measurement depends on how well the measuring instrument has been calibrated and on the skill of the operator. In general, different uncertainties can be expected with different measuring instruments. However, the same uncertainty may be more significant in some cases than in others.

For example, an uncertainty of 1 cm is not significant when a groundskeeper is marking out the lines on a soccer field, but is very significant when a carpenter is making a chair. The *relative error* considers the uncertainty in relation to the measurement. When expressed as a percent, this gives the *percentage error* of a measurement.

$$\text{Percentage error} = \frac{\text{Uncertainty of measurement}}{\text{Measurement}} \times 100\%$$

For example, the length of an object is (2.50 ± 0.05) cm and the percentage error is:

$$\text{Percentage error} = \frac{0.05 \text{ cm}}{2.50 \text{ cm}} \times 100\%$$
$$= 2.0\%$$

The percentage error has no units. This means that we can compare percentage errors even when measurements have different units.

Example 2 **Comparing measurements**

During a physical examination, a young man's height and mass were measured to be 1.78 m and 65 kg. Which measurement has the lower percentage error?

SOLUTION

Calculate the percentage error of each measurement.

The height has a precision of 0.01 m and an uncertainty of 0.005 m.

$$\text{Percentage error (height)} = \frac{\text{Uncertainty of measurement}}{\text{Measurement}} \times 100\%$$
$$= \frac{0.005 \text{ m}}{1.78 \text{ m}} \times 100\%$$
$$\doteq 0.281\%$$

The mass has a precision of 1 kg and an uncertainty of 0.5 kg.

$$\text{Percentage error (mass)} = \frac{\text{Uncertainty of measurement}}{\text{Measurement}} \times 100\%$$
$$= \frac{0.5 \text{ kg}}{65 \text{ kg}} \times 100\%$$
$$\doteq 0.77\%$$

The height measurement has the lower percentage error.

Often a measurement is quoted with its percentage error instead of the uncertainty.

Example 3 **Calculating percentage error for imperial measurements**

A compact disc has a diameter of $(4\frac{3}{4} \pm \frac{1}{16})$ inches. Express this measurement using percentage error.

SOLUTION

The uncertainty is $\frac{1}{16}$ of an inch.

$$\text{The percentage error} = \frac{\text{Uncertainty of measurement}}{\text{Measurement}} \times 100\%$$
$$= \frac{\frac{1}{16}\text{ inches}}{4\frac{3}{4}\text{ inches}} \times 100\%$$

Use a calculator.
$$= \frac{0.0625}{4.75} \times 100\%$$
$$\doteq 1.315\ 789\ 47\%$$

The diameter measures 4.75 inches $\pm$ 1.32%.

1. Explain how to compare the accuracy of the measurements (23.3 ± 0.05) cm and (6.48 ± 0.005) m.

2. Explain why the percentage error of a measurement has no units.

3. The length and width of a tabletop are measured using the same instrument. The measurements are reported as 2.02 m $\pm$ 0.248% and 1.65 m $\pm$ 0.303%. Explain why the percentage errors are not the same.

4. In *Tutorial 7.3*, you determined that the uncertainty of the sum or difference of two measurements is the sum of the uncertainties of the individual measurements. Do you think there is a similar relationship between the percentage errors? Justify your answer with an example.

EXERCISES

Checking Your Skills

1. Determine the percentage error for each measurement. Assume an uncertainty of one-half the precision.

   a) 11 cm   **b)** 0.8 g   **c)** 6.2 kg   **d)** 8.72 m

2. Determine the percentage error for each measurement. Assume an uncertainty of one-half the precision.

	Measurement tool	Precision	Measurement
a)	metric ruler	1 mm	24.7 cm
b)	graduated cylinder	1 mL	81 mL
c)	micrometer	0.01 mm	9.23 mm
d)	thermometer	0.1°C	101.8°C
e)	yardstick	$\frac{1}{16}$ inch	$13\frac{1}{4}$ inches
f)	Imperial scale	$\frac{1}{16}$ pound	$2\frac{1}{2}$ pounds

3. A nurse records the mass of a child as 32.4 kg and her height as 1.23 m. Determine which measurement has the lower percentage error.

4. A manufacturing company determines that the volume of a volleyball is 4800 cm^3 $\pm$ 1.6%. What are the greatest and least possible volumes?

5. A scale has a precision of 0.001 g. Determine the greatest and least possible mass of a container with a mass of 27.478 g. Express the mass of the container using percentage error.

6. Measure the picture of a postage stamp using a metric ruler. Record the length and width using the precision of the ruler. Express the length and width using percentage error.

7. Refer to exercise 6. Determine the uncertainty of the perimeter of the stamp. Calculate the percentage error of the perimeter.

Extending Your Thinking

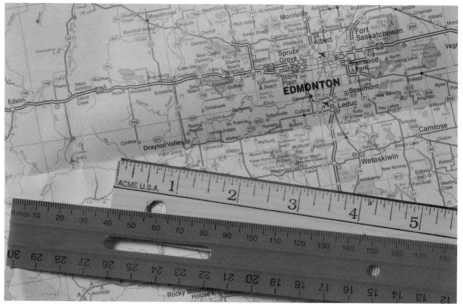

8. Two students measure the same line segment on a map. One student uses a metric ruler with a precision of 1 mm and determines the length to be 5.9 cm. The other student uses an imperial ruler with a precision of $\frac{1}{16}$ inch, and reports the length as $2\frac{5}{16}$ inches. Determine which measurement has the smaller percentage error.

PROJECT

In this Tutorial, you have learned how to compare the accuracy of measurements by calculating the percentage error. You will use this when you return to the Chapter Project and in the following projects in the Project Book.

• Barn Design
• Indoor Climbing Walls

COMMUNICATING THE IDEAS

Write to explain why percentage error is commonly used to describe the uncertainty associated with a measurement.

Applications of Percentage Error

In earlier Tutorials, you discovered the rules for estimating uncertainties when adding or subtracting measurements. In this Tutorial, you will investigate the rules for estimating uncertainty when multiplying or dividing measurements.

Example 1 **Determine the percentage error in a product of measurements**

A surveyor measures a rectangular plot of land. She determines that it is 43 m by 33 m. The length was measured with a percentage error of 2.5% and the width with a percentage error of 1.5%. What is the percentage error in the calculated area?

SOLUTION

The area is calculated as
43 m × 33 m = 1419 m^2.

The greatest and least possible lengths are 44.075 m and 41.925 m.

The greatest and least possible widths are 33.495 m and 32.505 m.

The greatest possible area is 44.075 m × 33.495 m = 1476 m^2.

The least possible area is 41.925 m × 32.505 m = 1362 m^2.

The uncertainty in the area is $\frac{1476 - 1362}{2}$ m^2 = 57 m^2.

The percentage error in the area is $\frac{57 \text{ m}^2}{1419 \text{ m}^2}$ × 100 = 4.0%.

If we find the sum of the percentage errors of the length and the width the result is 2.5% + 1.5% = 4.0%.

This is the percentage error in the calculated area. This demonstrates the following rule:

> If the uncertainties are small, the percentage error of a product of measurements is equal to the sum of the percentage errors of the individual measurements.

At this point you may suspect that a similar rule may also be true for quotients. The following *Investigation* examines this.

Investigation

The Percentage Error of the Quotient of Two Measurements

You will need a small marble, a graduated cylinder, water, and a scale with a precision of one decigram. Work with a partner to determine the density of the object.

1. Weigh the marble and record the mass, M, using the $\pm$ notation. Calculate the percentage error of M.

2. Put some water into the cylinder and record its volume. Add the marble to the water. The marble must be completely submerged. If it is not, start again. Record the new volume. Determine the volume, V, of the marble. Record the volume using the $\pm$ notation. Calculate the percentage error of V.

3. The density, D, is the mass per unit volume, so $D = \frac{M}{V}$. Calculate the density, D, of the marble.

4. Determine the largest possible density, D. This will occur when the mass is as large as possible and the volume is as small as possible.

5. Determine the smallest possible density, D.

6. Use the results of exercises 4 and 5. What would you say is the uncertainty for the density?

7. Use the results of exercises 3 and 6 to calculate the percentage error of the density.

8. Is the percentage error of the density related to the individual percentage errors of the mass and the volume? If it is, explain how it is related.

9. Repeat exercises 1 and 2 using 5 marbles. Divide the mass and volume measures by 5 to get the mass and volume of 1 marble. What do you notice about the percentage errors of the mass and volume?

10. Repeat exercises 3 to 8 using the measures from exercise 9. Is your answer to exercise 8 different?

If the uncertainties are small, the percentage error of a quotient is equal to the sum of the percentage errors of the individual measurements.

When we perform calculations with measurements, the result can be only as precise as the measurements. We need to report answers with an appropriate number of digits.

Recall the rectangular plot of land in *Example 1*. The length was about 43 m and the width was about 33 m. We say that the digits 4 and 3 in the measurement 43 m, and the digits 3 and 3 in the measurement 33 m are *significant digits*.

Significant digits are the meaningful digits of a number that represents a measurement. To determine the number of significant digits a measurement has, start from the first non-zero digit on the left. Count over to, and include, the first uncertain digit.

Example 2 Determine the number of significant digits

How many significant digits does each measurement have?

a) 120.7 s **b)** 0.004 cm **c)** 0.001 50 m

d) 12 000 mm **e)** 12 000 ± 1 kg **f)** 12 000 ± 1000 g

SOLUTION

a) 120.7 s: The first uncertain digit is 7, so all digits are significant. Thus 120.7 s has 4 significant digits.

b) 0.004 cm: The first uncertain digit is 4. The measurement has 1 significant digit.

c) 0.001 50 m: The first digit that is significant is 1, since the zeros to the left of 1 are holding the decimal place. The first uncertain digit is the final 0. This digit is meaningful. It is not holding the place. Thus, 0.001 50 m has 3 significant digits.

d) 12 000 mm: The first uncertain digit is 2. The zeros are holding the decimal place. Thus, 12 000 mm has 2 significant digits.

e) (12 000 ± 1) kg: The first uncertain digit is the final 0 since this could be either 9 or 1 (the limits for this mass are 11 999 and 12 001). Thus, (12 000 ± 1) kg has 5 significant digits.

f) (12 000 ± 1000) g: The first uncertain digit is 2, since this could be either 1 or 3 (the limits for this mass are 13 000 and 11 000). Thus (12 000 ± 1000) g has 2 significant digits.

The number of significant digits indicates precision. Suppose the area of the land in *Example 1* was reported as 1419 m². This has 4 significant digits, and so greater precision than the individual measurements. Precision depends on the measuring instrument; mathematical calculation can never improve precision. We agree to use the following convention.

When we calculate with measurements, a product, quotient, or root should be written with the same number of significant digits as the measurement with the least number of significant digits.

Since the length and width of the plot of land have 2 significant digits, the area of the plot of land should be reported as 1400 m². The percentage error is 4%, as discussed earlier.

Significant digits are used only when the numbers involved are measurements. For example, we can visualize a rectangle that is *exactly* 43 m long and *exactly* 33 m wide. The area of this rectangle is *exactly* 1419 m², and it should be written this way without using the convention.

DISCUSSING THE IDEAS

1. Use an example to explain how to estimate the percentage error of the quotient of two measurements. Include an explanation of how many decimal places to retain in the final result.

2. A volume is the product of three measurements. How will the percentage error of the volume relate to the percentage errors of the individual measurements?

3. The area of a compact disc is 70.9 cm². You have to determine the radius of the disc. Explain how many significant digits you should give in your answer.

4. Explain why it is always more appropriate to use the value for π in your calculator than any other approximation for π.

5. Suppose you need to measure the thickness of a penny with a metric ruler that has centimetre and millimetre divisions. You can either measure a single penny or the height of a stack of 10 pennies, then divide the height by 10. Which method would you choose, and why?

Checking Your Skills

1. A rectangular table measures 420 cm by 170 cm. The length is measured with a percentage error of 1.5% and the width with a percentage error of 2%.

   a) Calculate the possible maximum and minimum areas of the table.

   b) Estimate the percentage error in the area of the table.

2. A 500-mL flask is marked with increments of 50 mL.

   a) What is the uncertainty?

   b) What is the percentage error of a 150-mL measurement?

   c) What are the maximum and minimum possible volumes of the liquid when the flask is filled to the 400-mL mark?

   d) What is the percentage error of the volume in part c?

3. Use a metric ruler to measure the lengths of the sides of the following shape. Calculate the area of the shape and the percentage error of the area.

4. Use a metric micrometer that has been zero-corrected to measure the diameter of a dime.

   a) Calculate the percentage error of the diameter.

   b) Calculate the surface area of the tail of the dime.

   c) Calculate the percentage error of the area in part b.

UTILITY

If you need to review the use of the micrometer, refer to Utility 3, available in the *Applied Mathematics 10 Source Book*, or from your teacher.

5. This logo for a line of children's shirts is life size.

   a) Use an ordinary metric ruler to measure the diameter of the logo.

   b) Calculate the area of the logo.

   c) Determine the percentage error of the area.

6. A manufacturing company determines that the volume of a volleyball is 4800 cm$^3 \pm 1.9\%$.

   a) What are the possible maximum and minimum radii?

   b) Calculate the radius and its percentage error.

   c) How is the percentage error of the radius related to the percentage error of the volume? Explain.

7. An experiment is conducted to determine the density of a ball bearing. The mass of the ball bearing is measured to be 470 g $\pm$ 4%. The diameter is 5.1 cm $\pm$ 2%.

   a) Calculate the maximum and minimum densities of the ball bearing, and the percentage error.

   b) Which is more effective in reducing percentage error: a new balance that measures the mass as 470 g $\pm$ 1.5%, or a new caliper that measures the diameter as 5.10 cm $\pm$ 1%? Justify your answer with appropriate calculations.

8. Curb stones will line both sides of a walkway in a city park. Each curbstone has a length of (15.60 $\pm$ 0.05) cm; a gap of (1.20 $\pm$ 0.05) cm is left between the stones for mortar. The walkway is 2.7 km long.

   a) Estimate the number of curb stones that will be needed for the walkway. What is the percentage error in the number of curbstones?

   b) The city is currently negotiating to buy sufficient curbstones for the walkway. The price has not yet been agreed upon, but it will probably be $(1.90 \pm 0.20) per stone. Estimate the total cost of lining the walkway. What is the error in the total cost estimate?

Extending Your Thinking

9. Suppose $1000 is used to purchase an investment certificate. The interest earned is compounded annually. However, the exact interest rate is not known, and may fluctuate from year to year. It seems certain that the interest rate will be in the range $(10 \pm 1)\%$ every year. Estimate the value of the investment certificate after 20 years. What is the error in the total value after 20 years?

PROJECT

In this Tutorial, you have used measurements as the basis of calculations. You will use this skill when you return to the Chapter Project and in the following projects in the Project Book.

- Barn Design
- Estimating the Volume of Timber in a Woodlot
- Indoor Climbing Walls

COMMUNICATING THE IDEAS

Write a step-by-step method, suitable to display on a poster, to explain how to estimate the percentage error of a calculated area or volume.

Many industries today use mass-production methods. Components are often made in different factories and sent to a central point for assembly. For example, many different companies produce parts for GM cars, and these parts are shipped to the GM factory for assembly. It is very important that the components fit when assembled.

There is always a slight variation in the size of manufactured parts. Components can be assembled, provided that the actual sizes do not differ much from the specifications. The difference between the largest and smallest acceptable measurements is called the *tolerance range*.

For example, certain bolts are required to have a diameter of 1.24 cm. This is the target value. Diameters as large as 1.30 cm or as small as 1.18 cm are also acceptable. This specification stated as a *tolerance interval* is (1.24 ± 0.06) cm. The tolerance is ±0.06 cm, and the tolerance range is 0.12 cm.

Example 1 **Testing bulletproof vests**

To certify the ballistic resistance of police body armour, certain standards must be met during the testing process. One standard involves the armour-backing material, which is typically made from modelling clay. For the material to be bulletproof, the material must satisfy this condition:

When a (1.00 ± 0.01) kg cylindrical steel mass of diameter (44.5 ± 0.5) mm, with a hemispherical striking end, is dropped from a height of (2.00 ± 0.02) m onto the material, a depression of depth (25 ± 3) mm results.

Determine whether the following materials meet the specifications.

Test	Depression depth	Steel mass	Steel diameter	Height
A	23 mm	1007 g	45.0 mm	1.99 m
B	28 mm	900 g	4.40 cm	2.02 m
C	22 mm	0.99 kg	44.5 mm	195 cm

Write each tolerance interval in terms of its upper and lower limits.
To be acceptable:

- Depression depth must be between 22 mm and 28 mm

- Steel mass must be between 990 g and 1010 g

- Steel diameter must be between 44 mm and 45 mm

- Height must be between 1.98 m and 2.02 m

Test A: All of the parameters are within the specified limits, so the results do meet the specifications.

Test B: The lower limit of the specification range for mass is 990 g. A mass of 900 g is less than this, so the results do not meet the specifications.

Test C: The lower limit of the height specification range is 1.98 m, or 198 cm. A height of 195 cm is less than this, so the results do not meet the specifications.

Example 2 **Maintaining building codes**

As a building code inspector, you need to determine if the dimensions of elevator cars meet the tolerance requirements for access by a wheelchair. According to the local building code, there must be a lower activator to re-open the door placed (125 ± 25) mm from the floor and an upper activator placed (740 ± 25) mm from the floor.

What are the maximum and minimum distances between the two door re-opening activators?

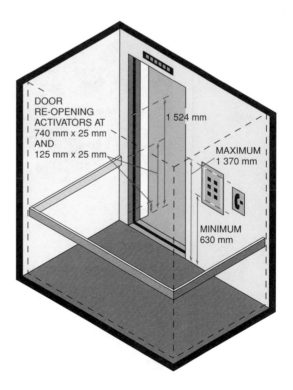

DOOR
RE-OPENING
ACTIVATORS AT
740 mm x 25 mm
AND
125 mm x 25 mm

1 524 mm

MAXIMUM
1 370 mm

MINIMUM
630 mm

The maximum distance between the activators is

$$[(740 + 25) - (125 - 25)] \text{ mm} = 665 \text{ mm}.$$

The minimum distance between the activators is

$$[(740 - 25) - (125 + 25)] \text{ mm} = 565 \text{ mm}.$$

Example 3 **Race car engine requirements**

The engine size of a race car is determined by calculating its cylinder volume. A race car typically has eight identical cylinders. A certain class of drag racing requires that an engine have a maximum size of 350 cubic inches. The race-car mechanic wishes to get close to 350 cubic inches without going over.

The desired engine volume is (349 ± 1) cubic inches and each cylinder has a diameter of (4.000 ± 0.002) inches. What are the maximum and minimum acceptable heights of each cylinder? Express these specifications as a tolerance interval for the height of the cylinders.

SOLUTION

The volume of a single cylinder is $\frac{\pi d^2 h}{4}$, where d is the diameter of the base of the cylinder and h is its height. The total engine volume, V, is 8 times the volume of one cylinder:

$$V = 8 \times \frac{\pi d^2 h}{4}$$
$$= 2\pi d^2 h$$

Rearrange the formula to isolate h.

Divide both sides by $2\pi d^2$.

$$h = \frac{V}{2\pi d^2}$$

Substitute the given values $V = 349$ cubic inches, and $d = 4.000$ inches.

$$h = \frac{349}{2\pi (4)^2}$$
$$\doteq 3.472$$

To determine the percentage error in h, use the results you learned in *Tutorial 7.5*. Calculate the percentage errors in V and d^2 and add them.

Percentage error in $V = \frac{1 \text{ m}}{349 \text{ m}} \times 100\% = 0.287\%$

Percentage error in $d = \frac{0.002 \text{ inches}}{4.000 \text{ inches}} \times 100\% = 0.050\%$

Percentage error in $d^2 = 0.050\% + 0.050\% = 0.100\%$

Percentage error in $h = 0.287\% + 0.100\% = 0.387\%$

Tolerance in $h = \pm 3.472$ inches $\times 0.387\% = \pm 0.013$ inches

Thus, the tolerance interval of the cylinder height is (3.472 ± 0.013) inches. The maximum and minimum acceptable heights are 3.459 inches and 3.485 inches.

DISCUSSING THE IDEAS

1. Explain the similarities and differences between tolerances and uncertainties.

2. How do you determine maximum or minimum measurements from tolerance?

3. For each of the Examples, what could happen if tolerance ranges were exceeded?

4. Why and when are tolerances used?

Checking Your Skills

1. Determine the maximum and minimum acceptable measurements for each tolerance interval.

a) (3.75 ± 0.05) mm

b) (0.0080 ± 0.0002) inches

2. Determine each tolerance interval for acceptable measurements given the largest and smallest measurements.

a) 7.9 g and 8.5 g

b) 3.0 cubic feet and 3.1 cubic feet

3. An orthographic diagram of a metal plate specifies a hole that is (0.8590 ± 0.0005) inches in diameter. A drill bit makes a $\frac{55}{64}$-inch hole. Is this measure within the tolerance interval?

4. A set of blueprints requires a metal rod to have a length of (3.0 ± 0.2) cm. Which of the following measurements are within the tolerance interval?

a) 3.3 cm   **b)** 2.08 cm   **c)** 3.09 cm   **d)** 2.98 cm

5. The orthographic diagrams below represent the top and side views of a drawer handle.

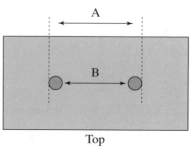
Top

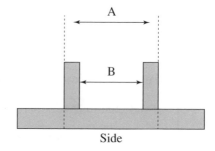
Side

$A = (10.50 \pm 0.02)$ cm $B = (8.20 \pm 0.04)$ cm

The tolerance intervals are as shown. Determine the maximum and minimum distances between the two centres.

6. A machined bolt is specified to have a diameter of (112.59 ± 0.01) mm. It will be inserted into a hole measuring (112.53 ± 0.01) mm. The bolt is designed to be larger than the hole. What is the greatest allowable difference between the diameters of the bolt and hole?

Extending Your Thinking

7. To carry a large electric current to a Light Rapid Transit (LRT) car, a wire must have a cross-sectional area of (45 ± 2) mm^2. What are the maximum and minimum acceptable diameters for this wire?

8. A steel ball bearing has a diameter of (0.80 ± 0.02) cm. Determine the volume of one ball bearing and its tolerance. What is the maximum number of these ball bearings that can be made from 1000 cm^3 of steel? What is your assumption?

PROJECT

In this Tutorial, you have worked with tolerances. You will use this in the Chapter Project and in the following projects in the Project Book.

- Barn Design
- Indoor Climbing Walls

COMMUNICATING THE IDEAS

Many of the human body's systems must operate within certain tolerances or else a person may become ill or die. Tolerances also play similar roles in the natural world of living organisms, and in society. Choose one area and explain how tolerances play an important role.

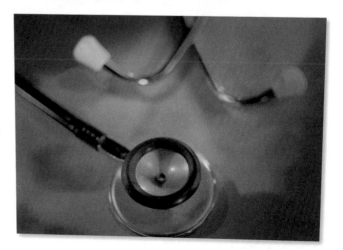

Building the Giant Replica

In the second part of this project you drew orthographic diagrams of an object. You will now choose an appropriate scale for the enlargement of the object, calculate the maximum and minimum volumes of material required to build the model, and then use the orthographic diagrams to create a model of the giant replica using appropriate material.

Your finished project will include:

- The object (if possible)

- A rough sketch of the object with measurements

- The orthographic diagrams of the object with measurements

- A written report that includes a brief description of the process of building the model, an explanation of the scale you selected for the enlargement, and all the calculations required to build the model

- The model you have made of the object

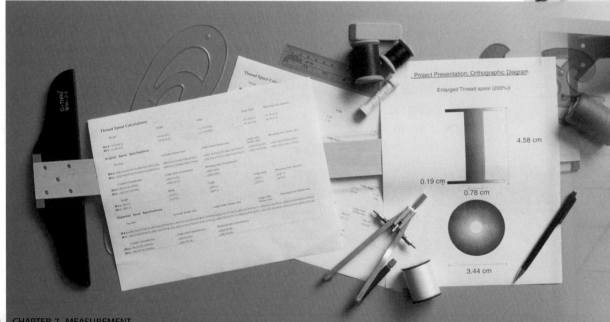

What Do I Need To Know?

Tutorial	Skills and Concepts	Important Results and Formulas
7.1	• Represent and manipulate scales in statement, rate, ratio, or linear form • Create enlarged or reduced drawings based on a specified scale	• 1 cm = 1 m or 1 : 100 has a scale factor $\frac{1}{100}$ or 0.01
7.2	• Draw and interpret pictorial and orthographic diagrams • Enlarge and reduce objects to a specified scale in three dimensions • Adjust scale given a new scale factor • Construct three-dimensional objects based on two-dimensional diagrams	
7.3	• Understand the concepts of precision and accuracy • Calculate the greatest possible uncertainty of any measurement • Calculate the greatest possible uncertainty when adding or subtracting measurements	• Uncertainty = half the precision of the instrument • When adding or subtracting lengths, the uncertainty for the resulting length is the sum of the greatest possible uncertainties of each length.
7.4	• Calculate the percentage error of any measurement	• Percentage error $= \frac{\text{Uncertainty of measurement}}{\text{Measurement}} \times 100\%$
7.5	• Determine maximum and minimum values in calculated products and quotients • Calculate the percentage error in calculated products and quotients • Understand and apply significant digits to calculations involving measurement	• If the uncertainties are small, the percentage error of a product or quotient of measurements is the sum of the percentage errors of the individual measurements
7.6	• Determine if measurements are within specified tolerance intervals	

What Should I Be Able To Do?

When you have completed the work in Chapter 7, you should be able to solve the problems that follow. Part A is investigative.

As you work through the exercises, refer to the *Student Reference, Utilities*, and the *Tutorials* as necessary.

Part A

You will need a micrometer, aluminum foil, hard green candy (Halls, Jolly Ranchers, etc.), glue, and sandpaper.

1. A jewellery designer must deal with very precise measurements to ensure that quality merchandise is produced. She makes an enlarged drawing of a silver ring with an emerald stone using a scale of 5 : 1. You are asked to use the scale drawing to construct the ring. You measure the dimensions of the ring on the scale drawing. The results are shown below.

outside diameter of band:	9.5 cm
width of band:	1.5 cm
stone length:	4.5 cm
stone width:	3.5 cm
stone depth:	1.5 cm

   a) Calculate the percentage error of each measurement.

   b) Use the scale and dimensions above. Create an orthographic diagram of the ring and stone. The ring is circular, but you will need to show the top, front, and side views since the stone is a rectangular prism.

   c) Using the scale, calculate the true dimensions of the ring.

   d) Construct an actual-sized model of the ring. Roll the foil into a long, thin cylinder to create the band. Use the sandpaper to reduce the hard candy to the size of the emerald.

   e) During the construction process, use the micrometer to ensure that the dimensions of the ring are within the following tolerance intervals specified by the designer:

   - outside diameter of band: actual size ± 0.05 cm
   - width of band: actual size ± 0.002 cm
   - stone length: actual size ± 0.025 cm
   - stone width: actual size ± 0.025 cm
   - stone depth: actual size ± 0.005 cm

   f) Using the above tolerance intervals, calculate the maximum surface area and volume of the stone.

   g) Assemble the ring with glue.

2. The scale on a map of British Columbia is 1 cm = 20 km.

   a) Represent this scale in ratio and linear form.

   b) Use the straight-line distances below. Determine the distance in kilometres between each pair of cities:

   Nanaimo to Port Alberni: 3.3 cm

   Prince George to Kelowna: 26.3 cm

   Dawson Creek to Prince Rupert: 34.7 cm

3. Draw an orthographic diagram of each object.

   a)   b)

   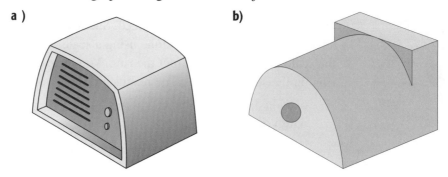

4. Use the scale of this orthographic diagram to draw a pictorial diagram of the object.

   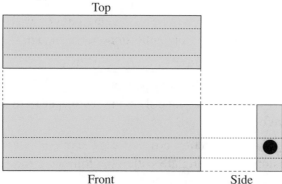

5. The length of an object was measured with a micrometer, a vernier caliper, a metric ruler, and a metre stick. The following measurements were obtained: 37.23 mm, 37.4 mm, 3.7 cm, and 4 cm.

   a) What is the uncertainty of each measurement?

   b) Express each measurement using the ± notation and percentage error.

6. The stem of the following pin must be shortened by 0.8 cm.

a) Use a metric ruler to measure the length of the stem of the pin.

b) What is the uncertainty of your measurement? Express your measurement using the ± notation.

c) Suppose exactly 0.8 cm were cut from the bottom of the pin. What would be the maximum and minimum lengths of the resulting stem?

7. Use an imperial ruler to measure the diameter of a standard CD.

a) What is the percentage error of this measurement?

b) Calculate the surface area of one side of the CD.

c) Calculate the percentage error of the surface area.

8. Acceptable masses for a machine part are between 31.8 mg and 32.4 mg. Express these masses as a tolerance interval.

9. The diagram of the bottom view of a screw is shown.

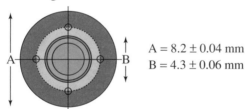

$A = 8.2 \pm 0.04$ mm
$B = 4.3 \pm 0.06$ mm

What are the maximum and minimum acceptable differences between the two radii?

10. From a map, the distance between two towns is 7 km, to the nearest kilometre. Suppose a person walks at a speed of 4 km/h, to the nearest 0.5 km/h. Find the range of times that the person could take for the journey.

The Chapter Project combines many skills and concepts into a single problem. Here are samples of student work from different stages of the Chapter Project. Review these samples to gain insights into your own project work.

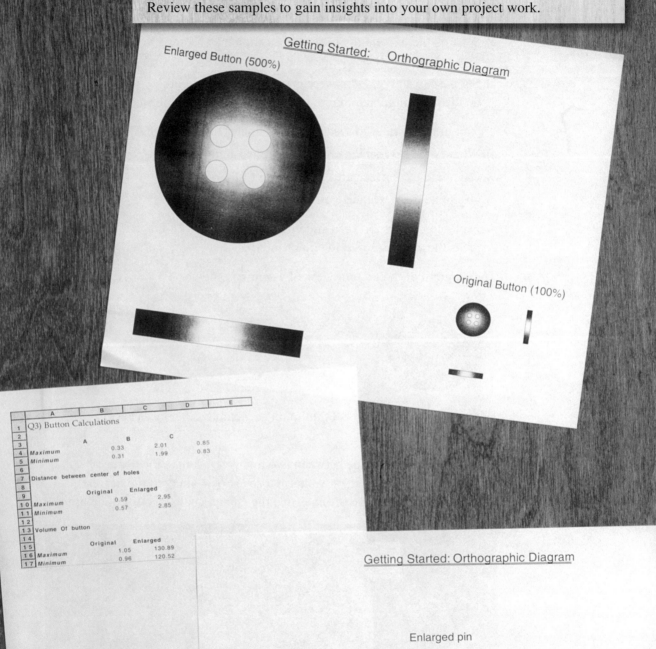

Getting Started: Orthographic Diagram

Enlarged Button (500%)

Original Button (100%)

	A	B	C	D	E
1	Q3) Button Calculations				
2					
3		A	B	C	
4	Maximum	0.33	2.01	0.85	
5	Minimum	0.31	1.99	0.83	
6					
7	Distance between center of holes				
8					
9		Original	Enlarged		
10	Maximum	0.59	2.95		
11	Minimum	0.57	2.85		
12					
13	Volume Of button				
14					
15		Original	Enlarged		
16	Maximum	1.05	130.89		
17	Minimum	0.96	120.52		

Getting Started: Orthographic Diagram

Enlarged pin

0.6 mm

1.76 mm

0.65 mm

1.35 mm

32 mm

1 Cm = 2 mm

11. Here are the student's orthographic diagrams of the object replicated. Do the orthographic diagrams accurately depict the object?

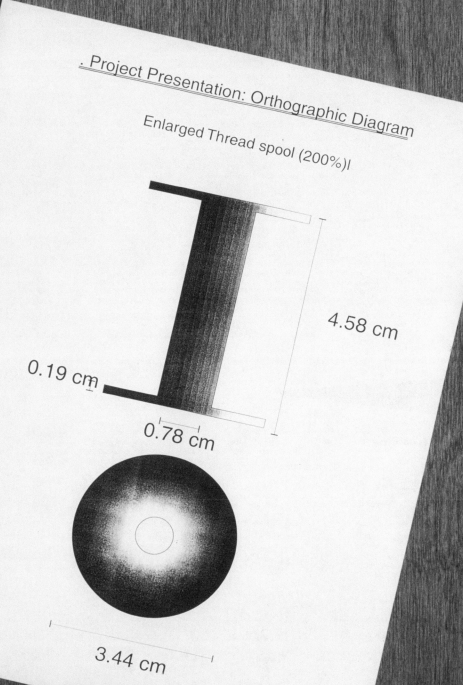

. Project Presentation: Orthographic Diagram

Enlarged Thread spool (200%)l

4.58 cm

0.19 cm

0.78 cm

3.44 cm

12. Here are the student's calculations for the dimensions of the replica. What scale factor did the student use? Are the calculations correct?

Thread Spool Calculations

Original Spool Specifications

	Height	Width	Ledge	Ledge depth	Mounting hole diameter
Max	4.59	3.45	1.16	0.20	0.79
Min	4.57	3.43	1.14	0.18	0.77

	Top Area	Cylinder Surface Area	Ledge (under) Surface Area	Ledge (side) Surface Area	Mounting hole Surface area
Max	8.88	15.68	7.89	2.17	10.50
Min	8.75	14.67	7.70	1.94	10.09

	Cylinder Circumference	Ledge (side) Circumference	Mounting hole Circumference
Max	3.71	10.84	2.48
Min	3.52	10.78	2.42

Expanded Spool Specifications

	Height	Width	Ledge	Ledge depth	Mounting hole diameter
Max	50.49	37.95	12.71	2.20	8.69
Min	50.27	37.73	12.48	1.98	8.47

	Top Area	Cylinder Surface Area	Ledge (under) Surface Area	Ledge (side) Surface Area	Mounting hole Surface area
Max	1074.79	1897.39	954.12	262.29	1270.29
Min	1058.75	1775.37	931.73	234.69	1220.57

	Cylinder Circumference	Ledge (side) Circumference	Mounting hole Circumference
Max	40.78	119.22	27.30
Min	38.70	118.53	26.61

Thread Spool Calculations

Original Spool Specifications

	Height	Width	Ledge	Ledge depth	Mounting hole diameter
Max	=4.58+0.01	=3.44+0.01	=1.145+0.01	=0.19+0.01	=0.78+0.01
Min	=4.58-0.01	=3.44-0.01	=1.145-0.01	=0.19-0.01	=0.78-0.01

	Top Area	Cylinder Surface Area	Ledge (under) Surface Area	Ledge (side) Surface Area	Mounting hole Surface area
Max	=PI()*((0.5*C4)^2)-(PI()*((0.5*F5)^2)))	=PI()*(C4-(2*D5))*(B4-(2*E5))	=(PI()*(0.5*C4)^2)-(PI()*(0.5*F5))^2	=PI()*(C4))*E4	=(PI()*(F4))*(B4-(2*E5))
Min	=PI()*((0.5*C5)^2)-(PI()*((0.5*F4)^2)))	=PI()*(C5-(2*D4))*(B5-(2*E4))	=(PI()*(0.5*C5)^2)-(PI()*(0.5*F4))^2	=PI()*(C5))*E5	=(PI()*(F5))*(B5-(2*E4))

	Cylinder Circumference	Ledge (side) Circumference	Mounting hole Circumference
Max	=PI()*(C4-(2*D5))	=(PI()*(C4))	=(PI()*(F4))
Min	=PI()*(C5-(2*D4))	=(PI()*(C5))	=(PI()*(F5))

Expanded Spool Specifications

	Height	Width	Ledge	Ledge depth	Mounting hole diameter
Max	=B4*11	=C4*11	=D4*11	=E4*11	=F4*11
Min	=B5*11	=C5*11	=D5*11	=E5*11	=F5*11

	Top Area	Cylinder Surface Area	Ledge (under) Surface Area	Ledge (side) Surface Area	Mounting hole Surface area
Max	=(PI()*((0.5*C18)^2)-(PI()*((0.5*F19)^2)))	=PI()*(C18-(2*D19))*(B18-(2*E19))	=(PI()*(0.5*C18)^2)-(PI()*(0.5*F19))^2	=PI()*(C18)*E18	=(PI()*(F18))*(B18-(2*E19))
Min	=(PI()*((0.5*C19)^2)-(PI()*((0.5*F18)^2)))	=PI()*(C19-(2*D18))*(B19-(2*E18))	=(PI()*(0.5*C19)^2)-(PI()*(0.5*F18))^2	=PI()*(C19)*E19	=(PI()*(F19))*(B19-(2*E18))

	Cylinder Circumference	Ledge (side) Circumference	Mounting hole Circumference
Max	=PI()*(C18-(2*D19))	=(PI()*(C18))	=(PI()*(F18))
Min	=PI()*(C19-(2*D18))	=(PI()*(C19))	=(PI()*(F19))

Utilities

Utilities 1–16 are printed in *Applied Mathematics 10*. The text of these Utilities is supplied with the Teacher's Resource Book for *Applied Mathematics 11*.

Plotting a Histogram on the TI-83

The TI-83 can display a histogram based on data you input. We will use the data from a class survey given in *Tutorial 1.3*. For convenience, these data are reproduced below.

0, 10, 15, 25, 35, 38, 35, 54, 58, 52, 42, 45, 40, 48, 44, 68, 0, 18, 30, 35, 30, 50, 55, 55, 5, 9, 45, 40, 45, 43, 65, 96

1. Access the equation editor by pressing [Y=]. Clear any equations entered in the list. Use the arrow key to highlight the equation, then press [CLEAR].

2. Access the list editor by pressing [STAT] [ENTER]. Clear any data in list L1. Use the arrow key to highlight L1, then press [CLEAR] [ENTER].

3. Enter the data in L1. Remember to press [ENTER] after each number.

4. To turn the plot on, press [2nd] [Y=] to access the STAT PLOT menu. Press [ENTER] to select plot 1. Highlight On and press [ENTER]. This is shown below left.

 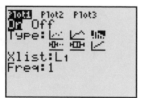

5. Select the type of graph by pressing the down arrow, then the right arrow 2 times to highlight the histogram icon. Press [ENTER]. The screen is shown above right.

6. To set the graph window, press [WINDOW] and choose appropriate bounds for the data. For these data, use Xmin = 0, Xmax = 100, Xscl = 3, Ymin = 0, Ymax = 4, Yscl = 1 and Xres = 1.

7. Press [GRAPH] and the histogram will be displayed (below left). Use the right arrow [▶] to move the icon to the position shown below right, to obtain the following readings.

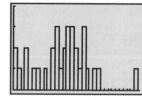 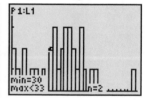

8. Press [TRACE] to show the minimum and maximum of the interval, and the frequency (above right).

9. The value assigned to Xscl determines the width of each rectangle of the histogram. To observe this effect, change the window setting to Xscl = 5. The choice of value for Xscl may affect the settings for Y. Try Xscl = 10 and adjust the other settings to display the histogram.

Determine a Regression Equation for Data Using the TI-83

The statistical features of the TI-83 can be used to determine the equation of the curve that comes closest to passing through the points of a scatterplot of data. For linear data, refer to Utility 14.

When we use the regression feature, the value of r^2, the coefficient of determination, indicates how well the chosen function fits the data. The closer that r^2 is to 1 or –1, the closer the equation fits the data. Another method used to determine the closeness of the fit is to graph the regression equation on the same screen as the scatterplot of the data, and estimate the closeness of the fit by eye.

For this utility, we will use the following data set as an example.

x	0	1	2	3	4	5
y	8	5.6	3.8	2.6	2	1.8

1. To calculate r^2, select DiagnosticOn. Press ⎣2nd⎦ **0**, to access the catalogue, then use the down arrow to move down through the list to DiagnosticOn, to obtain the screen below left. Press ⎣ENTER⎦ ⎣ENTER⎦ to obtain the screen below right.

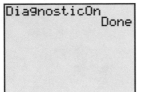

2. Access the list editor by pressing ⎣STAT⎦ ⎣ENTER⎦. Clear any data in lists L1 and L2 by using the arrow keys to highlight L1 (or L2) and pressing ⎣CLEAR⎦ ⎣ENTER⎦. Enter the data for x in list L1 and the corresponding data for y in list L2.

3. Choose an appropriate window setting. Consider the domain and range of the data. For the data above, use the standard window.

4. To graph the data, turn plot 1 on by pressing ⎣2nd⎦ ⎣Y=⎦ ⎣ENTER⎦, and selecting On. Press ⎣ENTER⎦, then select the scatterplot graph type using the arrow keys. Press ⎣GRAPH⎦ to display the scatterplot below.

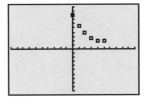

5. To find a quadratic equation that best fits the given data:

a) Press ⎣STAT⎦. Use the right arrow to select CALC.

b) Press 5 to select QuadReg. Press ⎣ENTER⎦ to have the calculator perform the quadratic regression on the screen below left. This means that the closest quadratic function that fits the data is (with coefficients to 3 decimal places) $y = 0.282x^2 - 2.639x + 7.979$. Since $r^2 = 0.9997$, this equation is a very close fit.

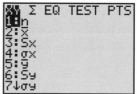

6. To find an exponential equation that best fits the given data:

a) Press [STAT]. Use the right arrow to select CALC.

b) Press **0** to select ExpReg. Press [ENTER] to have the calculator perform the exponential regression below left. The equation is $y = 7.459(0.732)^x$ and $r^2 = 0.974$ also indicates a close fit.

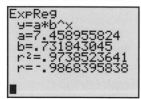

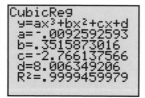

7. To find a cubic equation that best fits the given data:

a) Press [STAT]. Use the right arrow to select CALC.

b) Press **6** to choose CubicReg. Press [ENTER] to have the calculator perform the cubic regression above right. The equation is $y = -0.009x^3 + 0.352x^2 - 2.766x + 8.006$. Since $r^2 = 0.9999$, this equation is a very close fit indeed.

All equations in our example give values of r^2 close to 1 (or −1), but the cubic equation gives the closest fit.

8. To graph the regression equation on the same screen as the scatterplot, press [Y=] to access the equation editor. Clear any equations in the list, then paste the regression equation into Y₁. Press [VARS] **5** to get the screen shown below left. Use the right arrow to select EQ and press [ENTER], to get the screen shown below right using the cubic regression equation.

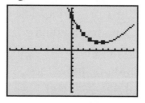

Press [GRAPH] to obtain the scatterplot and regression curve on the same screen.

The CALC Feature of the TI-83 Calculator

The CALC feature can be used when the TI-83 is in the graph mode to determine the coordinates of maximum points, minimum points, points of intersection of two curves or lines, and the zeros of a function.

To demonstrate this feature, use the equations $y = -2x^2 + 5x + 4$, and $y = x + 1$.

1. Ensure that all plots are turned off. To check, press [2nd] [Y=], then highlight any plot that is ON and press [ENTER]. Highlight Off and press [ENTER]. Access the equation editor by pressing [Y=]. To clear any equations in the list use the down arrow to highlight the equation, and then press [CLEAR] [ENTER].

2. Enter the equation $y = -2x^2 + 5x + 4$ in Y1 and $y = x + 1$ in Y2 of the equation editor list.

3. To choose an appropriate window for the equations consider the domain and range. For the equations given, use the standard window.

4. To graph the function on the same screen, press [GRAPH], (see below left).

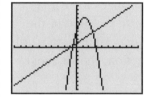 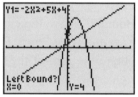

5. To find the coordinates of the maximum point of the quadratic function, press [2nd] [TRACE]. To access the CALC menu. Press **4**, to obtain the screen shown above right. To answer the prompt "Left Bound?", position the cursor to the left of the maximum point on the parabola and then press [ENTER]. The prompt changes to "Right Bound?" Use the right arrow key to move the cursor to the right of the maximum point of the parabola, and then press [ENTER]. The screen is shown below left. At the new prompt "Guess?", press [ENTER] and the coordinates of the maximum point are displayed, (see below right).

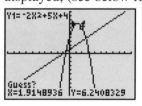 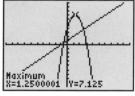

A similar process determines the coordinates of a minimum point between two "guesses".

6. To determine the zeros of a function, access the CALC menu by pressing [2nd] [TRACE]. Select **2**:zero. The prompt "Left Bound?" appears on the screen, shown below left.

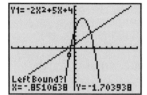

Use the right or left arrow key to position the cursor to the left of the zero of the function (to the left of its intersection with the x-axis). Press [ENTER]. The prompt changes to "Right Bound?" Move the cursor to the right of the zero and press [ENTER]. Press [ENTER] once more to obtain the zero of the function, shown above right.

7. To determine the point of intersection of two graphs, access the CALC menu by pressing [2nd] [TRACE]. Select **5**:intersect. The prompt "First curve?" appears. Use the right or left arrow keys to position the cursor close to the point of intersection, shown below left. If the equation shown is that of one of the curves whose point of intersection you are finding, press [ENTER]. The prompt changes to "Second curve?" and shows another equation. If this is the other equation, press [ENTER] [ENTER] to obtain the coordinates of the point of intersection, shown below right.

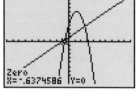

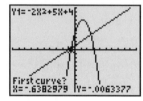

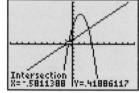

ZOOM Features on a TI-83

There are ZOOM features on the TI-83 that allow you to zoom in or out on a graph, and draw a box around a section of a graph and enlarge this section. Another use of the ZOOM feature is to set the viewing window. This utility will explain how to use the ZOOM feature to determine the coordinates of the point of intersection of the lines $y = 2x - 1$ and $y = -2x + 7$. The WINDOW should be standard and have values for both x and y from -10 to 10 with increments of 1. (If you are not sure how to return to the standard settings, refer to Utility 6.)

1. Turn off any plots currently turned on by pressing [2nd] [Y=]. Select any plots that are On using the arrow keys, then press [ENTER]. Use the arrow key to highlight Off and press [ENTER].

2. Press [Y=]. If any equations are listed in the equation editor, clear them by using the arrow keys and [CLEAR]. Enter the equation $y = 2x - 1$ as Y_1 and $y = -2x + 7$ as Y_2 of the list.

3. Set the viewing window. To choose the standard window, press [ZOOM] **6**.

4. Press [TRACE]. Use the arrow keys to move the cursor close to the point of intersection. The approximate x- and y-coordinates are displayed at the bottom of the screen.

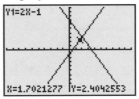

5. To determine the coordinates of the point of intersection more accurately, you may draw a box around the particular section of the graph you want to enlarge, or zoom in on the area around the cursor.

a) Use the ZBox:

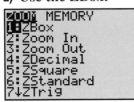 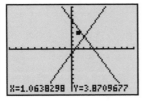

1) Press [ZOOM] **1** to select Zbox. The screen above right will appear with the position of the zoom cursor indicated.

2) Define the box around the point of intersection. Move the cursor up and to the left of the point of intersection, then press [ENTER] to obtain a screen similar to the one above right. Notice that the cursor has been replaced by a small box.

3) Use the right arrow key to enlarge the box to the desired length (below left) and the down key to enlarge the box to the desired width (below right). The box should enclose the point of intersection.

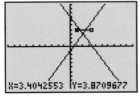 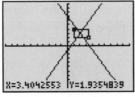

4) Press [ENTER] and the graphs are replotted within the new viewing window. Notice that the zoom cursor in the screen below appears in the centre.

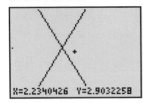 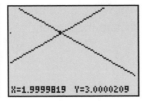

5) Move the cursor closer to the point of intersection, then repeat steps 1 to 4 until the point of intersection is determined to the desired accuracy (above right).

b) Use the Zoom In:

1) Press [ZOOM] and then right arrow to view the zoom memory. This shows the zoom factors. Select **4: Set Factors**. The zoom factors are positive numbers (not necessarily integers) that give the magnification or reduction factor used to **Zoom In** (or **Zoom Out**). Enter 10 for both settings, XFact and YFact, as shown below right. With these settings the x-scale and y-scale are multiplied (or divided) by 10 each time you zoom in (or out).

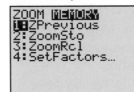 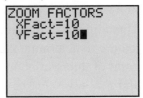

2) Press [ZOOM] **2**. A screen similar to the one below appears.

3) Move the cursor close to the point of intersection. Repeat steps 1 and 2 until the coordinates of the point of intersection are obtained to the degree of accuracy required.

When you use the ZOOM menu, remember:
- The viewing window settings change. Therefore, you will need to restore them later.
- Once you change the zoom factors, they will remain in memory even when you turn off the calculator.
- To cancel the **Zoom In** (or **Zoom Out**) command before you execute the command by pressing [ENTER], press [CLEAR].

Graphing Styles on the TI-83 Calculator

The TI-83 calculator can use 7 styles to display a graph. These are:

Style	Icon	Description
Thin line (default setting)		Line of thickness 1 pixel
Thick line		Line of thickness 2 pixels
Above		Shade region above graph
Below		Shade region below graph
Path	⌐0	Draws the leading edge of graph from left to right of screen
Animate	0	A circular cursor traces the leading edge of the graph without drawing a path
Dot	⋰	The graph appears as a series of dots

To change the graphing style for the graph of the equation $y = 3x + 5$:

1. Turn off any plots and clear any equations in the Y= list.

2. Set the viewing window to the standard setting by pressing [ZOOM] **6**.

3. Press [Y=] and enter the equation $y = 3x + 5$ in Y1.

4. The default graph style is the thin line, one pixel wide. To change the graph style, use the left arrow key to move the cursor to the left, past the = sign. The thin line icon will move. Press [ENTER] and the moving icon changes to a thick line (below left).

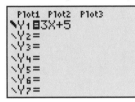
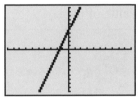

Press [GRAPH] to display the graph as a thick line (above right).

5. To change to another graph style, press [Y=] to access the equation editor, then repeat step 4, pressing [ENTER] repeatedly to rotate through the graph styles, shown below.

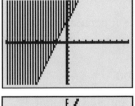
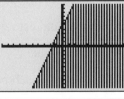

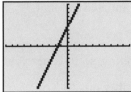

The animate screen has not been displayed.

Using the TVM Solver on the TI-83

The TI-83 can carry out financial calculations. It has a feature called the TVM (Time Value of Money) Solver. When interest is paid for the use of money, the value of any amount of money subject to interest changes with time. This change is the time value of money.

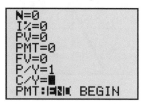

To access the TVM Solver, press [2nd] [x⁻¹], then [ENTER]. The screen above appears.

The variables represent the following quantities.

N: total number of payments

I%: annual interest rate as a percent

PV: present value

PMT: payment each period

FV: future value, or accumulated amount

P/Y: number of payments per year

C/Y: number of compounding periods per year

The calculator displays either positive or negative values for PV, PMT, and FV. A positive value indicates the amount is earned. A negative value indicates the amount is invested.

When you input four of the first five quantities, the calculator can provide the fifth. The five examples below demonstrate this. In each case, to input the known quantities use the arrow and [ENTER] keys.

1. Solve for N (the number of payments):

To buy a new car you must take out a loan of $10 593.30. You can afford a payment of $238 per month. The finance company offers an annual interest rate of 3.75% with compounding monthly. How many payments must you make? Enter the values in the screen on the left in the TVM Solver:

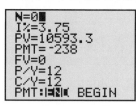

The payment will be made at the end of a payment period, so the word END should be highlighted.

To find the number of payments, move the cursor to the N line and press [ALPHA] [ENTER] to obtain the screen above right.

You must make 48 payments. That would be one payment each month for 4 years.

2. Solve for I (the rate of interest):

A certain university program will cost $20 000. What annual interest rate, compounded monthly, must you obtain if you can save \$288.50 per month for the next five years and hope to have the money for the course saved at that time?

Enter the values shown below left in the TVM Solver.

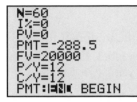

Use the arrow keys to move to the row for I%. Press [ALPHA] [ENTER] to obtain the screen above right.

If you can obtain an annual interest rate of at least 5.75% compounded monthly, you will have \$20 000 at the end of 5 years.

3. Solve for PV (the value now):

You plan to buy a car. You can make payments of \$525 per month and the interest rate advertised for car loans is 6.25%, compounded monthly. If the finance company offers the loan for 2 years, how much can you afford to borrow?

Enter the values in the TVM Solver as shown below left.

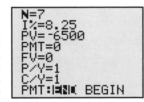

Use the arrow keys to move to the row for PV. Press [ALPHA] [ENTER] to obtain the screen shown above right.
You can afford to borrow \$11 815.45.

4. Solve for PMT (the payment):

You want to buy a house and take out a

30-year mortgage of \$100 000 at 8%, compounded monthly. What are your monthly payments?

Enter the data in the TVM Solver as shown below left.

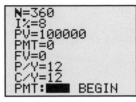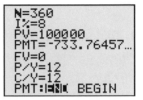

Use the arrow keys to place the cursor at PMT, then press [ALPHA] [ENTER] to obtain the screen above right. You must pay \$733.76 each month to pay off your \$100 000 mortgage in 30 years.

5. Solve for FV (the future value):

You decide to invest \$6500. The bank offers an interest rate of 8.25% compounded annually. What will your money be worth in 7 years if the interest rate remains unchanged?

Enter the data in the TVM Solver as shown below left.

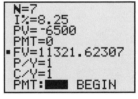

Use the arrow keys to place the cursor beside FV = and press [ALPHA] [ENTER] to obtain the screen above right. The investment will be worth \$11 321.62 in 7 years' time.

Using *The Geometer's Sketchpad*

1. To construct △ABC using points:

Click on this tool …   *… and do this:*

a) Draw 3 points.

b) Click on each point to display its label. To change a label, double-click and type a new letter. Make sure the labels are A, B, and C.

c) Hold down the Shift key and click on each point. This selects the points. When a point is outlined in black, it is selected.

d) From the Construct menu, choose Segment.

e) Click anywhere on the screen to deselect segments and points.

2. To construct the midpoint of AB:

Click on this tool …   *… and do this:*

a) Click on the side AB to select it. The two black squares on the line segment show that it has been selected.

b) From the Construct menu, choose Point at Midpoint.

c) Click on the midpoint to display its label, D. Double-click on D, then change it to M.

3. To construct △PQR using segments:

Click on this tool …   *… and do this:*

a) Draw a horizontal line segment by clicking on the screen, then drag. The segment is selected.

b) Click anywhere on the screen to deselect the segment.

c) Construct a point on one side of the segment.

d) Click on the point on one side of the segment. Double-click on the label and change it to R.

e) Repeat this procedure to label the points you have constructed on the segment R and Q.

f) Click on P and R. From the Construct menu, choose segment.

g) Click anywhere on the screen to deselect the points and segments.

h) Click on Q and R, then construct segment QR.

i) Drag a vertex of △PQR until all the angles are acute.

4. To construct a circle:

Click on this tool ...   *... and do this:*

a) Hold down the mouse button anywhere on the screen. Move the mouse. Click anywhere to deselect.

b) Drag the control point to make the circle larger or smaller.

5. To measure the length of a segment AB:

Click on this tool ...   *... and do this:*

a) Select points A and B.

b) From the Measure menu, choose Distance. The length of AB is displayed on screen.

6. To measure ∠ABC:

Click on this tool ...   *... and do this:*

a) Select points A, B, and C in that order.

b) From the Measure menu, choose Angle. The measure of ∠ABC is displayed on screen.

7. To label a point:

Click on this tool ...   *... and do this:*

a) Use the mouse to move the hand to the point. The hand turns black. Click, and the point is labelled.

b) To change the label, double-click on the label. A dialog box appears. Type the new label, then click O.K.

8. To construct the perpendicular bisector of segment AB:

Click on this tool ...   *... and do this:*

a) Click anywhere on the screen, hold down the mouse button, drag to form a segment, and then release the mouse button.

b) Move the hand to one endpoint and click to label it A. Move the hand to the other endpoint and click to label it B.

c) Select segment AB.

d) From the Construct menu, choose Point at Midpoint.

e) Select the midpoint and the segment AB.

f) From the Construct menu, choose Perpendicular Line. This line is the perpendicular bisector of AB.

TI-83 Programs

1. WORLDPOP

PROGRAM:WORLDPOP

: ClrAllLists

: 0 → Xmin

: 188 → Xmax

: 50 → Xscl

: 0 → Ymin

: 25 → Ymax

: 5 → Yscl

: Disp "INITIAL POP"

: Input P

: Disp"MAX POP"

: Input M

: Disp "RATE"

: Input R

: (R/100)/(M-P) → A

: 0 → L1(1)

: P → L2 (1)

: For (N,1,40)

: For (I,1,10)

: P+A*P*(M-P) → P

: End

: 10*N → L1(1+N)

: P → L2(1+N)

: End

2. LINES

This program is designed to draw the graphs of a linear system when the equations are presented as $ax + by = c$ and $dx + ey = f$, where $b \neq 0$, and $e \neq 0$.

Before you use this program:

- Turn off any plots.
- Clear any equations currently in the Y= list. Enter Y1 = −(A/B)X + C/B, and Y2 = −(D/E)X + F/E in the Y= list.
- Set the viewing window.

PROGRAM: LINES

: FnOff   (press [VARS] → **4 2** [ENTER])

: FnOn 1,2   (press [VARS] → **4 1 1, 2** [ENTER])

: Prompt A, B, C, D, E, F

: DispGraph

: Quit

absolute cell reference: in a spreadsheet formula, a reference to one particular cell of the spreadsheet that will not change when the formula is moved to a different cell

$B$3 indicates that the value or expression contained in cell B3 is to be used in the formula.

accelerate: make quicker; the rate of change of velocity with respect to time

accuracy: when referring to a measurement, an indication of how close the measurement comes to its true value

active cell: the cell of a spreadsheet into which an item of data is placed when you start to type

acute angle: an angle whose measure is less than 90°

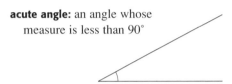

algebraic expression: a mathematical expression that contains at least one variable

$6x + 4$ is an algebraic expression.

altitude: the perpendicular distance from the base of a figure to the opposite side or vertex; the height of an aircraft above the ground

amortization period: the length of time over which the principal and interest of a loan are repaid

amount of an investment: the value of the principal plus interest

annuity: a series of regular, equal payments paid into, or out of, an account; see *Tutorial 5.7*

anomaly: irregularity of behaviour; for example, a point that is far away from the line of best fit

approximation: a number close to the exact value of a quantity or an expression; the symbols $\doteq$ and $\approx$ mean "is approximately equal to"

3.14 is an approximation for π.

arc: part of the circumference of a circle or other curve

BC is an arc of this circle.

area: the number of square units needed to cover a surface; common units used to express area include cm^2, m^2, and hectares; see *circle, rectangle, square,* and *triangle*

arithmetic sequence: a sequence of numbers in which each term after the first is formed by adding a constant to the preceding term

The numbers 1, 4, 7, 10, … form an arithmetic sequence, since each term after the first is formed by adding 3 to the previous number.

average: a single number used to represent a set of numbers; to find the average, all the numbers in the data set are added together and the sum is divided by the number of entries in the data set; see *mean*

The data set 1, 3, 4, 7, 7, 8 has 6 entries.
$$\text{Average} = \frac{1 + 3 + 4 + 7 + 7 + 8}{6}$$
$$= 5$$

average speed: the speed that, if the object travelled at that speed constantly, would result in the same total distance being travelled in the same total time; to calculate average speed, the total distance travelled during the given time period is divided by the total time

In 1 h, a car travels 100 km. The car stops for $\frac{1}{2}$ h, then travels 80 km in the next hour. Find the average speed of the car.

The total distance travelled is 180 km. The time required to travel this distance includes the time stopped of $\frac{1}{2}$ h.
$$\text{Average speed} = \frac{\text{Distance}}{\text{Time}}$$
$$v = \frac{d}{t}$$
$$= \frac{180 \text{ km}}{2.5 \text{ h}}$$
$$= 72 \text{ km/h}$$

axis of symmetry: a line about which a geometric figure is symmetrical

bar graph: a graph that displays data by using horizontal or vertical bars whose lengths are proportional to the numbers they represent

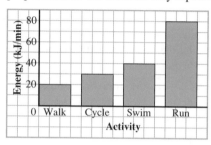

base: the side of a polygon, or the face of a solid, from which the height is measured; also, the factor repeated in a power

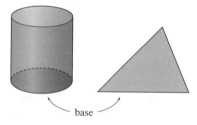

base

bias: an emphasis on characteristics that are not typical of the entire population

biased sample: a sample containing members of the population that are not representative

bisect: divide into two equal parts

blueprints: the initial drawings used in a construction project, originally on blue paper drawn in white lines; hence, the name "blueprints"

break-even point: the value at which a company's revenue from sales is equal to all costs of the production of their item(s); see *Tutorial 3.1*

broken-line graph: a graph that displays data by using points that are joined by segments

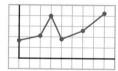

budget: a written plan to outline how money will be spent; see *Tutorial 5.8*

CBL: the Calculator-Based Laboratory; a data-collection device used with appropriate sensors and the TI-83 calculator

CBR: the Calculator-Based Ranger; a sonic motion detector used with the TI-83 calculator

calibrate: determine the scale of a measuring instrument by comparison to a standard

calibration equation: the equation used to calibrate an instrument

Canada Pension Plan (CPP) contributions: payments made by all employed Canadians between 18 and 70 years of age, and their employers, into a government-run pension fund; see *Tutorial 5.2*

canopy: the umbrella-like supporting surface of a parachute

cell: a location in a spreadsheet into which data may be entered

cell reference: the name of a cell in a spreadsheet, given by indicating the column and row to which it belongs

Cell B3 is the cell in column B and row 3 of the spreadsheet document.

central angle: the angle whose vertex is at the centre of a circle between two radii

central angle subtended by an arc: the angle at the centre of a circle between the radii from the ends of an arc of the circle

∠AOB is subtended by the arc AB.

chord of a circle: a line segment whose endpoints lie on a circle

circle: the set of points in a plane that are a given distance from a fixed point (the centre)

The area A of a circle with radius r and diameter d is:
$$A = \pi r^2$$
$$= \frac{\pi d^2}{4}$$

The circumference C of a circle is:
$$C = 2\pi r, \text{ where } r \text{ is the radius}$$
$$= \pi d, \text{ where } d \text{ is the diameter}$$

The area A of a circle with radius $r = 5$ cm is:
$$A = \pi(5 \text{ cm})^2$$
$$= \pi(25 \text{ cm}^2)$$
$$\doteq 78.5 \text{ cm}^2$$

The circumference C of a circle whose radius r is 5 cm is:
$$C = 2\pi(5 \text{ cm})$$
$$\doteq 31.4 \text{ cm}$$

circle graph: a diagram that uses parts of a circle to display data

circumcentre: the centre of a circle that passes through the vertices of a triangle

circumcircle: a circle that passes through all three vertices of a triangle

circumference: the distance around a circle; the length of the boundary of any plane region whose boundary is a simple closed curve

cold front: a term used in weather forecasts to indicate the leading edge of a cold air mass; see *Tutorial 1.5*

collecting like terms: putting together terms with exactly the same variable expressions, then simplifying by addition or subtraction

Collect like terms: $4(3x - 1) + 5x - 2$
$$= 12x - 4 + 5x - 2$$
$$= 12x + 5x - 4 - 2$$
$$= 17x - 6$$

collinear points: points that lie on the same line

commission: a fee or payment given to a salesperson, usually a specified percent of the person's sales; see *Tutorial 5.1*

common difference: the number obtained when any term is subtracted from the next term in an arithmetic sequence

For the arithmetic sequence: 1, –5, –11, –17, …, the common difference $= (-5) - 1$
$$= -6$$

complementary angles: two angles whose measures add up to 90°

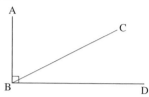

∠ABC and ∠CBD are complementary angles.

compound graphs: the graph obtained when more than one graph is drawn on a grid; see *Tutorials 1.1 to 1.4*

compound interest: when the interest due is added to the principal and thereafter earns interest, the interest earned is compound interest; see *Tutorial 5.5*

compounding: the process whereby interest is converted into principal; see *Tutorial 5.5*

concave polygon: a polygon with one or more interior angles greater than 180°

cone: a solid formed by a circular region (the base of the cone) and all the line segments joining points on the boundary of the region to a point not on the circular region

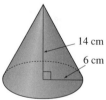

14 cm

6 cm

The volume of a cone can be found using the formula:

Volume = $\frac{1}{3}$(Base area)(Height)

= $\frac{1}{3}(\pi r^2)(h)$, where the circular base has radius r, and the height of the cone is h.

The volume of a cone whose circular base has a radius of 6 cm and a height 14 cm is:

$V = \frac{1}{3}(\pi \times (6 \text{ cm})^2)(14 \text{ cm})$

$\doteq 528 \text{ cm}^3$

congruent: figures that have the same size and shape, but not necessarily the same orientation

conjecture: a conclusion based on examples

consecutive integers: integers that come one after the other without any integers missing

34, 35, 36 are consecutive integers; so are –2, –1, 0.

consistent system of equations: a system of equations with at least one solution; see *Tutorial 3.4*

constant: a particular or fixed number

constant term: a number

constraint: a condition that restricts the acceptable range of values of variables, usually written as an inequality; see *Tutorial 4.4*

consumer price index: a record of the relative costs of selected items over a period of years

continuous data: data that can assume any value without a break

contour lines: lines on a map that join places of equal altitude; see *Tutorial 1.5*

contour map: a map that uses contour lines to show the outlines of hills and valleys at regular intervals above or below sea level. The closeness of the contour lines gives an indication of the slope of the land. A horizontal scale allows estimation of horizontal distances. See *Tutorial 1.5*

convex polygon: a polygon with all interior angles less than 180°

coordinate axes: the horizontal and vertical number lines on a grid that represent a plane

coordinate plane: a two-dimensional surface on which a coordinate system has been set up

coordinates: also called Cartesian coordinates; the numbers in an ordered pair that locate a point in the coordinate plane

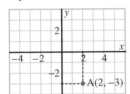

The coordinates of point A are (2, –3).

correlation coefficient: a measure of how closely data can be described by a certain type of function; the closer the value of the correlation coefficient to 1 or –1, the closer the data fit the function

corresponding angles in similar triangles: two angles, one in each triangle, that are equal

cosine: for an acute angle in a right triangle, the ratio of the length of the side adjacent to the angle to the length of the hypotenuse

cosine $\angle A = \frac{adjacent}{hypotenuse}$

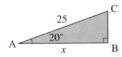

To determine AB in the diagram above:

$\cos \angle A = \frac{adjacent}{hypotenuse}$ Substitute the known quantities.

$\cos 20° = \frac{x}{25}$ Use a calculator to determine cos 20°.

$0.9397 \doteq \frac{x}{25}$ Multiply both sides by 25.

$23.5 \doteq x$

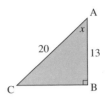

To determine $\angle A$ in the diagram above:

$\cos \angle A = \frac{adjacent}{hypotenuse}$ Substitute the known quantities.

$\cos x° = \frac{13}{20}$ Convert the fraction into a decimal.

$\cos x° = 0.65$ Use the $\cos^{-1}$ ("the angle whose cosine is") function on the calculator.

$x \doteq 49.5°$

Cosine Law: a trigonometric law used to solve triangles that are not right triangles

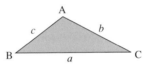

In any $\triangle ABC$,

$a^2 = b^2 + c^2 - 2bc \cos A$, so $\cos A = \frac{b^2 + c^2 - a^2}{2bc}$

$b^2 = a^2 + c^2 - 2ac \cos B$, so $\cos B = \frac{a^2 + c^2 - b^2}{2ac}$

$c^2 = a^2 + b^2 - 2ab \cos C$, so $\cos C = \frac{a^2 + b^2 - c^2}{2ab}$

Use the Cosine Law to solve problems when you know all 3 sides of a triangle and wish to find an angle, or when you know 2 sides and the included angle and wish to find the other side.

cost price: the price paid by a retailer to purchase an item for resale

counterexample: an example that shows a conjecture is false

cube: a rectangular solid whose length, width, and height are all equal

For a cube with sides of length s, the surface area of the cube is calculated by $S = 6s^2$; the volume of the cube is $V = s^3$.

If $s = 7$ cm

Surface area $= 6(7)^2$ cm^2

$\qquad = 294$ cm^2 and

Volume $= (7)^3$ cm^3

$\qquad = 343$ cm^3

cube root: a number that, when raised to the power 3, results in the given number

$\sqrt[3]{8} = 2$, since 2^3 is equal to 8.

cubic units: units that measure volume; common cubic units include cm^3 and m^3

cyclic quadrilateral: a quadrilateral whose vertices lie on a circle; see *Tutorial 6.5*

cyclone: a term used in weather forecasts to indicate a meeting of the warm and cold air masses that cause a storm; the air rotates counterclockwise (in the northern hemisphere) around the low-pressure centre.

cylinder: a solid with two parallel, congruent, circular bases

Surface area $= 2\pi rh + 2\pi r^2$

$\qquad = 2\pi(8)(20) + 2\pi(8)^2$

$\qquad \doteq 1005.3 + 402.1$

$\qquad \doteq 1407.4$ cm^2

Volume $= \pi r^2 h$

$\qquad = \pi(8)^2(20)$

$\qquad \doteq 4021.2$ cm^3

8 cm

20 cm

data: numeric or non-numeric facts or information

debt: money owing

deficit: when expenses exceed revenues

A business owed $15 000 and had only $12 000 in funds. The deficit is $3000.

degree (of polynomial): the highest power of any term in the polynomial

density: the mass of a unit volume of a substance; common units for measuring the density of a substance include g/cm^3, kg/m^3, g/mL, or kg/L

Find the density of an object that has a mass of 577.8 g and a volume of 214 cm^3.

Density $= \dfrac{\text{Mass}}{\text{Volume}}$

$\qquad = \dfrac{577.8 \text{ g}}{214 \text{ cm}^3}$

$\qquad = 2.7$ g/cm^3

dependent variable: the output of a relation, often denoted y; also called the responding variable

diagonal: a line that joins two vertices of a figure, but is not a side

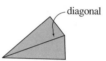

diagonal

diameter: a line segment that joins two points on a circle (or sphere) and passes through its centre; the diameter of a circle is twice the length of the radius; the diameter is the line of symmetry of a circle; see *circle*

diameter

O

direct variation: when the ratio of two variable quantities remains constant

If y varies directly as x, the equation that relates y to x is $y = mx$, where m is a constant; the graph of a direct variation is a straight line that passes through the origin.

discrete data: distinct data, intermediate points do not have meaning; see *Tutorial 1.2*

discretionary income: the amount of income left after expenses have been paid

distance: the space between two points; also, the distance travelled by an object that is moving at a constant speed for a time is determined from the relation Distance $=$ Speed $\times$ Time, where a consistent set of units must be used

If an object travels at a constant speed of 20 m/s for 2 min, the distance travelled is

$d = $ (20 m/s)(120 s)

$\quad = 2400$ m

distance formula: a formula used to determine the distance between two points whose coordinates are known

If $A(x_A, y_A)$ and $B(x_B, y_B)$,
then $AB = \sqrt{(x_B - x_A)^2 + (y_B - y_A)^2}$

For $A(-1, 3)$ and $B(2, -4)$

$$AB = \sqrt{(2 - (-1))^2 + (-4 - 3)^2}$$
$$= \sqrt{3^2 + (-7)^2}$$
$$AB = \sqrt{58}$$

dive position: a head first position in skydiving in which the skydiver will accelerate quicker than in other positions

domain of a relation or function: the set of all possible x-values (or valid input values) represented by the graph or equation

double-bar graph: a graph that uses horizontal or vertical bars to display data, in which the bars are side by side to allow for easier comparison; see *Tutorial 1.1*

effective annual interest rate: the rate that, with annual compounding, has the same effect as the stated rate

elimination method: to solve a linear system by eliminating one variable by addition or subtraction of multiples of these equations; see *Tutorial 3.5*

Employment Insurance (EI) premiums: contributions made by all employed Canadians and their employers into a government-run insurance plan that provides insurance against some unemployment situations; see *Tutorial 5.2*

equation: a mathematical statement that indicates that two expressions are equal

$2x + 5y = -4$

equation of a line: an equation that defines the relationship between the coordinates of every point on the line

The common forms for the equation of a line are:
The slope-intercept form, $y = mx + b$, where m is the slope of the line and b is the y-intercept of the line.

The standard form, $Ax + By + C = 0$, where A, B, and C are numbers.

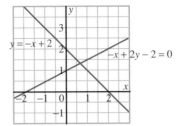

equidistant: the same distance apart

Points A and B are equidistant from the y-axis since they are both 3 units from the y-axis.

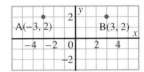

equilateral triangle: a triangle with three equal sides

error: the difference between the observed or approximate amount and the correct amount; see *measurement error*

evaluate an expression: substitute a value for each variable in the expression, then calculate the resulting arithmetic expression applying the order of operations rules

Evaluate $2x^2 + 3y - 4$, if $x = -3$ and $y = 5$.

Replace each letter with its value, placing each number in parentheses to prevent errors with signs.
$2x^2 + 3y - 4$
$= 2(-3)^2 + 3(5) - 4$
$= 2(9) + 3(5) - 4$
$= 18 + 15 - 4$
$= 29$

expenses: items that must be paid from income; for example, food, shelter, transportation, insurance; see *Tutorials 5.3* and *5.8*

experiment: a procedure, carried out under controlled conditions, that is used to test a hypothesis

exponent: a number that expresses a power and that tells us how many times the base of the power is used as a factor

2 is the exponent in the power 6^2 and 6 is the base. The laws of exponents are given below left, with examples to the right.

$a^m \cdot a^n = a^{m+n}$ $x^3 \cdot x^5 = x^{3+5} = x^8$

$(a^m)^n = a^{mn}$ $(x^3)^4 = x^{3 \cdot 4} = x^{12}$

$(ab)^m = a^m b^m$ $(4x)^3 = 4^3 \cdot x^3 = 64x^3$

$\left(\dfrac{a}{b}\right)^m = \dfrac{a^m}{b^m}$ $\left(\dfrac{x}{2}\right)^4 = \dfrac{x^4}{2^4} = \dfrac{x^4}{16}$

$\dfrac{a^m}{a^n} = a^{m-n}$ $\dfrac{x^8}{x^2} = x^{8-2} = x^6$

$a^{-m} = \dfrac{1}{a^m}$ $2^{-4} = \dfrac{1}{2^4} = \dfrac{1}{16}$

$a^0 = 1$ $7x^0 = 7 \cdot 1 = 7$

exponential function: a function in which the variable occurs in the exponent; see *Tutorial 2.1*

$y = 2^x$ is an exponential function.

expression: a meaningful combination of mathematical symbols, such as a polynomial

$3x - 2$ is an expression, as is $-13x^2 - 5x + 6$

extrapolate: estimate a value beyond the known values

To use the graph below to estimate the distance travelled after 10 h requires extrapolation; the last known value occurs when the time is 8 h.

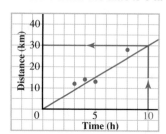

extremes: the highest and lowest values in a set of numbers

fair market value: an expert's determination of the value of a saleable item

feasible points: points on a graph that are possible solutions in the context of the problem posed

finance charge: the difference between the cash price and the sum of the payments made for an item

fixed cost: a cost, such as rent, that remains constant over a time period

float: the money in a till at the beginning of the business day

force: a push or a pull on an object in a certain direction

A force of 1 Newton (N) will cause a 1-kg object to accelerate at a rate of 1 m/s².

formula: an equation that describes the relationship between two or more quantities

The formula that describes how the volume, V, of a sphere is related to its radius, r, is $V = \frac{4}{3}\pi r^3$.

formula rearrangement: changing a formula to an equivalent form using the rules of equality

1. Rearrange the equation $y = mx + b$ to isolate x.
   $y = mx + b$
   Subtract b from both sides of the equation.
   $y - b = mx + b - b$
   $y - b = mx$
   Divide by m to isolate x.
   $\dfrac{y-b}{m} = \dfrac{mx}{m}$
   $\dfrac{y-b}{m} = x$

2. Make d the subject of the formula $F = \dfrac{12\,g}{d^2}$.
   $F = \dfrac{12\,g}{d^2}$
   Clear the fraction by multiplying both sides of the equation by d^2.
   $Fd^2 = 12\,g$
   Divide both sides of the equation by F to isolate d^2.
   $\dfrac{Fd^2}{F} = \dfrac{12\,g}{F}$
   $d^2 = \dfrac{12\,g}{F}$
   Take the square root of both sides of the equation to isolate d.
   $d = \pm\sqrt{\dfrac{12\,g}{F}}$

fractal curve: a curve constructed from a regular polygon by replacing each side with the generating shape, then repeating the process with each new side; see *Tutorial 6.5*

free fall: the portion of a skydive between exit and deployment of a parachute; movement under the force of gravity only

frequency: the number of times an event occurs in an experiment; the number of times that something occurs in a given time; a common unit is Hertz (Hz), named after Heinrich Hertz, which is the number of cycles that occur in 1 s

If you eat breakfast, lunch, and dinner every day, your meal frequency is 3 times a day. If a pendulum swings back and forth 10 times in 5 s, its frequency would be 10 cycles/5 s = 2 cycles/s = 2 Hz.

function: a rule that gives a single output number for every valid input number

function notation: the use of the function name, such as f, to indicate the output value for a particular input

The function $y = 2x - 5$ can be written in function notation as $f(x) = 2x - 5$.

graduated commission: a pay method where the rate of commission changes as certain goals are reached; see *Tutorial 5.1*

graph: a drawing that shows the relationship between certain sets of quantities by means of lines, points, or bars; see *Tutorials 1.3* and *1.4*

gross earnings: the amount of money earned before deductions; also called gross income or gross pay

gross profit: the difference between the cost price and selling price of an item; also called the *markup*

Lori's Fashions buys a coat for $29.00 and sells it for $49.99.
The gross profit on the coat is $(49.99 – 29.00), or $20.99.

growth equation: an equation that shows growth, such as $y = 200(2)^x$; see *Tutorial 2.1*

Guaranteed Investment Certificate (GIC): a type of investment offered by banks and trust companies that usually offers a higher rate of return than a bank account. The invesetment is made for a fixed period of time and is not cashable until the expiration of the fixed period.

half-life: the time taken for an item to reduce its quantity by half; see *Tutorial 2.1*

hectare: a metric unit used for land area; the area of a square with a side length of 100 m, so 1 ha = 10 000 m^2

hemisphere: half of a sphere

histogram: a graph that uses bars, where each bar represents a range of values and the data are continuous

Mathematics Test Mark

horizontal intercept: the horizontal coordinate of the point(s) where the graph of the line or function intersects the horizontal axis

imperial system: a system of measures used in Canada prior to 1976 and a variant of which is still used in the U.S.A.; devices using this measurement system often have each unit subdivided by halving, then halving the subdivisions

The relationship between some common imperial units and their relationship to metric units are given in the chart below.

Relationship between common imperial units	Relationship between common imperial units and SI units
Length	
1 mile = 1760 yards	1 mile = 1.609 km
1 yards = 3 feet	1 yard = 0.9144 m
1 foot = 12 inches	1 inch = 2.54 cm
Capacity (Volume)	
1 gallon = 4 quarts	1 gallon = 4.546 L
1 quart = 2 pints	
Mass (Weight)	
1 ton = 2000 pounds	1 pound = 0.454 kg
1 pound = 16 ounces	1 ounce = 28.35 g

implicit constraint: a constraint that is obvious but not specifically mentioned; for example, time spent watching television cannot be negative

income tax: money paid as tax to the federal and provincial governments based on the amount of income earned; see *Tutorial 5.2*

inconsistent system of equations: a system of equations with no solution; see *Tutorial 3.4*

independent variable: the input variable in a relation, often called *x*; also called the manipulated variable

initial value: the value at the start

inscribed angle: the angle between two chords of a circle that have a common endpoint on the circle

inscribed angle subtended by an arc: the inscribed angle formed by chords that intersect on the circle and whose other endpoints are the ends of the arc

∠ABC is an inscribed angle subtended by arc AC.

inscribed circle: a circle that is inside a figure so that every side of the figure is a tangent to the circle

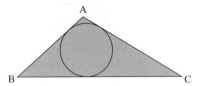

insurable earnings: the amount of money earned that is insured against unemployment

integers: the set of numbers that contains all positive and negative whole numbers, together with zero; see *number systems*

..., −3, −2, −1, 0, 1, 2, 3, ... is the set of integers.

intercepts: the horizontal and vertical coordinates of the points at which a graph crosses the horizontal and vertical axes

interest (simple): money paid for the use of money, usually at a predetermined percent. If *P* is the amount invested or borrowed, *r*, the rate of interest per annum, and *t*, the time in years, then *I*, the interest, is given by the formula $I = Prt$

Juanita purchased a $500 bond at an interest rate of 6.5% per annum. After 6 months, she received the following interest:

$I = \$500 \times 6.5\% \times \frac{6}{12}$

$\quad = \$500 \times 0.065 \times 0.5$

$\quad = \$16.25$

interpolate: estimate a value that lies between known values

intersection: the point or points common to two or more graphs

irrational numbers: the set of numbers that cannot be written in the form $\frac{m}{n}$, where *m* and *n* are integers and $n \neq 0$; see *number systems*

π and $\sqrt{2}$ are irrational numbers.

isobars: lines on a weather map that connect places with the same barometric pressure

isotherm: a line on a weather map that connects places of equal temperature; see *Tutorial 1.5*

lattice point: on a coordinate grid, a point at the intersection of two grid lines

least squares method: for a set of data, a method that is used by many calculators and computers to determine a line of best fit

like terms: terms that have the same variables

4x and −3x are like terms.

line graph: a graph in which the information is represented by a line or a series of line segments; see *Tutorials 1.1* and *1.4*

line of best fit: a line that passes as close as possible to a set of plotted points; it can be estimated by eye, or determined using the median-median method or the least square method

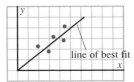

line of symmetry of a circle: a line about which the circle is symmetrical; see *diameter*

line segment: the part of a line between two points on the line, including the two points

linear equation and its graph: an equation that represents a straight line; can be written in the form $y = mx + b$ or $Ax + By + C = 0$

Slope-Intercept method: Graph the line $y = 3x + 2$.

This line has a slope of 3 and a y-intercept of 2. Mark the point (0, 2) on the y-axis. From that point, move up 3 for every 1 to the right. (Mark this point, then draw the line joining these points.)

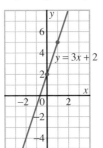

Intercept method: Calculate the points at which the line intersects the axes.

y-intercept: When $x = 0$, $y = 3(0) + 2 = 2$
x-intercept: When $y = 0$, $0 = 3x + 2$

$-2 = 3x$
$-\frac{2}{3} = x$

Plot, then join the intercepts $\left(-\frac{2}{3}, 0\right)$ and $(0, 2)$.

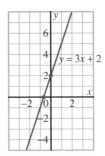

linear function: a function whose equation can be written in the form $y = mx + b$, and whose graph is a non-vertical line

linear inequality: a statement that one quantity is greater than (or less than) the other quantity. For example: $y > 3x - 1$

linear programming: the study of optimization problems that can be solved by finding the maximum or minimum value of a linear function subject to constraints represented by linear inequalities; see *Tutorial 4.4*

linear scale: the ruler-like scale given on a map to indicate the scale of the map

linear system: two or more linear equations in the same variables; see *Tutorial 3.1*

major arc: a part of a circle greater than half a circle

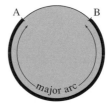

markup: the difference between the cost price and the selling price of an item; also called *gross profit*

mass: the amount of matter in an object

mean: the average of a set of numbers; see *average*

measurement error: the difference between a measure and its true value; see *Tutorial 7.3*

measurement standards: the standard set by the General Conference on Weights and Measures, in 1889, so that all persons would be dealing with the same measurements

median: the middle number of a set of numbers arranged in numerical order; if there are two middle numbers, their average is the median of the data set

For the data 2, 4, 8, 9, and 11 the median is 8.
For the data 2, 4, 6, 8, 9, and 11 the median is 7, since $\frac{6+8}{2} = 7$.

median-median line of best fit: to find the line of best fit for a set of data points using a particular method, in particular, the median-median method

metric system: also called the *SI system*; based on a decimal system, with each unit subdivided into tenths and prefixes showing the relation of a unit to the base unit; commonly used base units are:

Metre (m) for length   Gram (g) for mass
Litre (L) for capacity   Second (s) for time

Prefix	Multiplying Factor	Symbol
mega	1 000 000	M
kilo	1000	k
hecto	100	h
deca	10	da
	1	
deci	0.1	d
centi	0.01	c
milli	0.001	m
micro	0.000 001	μ
nano	0.000 000 001	n

Note: 1 L = 1000 cm³, so 1 mL = 1 cm³
1 tonne (sometimes called a metric ton) is used for mass: 1 t = 1000 kg
Convert 34.6 cm to m:
      from the table above, 1 cm = 0.01 m
                34.6 × 1 cm = 34.6 × 0.01 m
                34.6 cm = 0.346 m
Convert 246 cm² to mm²:
      from the table above, 1 cm = 10 mm
                (1 cm)² = (10 mm)²
                1 cm² = 100 mm²
                246 × 1 cm² = 246 × 100 mm²
                246 cm² = 24 600 mm²

Convert 35 mL to L:
      from the table above, 1 mL = 0.001 L
                35 × 1 mL = 35 × 0.001 L
                35 mL = 0.035 L

micrometer: a device for measuring small objects to the nearest 0.01 mm

midpoint: the point that divides a line segment into two equal parts

A ———————— M ———————— B

On a coordinate grid, if the endpoints are A(x_A, y_A) and B(x_B, y_B), the coordinates of M are:

$$x_M = \frac{x_A + x_B}{2} \qquad y_M = \frac{y_A + y_B}{2}$$

mill rate: the rate (in thousandths of a dollar) at which property tax is to be paid on the assessed value of the property; see *Tutorial 5.3*

minor arc: part of a circle that is less than half a circle

mortgage: a long-term loan on real estate that gives the person or firm that provides the money a claim on the property if the loan is not repaid

multiple bar graphs: several bar graphs represented on the same set of axes; see *Tutorial 1.4*

natural numbers: the set of counting numbers 1, 2, 3, 4, ...; see *number systems*

negative number: a number less than 0

net earnings: take home pay; see *Tutorial 5.1*

net loss: the difference between revenue and total cost when the result is negative

net of a rectangular box: a figure drawn on a plane that can be folded to create a rectangular box

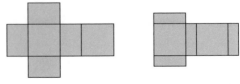

net profit: the difference between revenue and total cost when the result is positive

non-linear system: two or more equations in which at least one is not a linear equation

number systems:

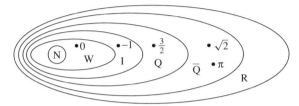

The *Natural numbers*, N, also called the counting numbers, are 1, 2, 3, 4, 5, ... If the number 0 is included, we get the *Whole numbers*, W: 0, 1, 2, 3, 4, 5, ...

The *Integers*, I, contain all of the whole numbers and all of their negatives: ... −2, −1, 0, 1, 2, ...

The *Rational numbers*, Q, consist of all numbers that can be expressed as fractions, with the denominator not equal to zero. Every integer is also a rational number, since every integer can be expressed as a fraction with denominator 1. All terminating or repeating decimals are rational numbers also.

Numbers such as $\sqrt{2}$ and π cannot be expressed as fractions that involve integers. They are called *Irrational numbers*, $\overline{Q}$.

The number system that consists of all rational numbers together with all irrational numbers is called the *Real number system*, R. It can be represented by all positions on a number line.

objective function: the function for which you require an optimal value, for example a profit function; see *Tutorial 4.4*

oblique triangle: a triangle that does not contain a 90° angle

obtuse angle: an angle greater than 90° but less than 180°

obtuse triangle: a triangle with one obtuse angle

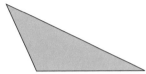

optimal value: the most favourable or best value

optimization problem: a problem in which the object is to find the maximum or minimum value of a quantity, subject to given conditions

order of operations: the rules that are followed to simplify or evaluate an expression:

Complete all operations within brackets following the order of operations.

Evaluate all exponents.

Complete all multiplication and division in the order they appear from left to right.

Complete all addition and subtraction in the order they appear from left to right.

Evaluate the following:

$5 - 2(4 + 2^3 \div 4)$	Begin with the exponent within the brackets.
$= 5 - 2(4 + 8 \div 4)$	Complete the division within the brackets.
$= 5 - 2(4 + 2)$	Complete the addition within the brackets.
$= 5 - 2(6)$	Complete the multiplication.
$= 5 - 12$	Finish by completing the subtraction.
$= -7$	

ordered pair: a pair of numbers, written as (x, y) that represent a point on the coordinate plane; see *coordinates*

orthographic diagram: a diagram used in industry that shows up to six views and internal features of an object. It usually shows the top, front, and side views. See *Tutorial 7.2*

outcome: a possible result of an experiment; a possible answer to a survey question

For the experiment of tossing a six-sided die, the possible outcomes are 1, 2, 3, 4, 5, or 6.

outlier: an observed value that differs markedly from the pattern established by most of the data

parabola: the name given to the shape of the graph of a quadratic function; see *Tutorial 2.2*

parallel lines: lines in the same plane that do not intersect

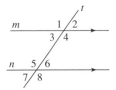

Lines *m* and *n* are parallel with a transversal, *t*. If two lines are parallel and cut by a transversal, then the following will be true:

The alternate interior angles will have equal measures (congruent). ∠3 = ∠6 and ∠4 = ∠5

The corresponding angles will have equal measures (congruent).
∠1 = ∠5 and ∠2 = ∠6   ∠3 = ∠7 and ∠4 = ∠8

The same-side interior angles add up to 180° (supplementary).
∠3 + ∠5 = 180° and ∠4 + ∠6 = 180°

If any one of these conditions is true then the lines must be parallel. Lines that are parallel will have the same slope.

parallelogram: a quadrilateral with opposite sides parallel

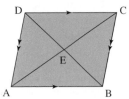

A parallelogram has the these properties:

The opposite sides have equal lengths. AB = CD and AD = BC

The opposite angles have equal measures (congruent).
∠A = ∠C and ∠B = ∠D

The diagonals bisect each other (cut each other into equal lengths).
AE = EC and DE = EB

pay periods: the time interval at which an employee is paid

payroll deductions: deductions made by the employer from the gross pay; see *Tutorial 5.2*

percent: means "out of 100"; symbolized by %

A percent can be written as a fraction with denominator 100, or as a decimal.
$45\% = \frac{45}{100} = 0.45$ **and** $150\% = \frac{150}{100} = 1.50$

1. **What percent is 33 out of 48?**
   We must determine *x*, where $\frac{33}{48} = \frac{x}{100}$.
   To isolate *x*, multiply both sides by 100.
   $$100 \times \frac{33}{48} = 100 \times \frac{x}{100}$$
   $$68.75 = x$$
   33 out of 48 is 68.75%.

2. **Find 7% of 45.95.**
   7% of 45.95 = 0.07 × 45.95, changing the percent to its decimal form
   $$= 3.2165$$
   7% of 45.95 is 3.2165.

3. **7.5 is 20% of what number?**
   Let the unknown number be *x* and write the question as:
   7.5 = 20% of *x*
   Use the decimal form of the percent.
   7.5 = 0.20 × *x*
   Solve for *x* by dividing both sides of the equation by 0.20.
   $$\frac{7.5}{0.20} = \frac{0.20x}{0.20}$$
   $$37.5 = x$$
   Thus 7.5 is 20% of 37.5.

percentage error: a comparison of the uncertainty of the measurement to the measurement, given as a percent

Percentage error in measurement
$$= \frac{\text{Uncertainty of measurement}}{\text{Measurement}} \times 100\%$$

perimeter: the distance around a closed figure; see *square, rectangle, triangle,* and *circle*

period: the length of time required to perform a complete cycle

perpendicular: at right angles

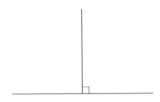

Two lines are perpendicular if their slopes are negative reciprocals of one another.

perpendicular bisector: the line that is perpendicular to a line segment and divides it into two equal parts

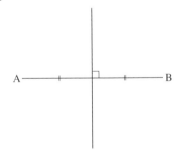

A ——|——|—— B

pi (π): the ratio of the circumference of a circle and its diameter; π ≐ 3.1416

pictorial diagram: a two-dimensional representation of a three-dimensional figure drawn from one perspective

piecework: payment based on the number of items produced

point of intersection: the point that is common to two or more figures

point of tangency: the point at which a tangent to a circle intersects the circle; see *tangent*; see *Tutorial 6.4*

polygon: a closed figure that consists of line segments that only intersect at their endpoints

The above figures are polygons.

These figures are not polygons.

The table gives the names of some common polygons.

Number of Sides	Polygon
3	Triangle
4	Quadrilateral
5	Pentagon
6	Hexagon
8	Octagon
10	Decagon
n	n-gon

population: the entire set of objects, people, or processes being studied

population pyramid: a graphical representation of the number of people of various age groups in a country; see *Tutorial 1.1*

positive number: a number greater than 0

power: see *exponent*

precision: an indication of how close a set of measurements are to one another; the smallest scale division of a measuring instrument

pressure: a measure of the amount of force that acts on a unit area of a surface; calculated by dividing the force acting on a surface by the area of the surface

If a force of 20 Newtons acts on a surface whose area is 4 m², what is the pressure on the surface?
Pressure = Force/Area
$$P = 20 \text{ N}/4 \text{ m}^2$$
$$= 5 \text{ N/m}^2$$
$$= 5 \text{ Pa}$$

principal: the amount of a loan or investment

prism: a solid with two congruent and parallel faces (bases), all other faces are parallelograms

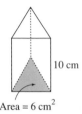

10 cm

Area = 6 cm²

The volume of a prism is the area of the base multiplied by the height.

Volume = (Area of base)(Height)

$V = A \times h$

$= (6 \text{ cm}^2)(10 \text{ cm})$

$= 60 \text{ cm}^3$

probability: an indication of the likelihood of an event occurring; if the outcomes of an experiment are equally likely, it is the ratio of the number of favourable outcomes to the total number of outcomes

profile: a drawing of the side view of a land surface that shows the slope of the land; see *Tutorial 1.5*

proportion: a statement that two ratios are equal

To solve for an unknown quantity within a proportion, first clear the fraction by multiplication.

$\frac{x}{12} = \frac{2}{5}$

$12 \times \frac{x}{12} = 12 \times \frac{2}{5}$

$x = \frac{24}{5}$

$x = 4.8$

$\frac{3}{x} = \frac{4}{5}$

$5x \times \frac{3}{x} = 5x \times \frac{4}{5}$

$15 = 4x$

$\frac{15}{4} = \frac{4x}{4}$

$3.75 = x$

pyramid: a solid with one face that is a polygon (base) and other faces are triangles with a common vertex

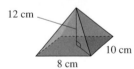

12 cm

10 cm

8 cm

The formula to calculate the volume, V, of a pyramid is:

Volume = $\frac{1}{3}$(Base area)(Height)

For the pyramid shown:

$V = \frac{1}{3}(8 \text{ cm} \times 10 \text{ cm})(12 \text{ cm})$

$= 320 \text{ cm}^3$

Pythagorean Theorem: for any right triangle, the area of the square on the hypotenuse is equal to the sum of the areas of the squares on the other two sides

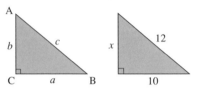

In right triangle ABC: $a^2 + b^2 = c^2$.

Use the values for the right triangle shown to substitute into the formula.

$10^2 + x^2 = 12^2$ Simplify each side.

$100 + x^2 = 144$ Isolate the variables.

$100 + x^2 - 100 = 144 - 100$

$x^2 = 44$ To solve, take the square

$x \doteq 6.6$ root of both sides.

quadrant: one of the four regions into which the coordinate axes divide the plane, usually numbered as shown in the diagram

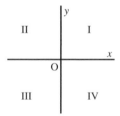

quadratic equation: an equation of the form $y = ax^2 + bx + c; a \neq 0$

quadratic function: a function with defining equation $f(x) = ax^2 + bx + c$, where a, b, and c are constants and a cannot be a zero; see *Tutorial 2.2*

quadrilateral: a four-sided polygon; see *polygon*

radical: the root of a number

$\sqrt{5}, \sqrt[3]{5}, \sqrt{2.6}$

radius: the distance from the centre of a circle to any point on the circumference; also, a line segment that joins the centre of a circle to any point on the circumference

The radius of a circle is half the length of its diameter.

range: the difference between the highest and lowest values in a set of data

range of a function or a relation: the set of output numbers of a function or a relation

rate: a certain quantity or amount of one thing considered in relation to one unit of another

Speed is the rate at which distance travelled changes in relation to one unit of time.

The slope of a line is the rate at which the line rises for one unit of horizontal run.

ratio: a comparison of two or more quantities with the same units

A rectangular box has length 18 cm, width 5 cm, and height 8 mm. To give the ratio of the lengths of its sides, first change all lengths to the same units, mm, then reduce by dividing by common factors:
180 : 50 : 8 = 90 : 25 : 4

rational numbers: the set of numbers that can be written in the form $\frac{m}{n}$, where m and n are integers and $n \neq 0$; see *number systems*

real numbers: the set of numbers that includes both rational and irrational numbers; that is, all numbers that can be expressed as decimals; see *number systems*

reconcile an account: check the amount of each deposit and withdrawal recorded in a register against the bank statement of the account to see if they agree; see *Tutorial 5.5*

rectangle: a quadrilateral that has four right angles

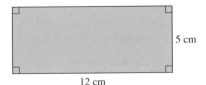

12 cm

5 cm

Perimeter = 2 × Length + 2 × Width

$$P = 2l + 2w$$

Area = Length × Width

$$A = lw$$

For the rectangle shown:

$P = 2(12 \text{ cm}) + 2(5 \text{ cm})$ $A = (12 \text{ cm})(5 \text{ cm})$

$\quad = 24 \text{ cm} + 10 \text{ cm}$ $= 60 \text{ cm}^2$

$\quad = 34 \text{ cm}$

recursive relation: a rule where a number in a list, other than the first number, is specified in terms of some of the numbers that come before it

The list 3, 6, 12, 24 is recursive, since each successive term after the first is twice the previous one.

Registered Retirement Savings Plan (RRSP): a savings plan for individuals who earn income, where funds contributed and interest earned are not taxed until the funds are withdrawn

regression curve: a best fit curve or straight line drawn through data points by a least squares fitting process

regular polygon: a polygon with all sides and all angles equal

The polygons below are regular polygons.

relation: a rule that produces one or more output numbers for every valid input number

relative error: the error as a fraction of the measurement itself, often expressed as a percent; see *Tutorial 7.4*

remove fractions from an equation: write an equivalent equation that does not contain fractions; obtained by multiplying each term by the LCM of the denominators

Simplify $\frac{5}{2}x - 3x + \frac{2}{7}x = 9$.

Determine the LCM of the denominators. This is 14.

Multiply each term by the LCM, 14.

$$14(\tfrac{5}{2}x) - 14(3x) + 14(\tfrac{2}{7}x) = 14(9)$$

Simplify $35x - 42x + 4x = 126$

$$-3x = 126$$

$$x = -42$$

residual: the vertical distance between a plotted point and a line of best fit

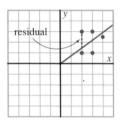

retail price: the price paid by consumers

revenue: money earned by the sale of goods or services

The sale of 158 show tickets that cost $20 each produces a revenue of $3160.

reverse shading: a method used to indicate a solution region when there are many overlapping graphs; see *Tutorial 4.3*

rhombus: a parallelogram with four equal sides

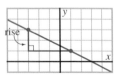

right angle: a 90° angle

right triangle: a triangle with one right angle

rise: the vertical distance between two points; see *slope*

rough sketch: a drawing that is not accurate, but is representative of the data being considered

run: the horizontal distance between two points; see *slope*

SI system: see *metric system*; SI stands for Système Internationale des unités

salary: a fixed amount of money earned by an individual over a specific period of time

sample: part of a population chosen to represent the total population in a study

sampling: the process used to choose part of a population to represent the total population in a study

scale: for a map, model, or diagram, the ratio of the distance between two points to the distance between the actual locations; the numbers on the coordinate axes

scale break: a small zig-zag mark on a graph's scale to indicate a break in the scale

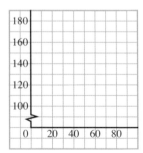

scale drawing: a drawing that either enlarges or reduces the original by a particular factor; see *Tutorial 7.1*

scale factor: the ratio of corresponding sides on similar figures; see *Tutorial 7.1*

scatterplot: a graph of data that are a series of points with no line shown to represent the data

Height (cm)	154	162	172	178
Mass (kg)	56.3	60.1	72.2	64.3

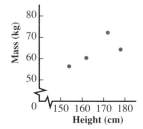

scientific notation: a number expressed as the product of a number greater than −10 and less than −1, or greater than 1 and less than 10, and a power of 10; used to express very large and very small numbers

47 000 = 4.7×10^4, and −26 = -2.6×10^1

secant: a line that intersects a circle at two points; see *Tutorial 6.4*

semicircle: half a circle

significant digits: the meaningful digits of a number that represent a measurement; see *Tutorial 7.5*

similar figures: figures that have the same shape but not necessarily the same size

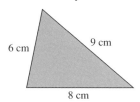

When two figures are similar, their corresponding angles will have equal measures, and their corresponding sides are in proportion (all have the same scale factor). The symbol ~ is used to indicate two figures are similar.

To find an unknown side of one similar figure, use a proportion.

$$\frac{9}{6} = \frac{8}{y} = \frac{6}{x}$$

Scale factor $= \frac{9}{6}$

$\quad\quad\quad\quad = \frac{3}{2}$

$\quad\quad\quad\quad = 3 : 2$

To find *x*, solve the following proportion.

$$\frac{3}{2} = \frac{6}{x}$$

$$2x \times \frac{3}{2} = 2x \times \frac{6}{x}$$

$$3x = 12$$

$$x = 4$$

To find *y*, solve the following proportion.

$$\frac{3}{2} = \frac{8}{y}$$

$$2y \times \frac{3}{2} = 2y \times \frac{8}{y}$$

$$3y = 16$$

$$y \doteq 5.33$$

similar objects: objects that have the same shape but not necessarily the same size

All the corresponding angles will have equal measures and all dimensions will be proportional.

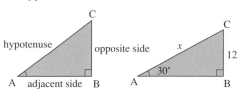

simple interest: see *interest* (simple)

sine: for an acute ∠A in a right triangle, the ratio of the length of the opposite side to the length of the hypotenuse

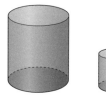

$\sin \angle A = \frac{\text{opp}}{\text{hyp}}$ Substitute in the known quantities.

$\sin 30° = \frac{12}{x}$ Use a calculator to determine the sine ratio.

$0.5 = \frac{12}{x}$ Multiply to clear the fraction.

$x \times 0.5 = x \times \frac{12}{x}$

$x \times 0.5 = 12$ Divide to isolate *x*.

$\frac{x \times 0.5}{0.5} = \frac{12}{0.5}$

$x = 24$

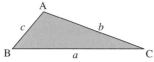

$\sin \angle A = \dfrac{\text{opposite}}{\text{hypptenuse}}$ **Substitute in the known quantities.**

$\sin x° = \dfrac{24}{30}$ **Convert the fraction into an equivalent decimal.**

$= 0.8$ **Use $\sin^{-1}$ (the angle whose sine is a function).**

$x \doteq 53.1°$

Sine Law: a trigonometric law used to solve triangles

Use the Sine Law in an oblique triangle where two angles and one side are known.

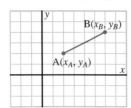

In any triangle ABC: $\dfrac{\sin A}{a} = \dfrac{\sin B}{b} = \dfrac{\sin C}{c}$ **and** $\dfrac{a}{\sin A} = \dfrac{b}{\sin B} = \dfrac{c}{\sin C}$

sky surfing: a type of skydiving in which the skydivers' feet are tied to a small board so that the skydivers can perform loops, spins, and the like

slope: a measure of the steepness of a line; the tangent of the angle made by the line with the x-axis

The slope of a line segment joining $A(x_A, y_A)$ and $B(x_B, y_B)$ is: Slope $= \dfrac{\text{Rise}}{\text{Run}} = \dfrac{y_A - y_B}{x_A - x_B}$

(graph showing segment from $A(x_A, y_A)$ to $B(x_B, y_B)$)

slope, y-intercept form: the equation of a line in the form $y = mx + b$, where m is the slope of the line and b is the y-intercept of the line

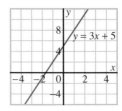

The equation $y = 3x + 5$ is that of a line with a slope of 3 and a y-intercept of 5.

solve a linear equation: to determine the value(s) of the unknown that, when substituted for the unknown in the equation, result(s) in a true statement

Solve the equation $3x + 5 = 5x - 4$.
Use inverse operations to move all the terms in the variable to one side of the equation.

$3x + 5 - 3x = 5x - 4 - 3x$ **Subtract 3x from both sides.**

$3x - 3x + 5 = 5x - 3x - 4$ **Rearrange to collect like terms.**

$5 = 2x - 4$ **Simplify.**

$5 + 4 = 2x - 4 + 4$ **Isolate the term in x; add 4 to both sides.**

$9 = 2x$ **Simplify.**

$\dfrac{9}{2} = \dfrac{2x}{2}$ **Isolate x; divide both sides by 2.**

$4.5 = x$

solve a linear system: to find all the ordered pairs that satisfy all equations in a linear system; see *Tutorials 3.1, 3.3,* and *3.5*

solvent: the situation where a business has an overall net profit for the year; that is, the business was able to meet all its liabilities

solving linear equations: see *solve a linear equation*

speed: see *average speed*

sphere: the set of points in space that are a given distance (radius) from a fixed point (centre)

Surface Area, $S = 4\pi r^2$
$= \pi d^2$

Volume, $V = \dfrac{4}{3}\pi r^3$
$= \dfrac{\pi d^3}{6}$

spread stable position: a position in sky diving in which the sky diver falls with trunk parallel to the ground with the arms folded at the elbow and the knees bent

spreadsheet: a computer-generated arrangement of data in rows and columns, where a change in one value can result in appropriate calculated changes in the other values

square: a rectangle with four equal sides

11 cm

Perimeter = 4 × Length of side

$$P = 4s$$

Area = (Length of side)^2

$$A = s^2$$

For the square shown: $P = 4(11 \text{ cm})$

$$= 44 \text{ cm}$$

$$A = (11 \text{ cm})^2$$

$$= 121 \text{ cm}^2$$

square root: a number which, when multiplied by itself, results in the given number

5 and –5 are the square roots of 25, since $5^2 = 25$ and $(-5)^2 = 25$. The notation $\sqrt{25}$ is reserved for the positive square root only.

stacked bar graph: a series of bar graphs on the same set of axes with bars stacked on top of each other, see *Tutorial 1.1*

standard form: for the equation of a line, the standard form is $Ax + By + C = 0$, where A, B, and C are integers; see *equation of a line*

statistics: the branch of mathematics that deals with the collection, organization, and interpretation of data

substituting into an expression: in an algebraic expression, replacing the letters with the indicated numbers or expressions each time they occur and simplifying according to the order of operations

Substitute $r = 4.5$ and $t = 3v$ into the expression $8r^2 - 2t$.

$$8r^2 - 2t = 8(4.5)^2 - 2(3v)$$
$$= 8(20.25) - 6v$$
$$= 162 - 6v$$

supplementary angles: two angles whose sum is 180°

∠1 and ∠2 are supplementary.

surface area: a measure of the area on the surface of a three-dimensional object; see *cube, cylinder,* and *sphere*

survey: an investigation of a topic to find out people's views

system of equations: when two or more equations are considered simultaneously

system of inequalities: when two or more inequalities are considered simultaneously

tangent: for an acute ∠A in a right triangle, the ratio of the length of the opposite side to the length of the adjacent side

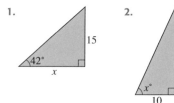

1.

15

42°

x

2.

22

x°

10

1. **In the triangle shown above left,**

$$\tan \angle A = \frac{\text{opposite}}{\text{adjacent}}$$ Substitute the known values.

$$\tan 42° = \frac{15}{x}$$ Use a calculator to obtain the value of tan 42°.

$$0.9004 = \frac{15}{x}$$ Clear the fraction.

$$0.9004 \times x = x \times \frac{15}{x}$$

$$\frac{0.9004x}{0.9004} = \frac{15}{0.9004}$$

$$x \doteq 16.659$$

2. **In the triangle shown above right,**

$$\tan \angle A = \frac{\text{opposite}}{\text{adjacent}}$$ Substitute the known values.

$$\tan x° = \frac{22}{10}$$ Convert the fraction into an equivalent decimal.

$$\tan x = 2.2$$ Use tan^{-1} (the "angle whose tangent is" function).

$$x \doteq 65.6°$$

tangent to a circle: a line that intersects the circle at only one point

tax exempt: a part of earned income on which the individual does not pay tax, such as CPP, RRSP, EI, and Registered Pension Plan contributions

taxable income: the part of the gross earnings on which income tax must be paid

term deposit: an account whose rate of interest is guaranteed for a specified term where withdrawal before the end of the term may result in the loss of interest

terminal velocity: the speed of a body falling under gravity when the net downward force is zero, beyond which there is no further acceleration

tessellation: a tiling pattern that covers the plane with no gaps or overlaps

thermocouple: an electrical device for measuring temperature differences

three-dimensional: having length, width, and depth, or height

ticketed price: the price placed on an item offered for sale

tolerance interval: the interval between the greatest and least acceptable measurements; see *Tutorial 7.6*

tolerance range: the difference between the largest and the smallest acceptable measurements; see *Tutorial 7.6*

trajectory: the path of an object as it moves through the air

transit: a device used by surveyors to measure horizontal angles and distances

trend: general pattern of a relationship; general direction, or tendency of the data

triangle: a three-sided polygon

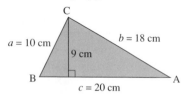

Perimeter = Sum of the three sides

$$= a + b + c$$
$$= 10 \text{ cm} + 18 \text{ cm} + 20 \text{ cm}$$
$$= 48 \text{ cm}$$

Area $= \frac{1}{2}$(Base)(Height)

$$= \frac{1}{2}bh$$
$$= \frac{1}{2}(20 \text{ cm})(9 \text{ cm})$$
$$= 90 \text{ cm}^2$$

An alternative formula, known as Heron's formula, is useful for finding the area of a triangle when the lengths of the three sides are known but the height is not.

Area $= \sqrt{s(s-a)(s-b)(s-c)}$ where $s = \frac{1}{2}(a+b+c)$

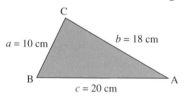

For the triangle shown:

$s = \frac{1}{2}(10 + 18 + 20)$ cm

$\quad = \frac{1}{2}(48)$ cm

$\quad = 24$ cm

$A = \sqrt{24(24-10)(24-18)(24-20)}$

$\quad = \sqrt{24(14)(6)(4)} \text{ cm}^4$

$\quad = \sqrt{8064} \text{ cm}^4$

$\quad \doteq 90 \text{ cm}^2$

The interior angles in any triangle add up to 180°. If the measures of two angles within a triangle are known, the third can be calculated by adding the measures of the two known angles and subtracting this from 180°.

if $\angle A = 35°$ and $\angle B = 48°$

then $\angle C = 180° - (35° + 48°)$

$\quad = 97°$

trigonometric ratios: see *cosine, sine,* and *tangent*

two-dimensional: having length and width, but no thickness, height, or depth

uncertainty of measurement: one-half the precision of the instrument used to make the measure; see *Tutorial 7.3*

unit price: the price of one item, or the price for a particular mass or volume of an item

validity: an indicator of how well a test measures what it is supposed to measure; a sample statistic is valid if it closely approximates the quantity for the population

variable: a letter or symbol used to represent a quantity that can vary

variable cost: cost, such as materials, that changes with the number of items produced

vernier caliper: an instrument that can be used to measure an object to the nearest 0.01 cm

vertex: the corner of a figure or solid

vertex

vertex of a parabola: the point where the axis of symmetry of a parabola meets the parabola; the minimum or maximum point or value of a parabola; see *Tutorial 2.2*

vertical exaggeration: to increase the vertical scale compared to the horizontal scale

vertical intercept: the vertical coordinate of the point at which the graph of the line or function intersects the vertical

volume: the amount of space occupied by an object

wage: monies that are earned hourly, daily, or by piecework. This may include gratuities or overtime pay; see *Tutorial 5.1*

warm front: a term used in weather forecasts to indicate the leading edge of a warm air mass; see *Tutorial 1.5*

weather map: a map that connects places with the same barometric pressure and places with the same temperature by using isobars and isotherms. These maps are used to help predict the weather.

whole numbers: the set of numbers 0, 1, 2, 3, ...; see *number systems*

wholesale price: see *cost price*

x-axis: the horizontal number line on a coordinate grid

x-intercept: the *x*-coordinate where the graph of a line or function intersects the *x*-axis; see *horizontal intercept*

y-axis: the vertical number line on a coordinate grid

y-intercept: the *y*-coordinate where the graph of a line or function intersects the *y*-axis; see *vertical intercept*

zeros of a function: the values of x for which a function $y = f(x)$ has the value 0

Answers

CHAPTER 1 GRAPHS
TUTORIAL 1.1
Practise Your Prior Skills, page 4

1. a) $0–9   **b)** 23

2. a) Frequencies: 3, 3, 4, 3, 2, 7, 4, 1, 1, 2
   c) 180-184 cm

3. a) $12 000
   b) $24, $22. Explanations may vary. As sales increase, the overhead costs contribute less to the sale price per unit.
   c) 600   **d)** $2000, initial production costs.

4. a) 28   **b)** Britain, Netherlands

EXERCISES, page 14
Checking Your Skills

1. a) Estimates may vary. About 4.3 million male births and 4 million female births per year. 4.3 : 4
   b) Explanations may vary. In each category, there are more males than females.
   c) No; explanations may vary.
   d) Explanations may vary. There are fewer people as the age ranges increase because people die.
   e) Estimates may vary. About 66 million

2. a) Canadian population slightly decreased in the first three age ranges, or in the last 30 years. Ethiopian population greatly decreases in the same time period. Conclusions may vary. Ethiopia has a higher infant mortality rate than Canada.
   b) No, Ethiopian birth rate has grown steadily without significant swellings or reductions.
   c) Canadian life span exceeds Ethiopian life span. More than 15% of Canadians are over 60 whereas less than 5% of Ethiopians survive that age.
   d) Ethiopia

3. a) 26: 25, no significant change
   b) The 25–45 age group exceeds the age groups directly before and after it. 1946–1966
   c) There are not many people ages 52–60 on the 1991 graph.
   d) There are not many people ages 16–22 on the 1961 graph.

4. a) August   **b)** September and October
   c) August
   d) Low sales in the winter months, greater sales in summer months
   e) Peak in summer and decline through the winter
   f) There are no sales through February and March. Explanations may vary.

5. a) 1999

b) There is almost no growth for 0–14 and 15–44. There will be an increase in 45–64 during the years 2000–2010. The greatest increase will be in senior citizens from now till 2036. Overall there is a gradual increase.
   c) 30, 44   **d)** Estimates may vary; 2038

6. a) $112 500   **b)** $237 500   **c)** $125 000   **d)** $75 000

7. a) B represents total costs, A represents revenue
   b) 1000   **c)** $20 000   **d)** $10 000

8. a) 16 December 1995, 23 March 1996, 6 April 1996
   b) 4 November 1995   **c)** 9 December 1995
   d) Influenza A peaks over a period of 6 weeks and then falls quickly for 4 weeks. It then follows a rise and shrink cycle until it completely dies.
   e) Influenza A   **f)** Explanations may vary.

Extending Your Thinking

9. Descriptions may vary.

TUTORIAL 1.2
Practise Your Prior Skills, page 21

1. The intercepts are (0,6) and (2.4,0).

Investigation 1, page 22

1. 70 m, 65 m

2. There were no summer games in 1982. The years 1940 and 1944 are missing data entries. (World War II)

3. Values between summer Olympics are meaningless.

4. Conclusions may vary. Performance has improved over time.

5. Answers may vary.

Investigation 2, page 23

Answers may vary.

EXERCISES, page 26
Checking Your Skills

1. a) Continuous   **b)** Discrete   **c)** Discrete
   d) Discrete   **e)** Continuous   **f)** Continuous

2. b) Continuous since there is still population in the in-between years
   c) Estimates may vary; 3.9 million, interpolation
   d) Estimates may vary; 4.1 million, extrapolation

3. b) Continuous   **c)** Estimates may vary; $54.5 billion
   d) Answers may vary; $61.1 billion

4. a) May–September, November, December
   b) January–April, October   **c)** Borrow funds, finance
   d) Costs

5. a) 0–6 months, 2 years 3 months–2 years 7 months, 4 years 5 months–4 years 8 months.
   b) $6\frac{1}{2}$ months, 1 year 6 months to 1 year 9 months, 2 years 3 months, 2 years 7 months, 4 years 5 months, 4 years 8 months
   c) Responds with decrease   **d)** Increases

e) Answers may vary. To show the interdependence of the species

6. a) Continuous except at $x = 1.5$ h   **b)** 400 pounds
c) First: The flight of the helicopter drains fuel. Second: The helicopter refuels completely. Third: The helicopter sits for half an hour. Fourth: The flight of the helicopter drains fuel. Fifth: The helicopter sits for fifteen minutes.

7. a) Answers may vary. 17 per 1000, 10.3 per 1000, 8 per 1000
b) Explanations may vary. Decreasing death rate. Downward sloping curve.
c) Answers may vary, 14.8 per 1000. It was lower than the actual figure. World War I
d) 5 per 1000. Descriptions may vary.

8. a) No, the points should not be joined since the amount increases at the end of the year when the interest is earned.
b) Approximately $1617.43

Extending Your Thinking

9. Answers may vary.
a) Birth rates decreased during the Great Depression, the society aged, and the median age increased.
b) Baby boomers were born. The proportion of children increased, lowering the median age.
c) Since 1970 there has been a general decline in the birth rate. This results in an increase in the median age of our society.

TUTORIAL 1.3
Investigation 1, page 31

1. Height: 2 vs. 4 units; Width: 2 vs. 4 units; Area: 4 vs. 16 square units

2. The area is quadrupled.

3. Height: 2 vs. 4 units; Width: 2 vs. 2 units; Area: 4 vs. 8 square units

4. The area is doubled.

5. Diagram B; explanations may vary.

6. Explanations may vary. The construction levels did not quadruple.

Investigation 2, page 32

2. A appears to change the least, B appears to change the most.

3. Changes the look of the graph; reduce the range.

4. Labelled scales and units

5. Answers may vary; shows changes.

Investigation 3, page 33

3. E   **4.** A and B
5. Answers may vary.   **6.** Answers may vary.

EXERCISES, page 35
Checking Your Skills

1. a) $2 000 000, $8 000 000   **b)** The bill sizes are not equal.

2. The pie pieces do not represent true data values.

3. The slanted graph suggests that the upper years are greater than they are.

4. Answers may vary; no scale

5. a) How you can increase salary based on increased ability and experience.
b) No vertical or horizontal scale is given.

Extending Your Thinking

6. Answers may vary.

TUTORIAL 1.4
EXERCISES, page 40
Checking Your Skills

1. b) Answers may vary.

2. a) Descriptions may vary.   **b)** Descriptions may vary.

4. Answers may vary.

6. b) Answers may vary.

Extending Your Thinking

8. Answers may vary.

TUTORIAL 1.5
Investigation 1, page 45

1. 100 m   **2.** 400 m; between 0 m and 100 m

3. 650 m   **4.** Over 700 m; within 100 m

5. No. Explanations may vary. **6.** No; explanations may vary.

7. Cliffs, mountains, canyon

8. U

9. V

EXERCISES, page 49
Checking Your Skills

1. 1D, 2E, 3B, 4C, 5A

2. a) 1300 m   **b)** 600 m   **c)** 390 m   **d)** 400 m

5. a) Answers may vary.   **b)** Vancouver
c) Answers may vary.

6. Answers may vary.

Extending Your Thinking

7. Answers may vary.

CONSOLIDATING YOUR SKILLS
What Should I Be Able to Do?, page 55

1. b) Discrete

d) ii, y values are close to min and max y values in table and therefore concentrates on the 5 mentioned years.

2. a) October **b)** March, October
c) September **d)** October
e) 76 **f)** 96 **g)** 172

3. Discrete

4. b) Continuous **c)** 28.0 cm
d) 20.8 cm **e)** 27 weeks, 3 days

5. a) Western **b)** 900 m; 400 m
c) Mountain, south **d)** 1598 m

CHAPTER 2 NON-LINEAR FUNCTIONS
TUTORIAL 2.1
Practise Your Prior Skills, page 64

1. a) x^{12} **b)** 3 **c)** $\frac{1}{3x^3}$ **d)** $\frac{3}{y^4}$

2. a) All real numbers **b)** $x \geq 1$, $g(x) \geq 0$
c) All real numbers; $h(x) \geq 2$

Investigation 1, page 64

4. $y = 600\left(2^{\frac{x}{30}}\right)$
5. $500(1.023^x)$

Investigation 2, page 66

Answers may vary.

EXERCISES, page 71
Checking Your Skills

1. b) $y = 2000\left(2^{\frac{t}{5}}\right)$
d) 10 556, 55 715

2. b) $y = 12\ 349.85(1.01^x)$ **c)** During the 1970s
d) Answers may vary.
e) $y = 0.000\ 040\ 03(1.016^x)$. Answers may vary.

3. a)

Year	Populations (millions)	Year	Populations (millions)
1995	2.30	2003	3.03
1996	2.38	2004	3.13
1997	2.46	2005	3.24
1998	2.55	2006	3.36
1999	2.64	2007	3.48
2000	2.73	2008	3.60
2001	2.83	2009	3.72
2002	2.93	2010	3.85

b) $y = 2\ 300\ 000(1.035^x)$
d) Approximately 4 500 000
e) 2018

4. a) $A = 100\ (0.5^{0.000\ 18t})$ **c)** 8.2%
d) Approximately 7535 years

5. a) 25 years **b)** 6% **c)** 82 years

6. a) $y = 7000(1.09)^x$ **b)** 8 years **c)** $19 688

7. a) $y = 39.20(1.52)^x$ **b)** Approximately 2 600 000

Extending Your Thinking

8. a) $T = 76(0.992^t) + 24$; 220 s **b)** $T = 100(0.9943^t)$

TUTORIAL 2.2
Investigation 1, page 75
Part A

Answers may vary.

Part B

2. (1, 5); maximum height of 5 m after 1 s. **3.** 0.3 s; 1.7 s
4. (0, 0), (2, 0); the ball was in the air for 2 s.
5. It is one-half the total time the ball was in the air.

Investigation 2, page 77

1. a) Parabola, yes it has a minimum **b)** (1, 0), (3, 0); 0
c) (0, 3); 0; 3. Since $x = 0$, y = constant term.
d) (2, −1) **e)** $x = 2$ **f)** real numbers ≥ -1

2. i) a) Parabola, maximum **b)** (−3, 0), (1, 0); 0
c) (0, 3); 0; 3 **d)** (−1, 4)
e) $x = -1$ **f)** Real numbers ≤ 4
ii) a) Parabola, minimum **b)** None
c) (0, 7); 0; 7 **d)** (2, 3)
e) $x = 2$ **f)** Real numbers ≥ 3
iii) a) Parabola, minimum **b)** (1, 0); 0
c) (0, 5); 0; 5 **d)** (1, 0)
e) $x = 1$ **f)** Real numbers ≥ 0
iv) a) Parabola, maximum **b)** (0, 0); 0
c) (0, 0); 0; 0 **d)** (0, 0)
e) $x = 0$ **f)** Real numbers ≤ 0
v) a) Parabola, maximum **b)** none
c) (0, −1); 0; −1 **d)** (0, −1)
e) $x = 0$ **f)** Real numbers ≤ -1
vi) a) Parabola, maximum **b)** (−1, 0), ($\frac{1}{3}$, 0); 0
c) (0, 1); 0; 1 **d)** ($-\frac{1}{3}$, $\frac{4}{3}$)
e) $x = -\frac{1}{3}$ **f)** Real numbers $\leq \frac{4}{3}$

EXERCISES, page 79
Checking Your Skills

1. a) i and ii **b)** Explanations may vary.

2. a) (−1, −2); $x = -1$; −2, 0; R; $y \geq -2$
b) (3, 4); $x = 3$; 1, 5, −5; R; $y \leq 4$
c) (2, −1); $x = 2$; no zeros, −5; R; $y \leq -1$
d) (−4, −8); $x = -4$; −7, −1, 6; R; $y \geq -8$

3 a) $x = -1.25$;
(−1.25, −6.125);
(−3, 0), (0.5, 0), (0, −3);
x and y real numbers
and $y \geq -6.125$

b) $x = -1$;
(−1, 35);
(−3.65, 0), (1.65, 0); (0, 30);
x and y real numbers and
$y \leq 35$

c) $x = 3.5$
(3.5, −2.25)
(2, 0), (5, 0); (0, 10);
x and y real numbers and $y \geq -2.25$

3. d) $x = -3.88$;
(−3.88, 68.06);
(−8, 0), (0.25, 0); (0,8);
x and y real numbers
and $y \leq 68.06$

e) $x = 2$;
(2, 5);
(−1.2, 0), (5.2, 0); (0, 3);
x and y real numbers
and $y \leq 5$

f) $x = 0.50$;
 $(0.50, 6.75)$;
 $(-1, 0), (2, 0); (0, 6)$;
 x and y real numbers and $f(x) \leq 6.75$

4. a) $(-6, 0), (2, 0)$ **b)** $(-8, 0), (0.25, 0)$
 c) $(0.5, 0), (5, 0)$ **d)** $(-1, 0), (2, 0)$

5. b) $t \geq 0, h \leq 82$ **c)** 51.4 m

6. b) $(15.6, 1197.5)$ **c)** 12.7 s
 d) $0 \leq t \leq 31.3, 0 \leq h \leq 1197.5$

Extending Your Thinking

7. a) Quadratic   **b)** $(1, 0), (5, 0)$ **c)** $x = 3$
 d) i) $(3, 0), (7, 0), x = 5$ **ii)** $(-2, 0), (6, 0), x = 2$

TUTORIAL 2.3
EXERCISES, page 90
Checking Your Skills

1. a) $h(t) = -4.9t^2 + 20t + 50$ **b)** $h(t) = -4.9t^2 + 10t$
 c) $h(t) = -4.9t^2 + 3000$ **d)** $h(t) = -0.815t^2 + 50t$

2. a) $y = 2x^2 - 5x + 1$, minimum
 b) $y = -x^2 + 20x$, maximum
 c) $y = x^2 - 7x + 10$, minimum
 d) $y = -5x^2 + 100x$, maximum

3. a)

($) Price/Canoe	500	550	600	650
Number Sold	60	56	52	48
($) Total Revenue	30 000	30 800	31 200	31 200

b) $R = -0.08S + 100$ **d)** $625; $31 250

4. a)

($) Price/Ticket	50	60	70	80	90
Number Sold	200	195	190	185	180
($) Total Revenue	10 000	11 700	13 300	14 800	16 200

$R = -0.5S + 225$
 c) $225; $25 312.50

5. b) $y = 300x - 2800$ **c)** 17.7 months
 d) $7000

6. a) $h(t) = -4.9t^2 + 100t$ **c)** 510.2 m
 d) 20.4 s   **e)** 684.1 m

7. a) $h(t) = -4.9t^2 + t + 35$ **c)** 35.05 m
 d) 2.8 s

8. a) $(0, 0), (3.4, 0.73), (6.8, 0)$ **b)** $y = -0.06x^2 + 0.43x$

9. a) $(0, 0), (22.5, 4.2), (45, 0)$ **b)** $y = -0.0083x^2 + 0.37x$

10. b) 3.2 m   **c)** 7.95 m

11. b) 4.9 m   **c)** 5.9 m   **d)** 2.5 m

Extending Your Thinking

12. 1.43 s

TUTORIAL 2.4
Investigation 1, page 95

3. $(-1.45, 2.1), (3.45, 11.9)$

4. Descriptions may vary, when $y > 0$, $x < -1.45$ and $x > 3.45$ and when $y < 0$, $-1.45 < x < 3.45$.

5. $3.45, -1.45$. The zeros are the x–intercepts   **6.** Equal

7. Descriptions may vary. *Method 1:* graph the equations $y = x^2$ and $y = 5x - 4$ and find points of intersection. *Method 2:* find the zeros of $x^2 - 5x + 4 = 0$

8. a) $-\frac{1}{3}, -2$ **b)** $-1.14, 4.53$

Investigation 2, page 96
Activity A

d) $y = 0.5x^2 - 0.5x$

Activity B

d) $y = 4x^3 - 98x^2 + 588x$

Activity C

d) $y = 100(1.035)^x$

2. $0.5x^2 - 0.5x = 200$; 20

3. $4x^3 - 98x^2 + 588x = 750$; 6.66 cm by 14.68 cm by 7.68 cm

4. $100(1.035)^x = 10\ 000$; 133.88 min

5. Answers may vary.   **6.** Answers may vary.

EXERCISES, page 100
Checking Your Skills

1. a) 1.85   **b)** $4.03, -4.03$ **c)** 2.33

2. a) $h = 0$; $-4.9t^2 + 75.0t + 2.3 = 0$ **b)** 15.3 s
 c) No   **d)** 285.8 m

3. a) $h = 0$; $-4.9t^2 + 8.8t + 3 = 0$ **b)** 2.09 s
 c) 1.8 s

4. a) 2 cm; $A = 4\pi - \pi r^2$ **b)** 1.45 cm   **c)** 10 cm^2

5. a) $y = -93.86x^2 + 3219.29x - 7040$ **b)** $14.70, $19.60
 c) $14.70, $19.60   **d)** $17.15

6. 105.60 km/h   **7.** 25

8. a) $V = 8\pi r^2 + \frac{4}{3}\pi r^3$ **b)** 3.22 m

9. a) $V = 11\ 250\pi h + \frac{1}{6}\pi h^3$ **b)** 149.03 m

10. 2026

11. a) Exponential equation, $y = 1000.01(1.105)^x$
 b) 11.0 years   **c)** 10.5%

12. b) Exponential, $y = 99.98(0.6)^x$ **c)** 9

Extending Your Thinking

13. a) 1440 min   **c)** 35 848.5 km
 d) 265 266.7 km   **e)** 11 052.8 km/h

CONSOLIDATING YOUR SKILLS
What Should I Be Able To Do?, page 107

1. b) Quadratic, $y = 0.004x^2 - 13.994x + 13\ 701.112$
 d) Yes, $(1957, 7.54)$ **e)** 17.92, 29.78   **f)** 7.68

2. a) $y = 1000\ (1.15)^x$ **c)** 27 858.6   **d)** 28.22 h

3. $(2.25, -15.125)$; x and y real numbers and $y \geq -15.125$; $x = 2.25$; $(-0.5, 0), (5, 0), (0, -5)$

4. 26.5

5. a) $h(t) = -4.9t^2 + 60t + 20$ **c)** 203.7 m, 6.1 s

   d) 12.6 s

6. b) $102.412(0.876)^x$ **c)** 73.55 kPa

7. 2.7 cm

CHAPTER 3 LINEAR SYSTEMS
TUTORIAL 3.1
Practise Your Prior Skills, page 114

1. $(-8, 0)$ and $(0, 4)$

2. a) $y = -\frac{2}{3}x + 2$ **b)** $y = \frac{5}{2}x + \frac{1}{2}$

3. a) 2; -3 **b)** -4; 6   **c)** $-\frac{1}{3}$; -5

4. $y = \frac{3}{4}x - 2$ or $3x - 4y - 8 = 0$ **5.** $2x + y = 5$

Investigation 1, page 115

Answers may vary.

EXERCISES, page 121
Checking Your Skills

1. b

2. a) $(-2, -6)$ **b)** $(-1, -8)$ **c)** $(3, -2)$

3. a) $(-1, 6)$ **b)** $(-3, -5)$ **c)** $(-4, 2)$

4. b) Mass of one apple = 0.083 kg; Mass of the crate = 1.01 kg

5. b) $(40, 800)$ **c)** 40 s   **d)** 800 m

6. a) $(80, 280)$ **c)** 80 s   **d)** 280 m

7. a) Payment Plan with a Membership $(C = V + 30)$

Number of Visits	0	2	4	6	8	10	12
Cost ($)	30	32	34	36	38	40	42

Payment Plan without a Membership $(C = 5V)$

Number of Visits	1	2	4	6	8	10	12
Cost ($)	5	10	20	30	40	50	60

   c) 8 visits

8. a) $(300, 2.35)$ **b)** 300 h, $2.35   **c)** $1.40

9. b) $(5000, 3400)$ **c)** 5000 brochures, $3400
   d) Quick and Clear, Miles Ahead   **e)** $0.80, $0.65

10. a) $(75\,000, 125\,000)$
   b) 75 000 t of waste, 125 000 t of ash
   c) Model 1 will produce less ash; Model 1 = 90 000 t VS.
   Model 2 = 100 000 t
   d) Model 2 will produce less ash; Model 1 = 160 000 t VS.
   Model 2 = 150 000 t

11. b) 95 min
   c) Plan B is better for 100 min/month; Plan A = $66.50 VS.
   Plan B = $65.00
   d) Plan A is better for 50 min/month;
   Plan A = $39.00/50 min VS. Plan B = $52.50/50 min
   e) When phone usage does not exceed 95 min

Extending Your Thinking

12. b) $(-13.5, 26.8)$ and $(29.5, 5.2)$ **c)** 48.1 km

   d) No; $x^2 + y^2 = 900$ is not a linear equation.

TUTORIAL 3.2
Practise Your Prior Skills, page 125

1. $d = r \times t$; $60 = 0.75r$

2. $I = P \times r \times t$; $T = 15\,000 \times 0.08 \times 1$

EXERCISES, page 129
Checking Your Skills

1. Let x dollars be the cost of 1 shirt. Let y dollars be the cost of 1 sweater. $2x + 4y = 98$; $x + 3y = 69$

2. Let x dollars be the cost of 1 CD. Let y dollars be the cost of 1 tape. $3x + 2y = 72$; $x + 3y = 52$

3. Let the initiation fee be x dollars. Let the monthly fee be y dollars. $x + 5y = 170$; $x + 10y = 295$

4. Let the cost of 1 football be x dollars. Let the cost of 1 soccer ball be y dollars. $3x + y = 155$; $2x + 3y = 220$

5. Let x be the number of oil shares. Let y be the number of Zinco Mines shares. $x + y = 450$; $7.50x + 3.25y = 2100$

6. Let x dollars be invested at 7%. Let y dollars be invested at 10%. $x + y = 500$; $0.07x + 0.10y = 44$

7. Let x dollars be invested at 4.5%. Let y dollars be invested at 5%. $x + y = 800$; $0.045x + 0.05y = 39.75$

8. Let the speed of the plane in still air be s km/h . Let d be the distance travelled. $d = 2s + 40$; $d = 3s - 60$

9. Let t represent the time travelled. Let d represent the distance travelled. $d = 75(t + 2)$; $125t = 75(t + 2)$

10. Let s represent the speed in still water. Let d represent the distance travelled. $d = 4s + 32$; $d = 7s - 56$

11. Let x dollars be invested at 4%. Let y dollars be invested at 6%. $x + y = 1250$; $0.04x - 0.06y = 0$

Extending Your Thinking

12. 48.5 km/h, 727.5 km/h   **13.** $6.00/kg, $3.50/kg

TUTORIAL 3.3
Practise Your Prior Skills, page 131

1. a) $-x + 7y$ **b)** $3x - 2y + 5$ **c)** $2x + 12y$

2. a) $x + 2y = 6$ **b)** $4x - 3y = 8$ **c)** $x + 2y = 136$

3. a) $x = 1.5$ **b)** $x = -1$ **c)** $x = -6.25$

4. a) $y = -3x + 12$ **b)** $y = 5x - 8$ **c)** $y = \frac{2}{3}x + 3$

EXERCISES, page 136
Checking Your Skills

1. a, c

2. a) $(9, 105)$ **b)** $(2, 3)$ **c)** $(-2, -6)$

   d) $(-1, -8)$ **e)** $\left(3\frac{5}{11}, -3\frac{4}{11}\right)$ **f)** $(3, -2)$

3. a) $\left(\frac{1}{3}, 4\frac{2}{3}\right)$ **b)** $\left(3\frac{1}{3}, 1\frac{1}{3}\right)$ **c)** $(4, 3)$

   d) $(-3, -5)$ **e)** $(2, -3)$ **f)** $(0, -4)$

4. Approximately 6.36 h

5. a) Plan 1   **b)** 160 km; $60

6. a) 3 h   **b)** Pyramid stables; answers may vary.

7. Approximately $3.44/kg   **8.** 4 h; 7 h

9. a) Let the total earnings be E dollars. Let the sales revenue be S dollars.
b) $E = 0.04S + 500$; $E = 0.02S + 700$
c) $S = \$10,000$, $E = \$900$
d) $10 000   **e)** Second plan, $860

10. a) $d = 120t$; $d = 170t - 510$ **b)** 10.2 min   **c)** 1224 m

11. a) Amount of Meat: $0.25x$, $0.5y$, 1250
b) $0.25x + 0.50y = 1250$; $x - 3y = 0$
c) 3000; 1000   **d)** 4000

12. 5 cans of pop, 20 candy bars

13. $4.50, $0.75/additional word

14. Answers may vary.

Extending Your Thinking

15. 20 goals

TUTORIAL 3.4
Investigation 1, page 142

1. a) Graphs are the same line; 7; 10, $-\frac{10}{7}$
b) Infinite set of ordered pairs
c) Infinite number of solutions.
d) One line is a multiple of the other.
e) There will be an infinite number of solutions
f) Answers may vary.

2. a) Parallel lines; $\frac{2}{5}$; (0, −3), (7.5, 0); (0, 1), (−2.5, 0)
b) None
c) The lines have the same slope but different y-intercepts.
d) When there is no point of intersection or parallel.
f) None
g) When graphs are two parallel lines with no point in common, the system is inconsistent.

3. a) The graphs intersect at the point (3, 1).
b) One point
c) The equations have different slopes and y-intercepts and are independent.

Investigation 2, page 144

1. (3, 1)   **2.** (3, 1)

3. Every line intersects at the same point.

4. Dependent equations are the same line. The solution (3, 1) is unchanged in equations ③ and ④ since ③ is identical to ① and ④ is identical to ②.

5. Answers may vary.

6. In a system of two equations, introducing dependent equations, which are multiples of the original equations, does not change the solution of the system.

Investigation 3, page 144

1. $7x - 2y = 19$

3. This line intersects the others at the same point.

4. $3x + 4y = 13$

6. This line intersects the others at the same point.

7. Answers may vary.

EXERCISES, page 147
Checking Your Skills

1. a

2. a) One solution   **b)** Infinite number of solutions
c) No solutions

3. a) A and C, B and C   **b)** A and B

4. a) No solution   **b)** Infinite number of solutions
c) No solutions

5. a) Answers may vary.
$4x + 2y = 20$ $x - 3y = 12$
$6x + 3y = 5$ $5x - 15y = -60$
b) Answers may vary.
$x - 3y = 12$ $2x + y = 10$
$6x + 3y = 5$ $2x - 6y = 24$
c) Answers may vary.
$2x + y = 10$ $x - 3y = 12$
$4x + 2y = 20$ $2x - 6y = 24$

6. Answers may vary.
a) $3x - 4y = 5$ **b)** $4x - 4y = 5$ **c)** $6x - 8y = 24$

7. a) 3   **b)** $6x + 9y = 15$ **c)** $2y = 14$; $y = 7$
d) Substitute   **e)** $x = -8$

Extending Your Thinking

8. a) Yes   **b)** Yes

TUTORIAL 3.5
EXERCISES, page 153
Checking Your Skills

1. a) (3, 4)   **b)** (−1, 3)   **c)** (4, 3)

2. a) (5, 3)   **b)** (−1, 5)   **c)** (3, 4)

3. 35 km/h; 765 km/h   **4.** 100, 200

5. 466.7 km; 133.3 km

6. a) $v + t = 100$ **b)** $8v + 12t = 980$
c) 55 plates; 45 plates

7. b) $120r + 100f = 49\,000$; $180r + 150f = 73\,500$
c) Infinitely many solutions, for example $r = 100, f = 370$

8. 4; 8

9. a) $240m + b = 23$; $620m + b = 31$
b) $m = 0.02$, $b = 17.96$ **c)** $T = 0.02d + 17.96$
d) $T = 89.58°C$

10. b) 30.96; −47.99; $T = 30.96v - 47.99$ **c)** 44.89°C

11. a) Suppose f pounds of French roast, and k pounds of Kenyan roast is used.
b) $f + k = 50$; $4.95f + 3.75k = 217.50$
c) 25 pounds.; 25 pounds.

Extending Your Thinking

12. a) $x + y = 4$ **b)** $0.1x + 0.05y = 0.32$
  c) The nurse used 2.4 L of 10% solution and 1.6L of 5% solution.

13. a) $x + y = 500$; $0.6x + 0.35y = 250$
  b) 300 g of 60% silver alloy and 200 g of 35% silver alloy

CONSOLIDATING YOUR SKILLS
What Should I Be Able To Do?, page 161

1. a) $C = 10\ 000 + 8n$; $R = 10n$
  b) 5000 widgets; $50 000   **c)** $N = 50\ 000 + 5n$
  d) 13 333 widgets   **e)** (10 000, $100 000)
  g) $30 000; $50 000; $20 000
  h) Yes, explanations may vary. The profit will be greater.
  i) 14 286 widgets. Yes, explanations may vary.

2. (7.4, 6.8)   **3.** $\left(-\frac{8}{7}, 4\frac{3}{7}\right)$ **4.** (−2, 3)

5. a) 118.57 min, $73.71   **b)** Company A

6. a) $2L + 2W = 20$; $L - W = 3$; $L = 6.5m$, $W = 3.5m$

7. a)

	Number of People	Ticket Sales Revenue
Number of Adults	x	$10x$
Number of Students	y	$6y$
Totals	200	$1680

  b) $x + y = 200$; $10x + 6y = 1680$ **c)** 120; 80

8. a) $12x + 15y = 960$; $20x + 25y = 1600$
  b) Infinitely many solutions

9. a) One   **b)** Infinitely many   **c)** None

10. 2.78 s

CHAPTER 4 LINEAR PROGRAMMING
TUTORIAL 4.1
Practise Your Prior Skills, page 170

1. a) 6   **b)** 3, 4

2. a) $x \geq 2$ **b)** $x < 3$ **c)** $x > -1.5$

4. a) $x > -4$ **b)** $x \geq -2$ **c)** $y \leq -12$
  d) $x < -3$ **e)** $x > 6$

5. a) $y = -\frac{2}{3}x + 3$; $-\frac{2}{3}$; 3   **b)** $y = \frac{1}{2}x - 3$; $\frac{1}{2}$; −3

Investigation 1, page 171

3. Yes.

4. All x-coordinates in the region left of the line are less than 3.

5. All x-coordinates in the region right of the line are greater than 3.

9. Answers will vary. Draw a dotted line $x = 4$ and shade the region to the right of the line.

10. Draw a solid line $y = 1$ and shade the region below the line.

Investigation 2, page 172

4. Yes, they all fall on the line $x + 3y = 3$.

7. All points on or above the line will do.

8. $x + 3y < 3$

9. Answers will vary. Draw the equality, test points to the left and right, and shade the appropriate region.

TUTORIAL 4.2
EXERCISES, page 178
Checking Your Skills

3. Descriptions may vary.
  a) (0, −3) and (3, 1)   **b)** (3, 1) and (6, 0)
  c) (5, −2) and (10, 0)   **d)** (0, 2.5) and (10, 2)
  e) (3, 0) and (5, 1)   **f)** (0, 0) and (2, −3)
  g) (1, −12) and (8, 0)   **h)** (−2, 10) and (0, 4)

7. a) No more than 400 with a possible maximum equal to 400
  b) Fractional cycles are meaningless. The graph will be a group of points, not a shaded region.

8. a) Time is continuous since fractions of an hour are meaningful.

9. a) Explanations may vary. Isolate y on the left and divide both sides by the y term's coefficient.
  c) Fractions of a cycle are meaningless. (8, 15), (16, 9)

10. b) Explanations may vary. (5, 0), (10, 1)

Extending Your Thinking

11. $300x + 100y \leq 12\ 000$

TUTORIAL 4.3
EXERCISES, page 187
Checking Your Skills

1. a) $y < 2x + 3$; $y < 0.5x + 1$
  b) $y > -1.5x - 2.5$; $3y < 2x - 3$

2. a) $y \leq 2$ **b)** $x > -2$ **c)** $x - y > 0$

6. a) Explanations may vary.

7. a) Explanations may vary.

8. a) $x \leq 20$, $y \leq 30$, $x + y \leq 40$

Extending Your Thinking

10. a) $x > 0$, $y > 0$; $x + y \leq 10$; $xy \geq 20$ **b)** Yes

TUTORIAL 4.4
EXERCISES, page 195
Checking Your Skills

1. a) x motorcycles/day, y ATVs/day
  b) $x \leq 25$, $y \leq 35$; $x + y \leq 50$ **c)** $x \geq 0$; $y \geq 0$

2. a) x hours of basketball, y hours of golf
  b) $x \geq 0$, $y \geq 0$; $x + y \leq 12$; $12x + 7y \geq 100$

3. a) a type A flashlights, b type B flashlights
  b) $a \leq 50$, $b \leq 60$, $3a + 2b \leq 180$, $a \geq 0, b \geq 0$

4. a) x hours walking, y hours swimming
  b) $y \geq 0$, $y \leq 3$; $x + y \leq 5$; $5x + 6y \geq 29$, $x \geq 0$
  c) No, it's not possible.

5. *m* mountain bikes, *t* touring bikes
$m \geq 10, t \geq 10; 5x + 4y \leq 110$

6. a) *a* Type A tents, *b* Type B tents
$a \geq 10, b \geq 10; a + b \geq 50; 2a + 3b \leq 144; a + 2b \leq 84;$
$2a + b \leq 90$

b) Answers may vary; for example 23 type A tents and
30 type B tents or 25 type A's and 29 type B's

7. a) $x > y; 2x + 2y \leq 120; xy \geq 280, x > 0, y > 0$

Extending Your Thinking

8. Answers may vary.

TUTORIAL 4.5
Investigation, page 200

2. $P = 10x + 15y$ **3.** $12 = 2x + 3y$

4. (6, 0) represents 6 swim suits and no leotards.
(0, 4) represents no swim suits and 4 leotards.
(3, 2) represents 3 swim suits and 2 leotards.
All are feasible except (4.5, 1).

6. They are parallel lines.

7. (20, 10) is maximum with profit of \$350, (0, 0) is minimum
with \$0 profit.

8. **2.** $P = 10x + 5y$ **4.** Feasible points are whole numbers.
5. Answers may vary.   **6.** Parallel lines

7. (20, 10) is maximum with \$250 profit, (0, 0) is minimum
with \$0 profit.

9. The maximum value is less in exercise 8. The minimum
value is equal in exercise 8. The locations of the points are
the same.

10. The maximum or minimum values of the objective function
occur at the intersection of lines representing the
constraints.

EXERCISES, page 207
Checking Your Skills

1. a) $C = 40$ **b)** $T = 18$

2. $T = 48, 0$ **3.** 30 Type A jackets and 12 Type B jackets

4. 6 section A questions and 6 section B questions

5. 5 units, 5 units   **6.** 1410 km

7. a) 10 hats of the first type and 7.5 hats of the second type
b) Round the fractional value, ensuring that the new
numbers satisfy the constraints

Extending Your Thinking

8. 4.3 oz of cereal A, 2.9 oz of cereal B

CONSOLIDATING YOUR SKILLS
What Should I Be Able To Do?, page 213

1. Answers will vary.

3. a) (4, 6)   **b)** $C = -8$

5. a) Negative hours are meaningless. Sum of hours on
machine M is 24 and likewise on machine N.
b) Answers may vary, (4, 4), (1, 4)

6. a) Total time must not exceed 10 h and total energy burned
must not be less than 4800 calories.
b) Yes

7. a) $x \geq 0, y \geq 0, xy > 3, 2x + 2y \leq 8$

8. a) $P = 300x + 200y$
b) $x \geq 0; y \geq 0; x + y \leq 80; 3x + y \leq 120$
c) 20 ha corn, 60 ha wheat

9. 12 First class passengers; 36 Economy Class passengers

CHAPTER 5 FINANCE
TUTORIAL 5.1
Practise Your Prior Skills, page 222

1. a) 0.12   **b)** 0.07   **c)** 1.50   **d)** 0.06

2. a) \$3909.12   **b)** \$4.10

3. Approximately 5%

Investigation, page 222

1. (40, 240)

2. Answers may vary; the rate of pay increases to an overtime
rate.

3. 6, 9   **4.** The rate of pay in dollars per hour

5. \$510; 40 h @ \$6/h plus 30 h @ \$9/h

EXERCISES, page 226
Checking Your Skills

1. Answers may vary. An employer pays an employee only
when sales are made. An employee earns more when she
increases her sales.

2. Biweekly is 26 payments in one year; semi-monthly is 24
payments in one year.

3. Explanations may vary. If the first payday of the year is
January 1, there will be 53 paydays. It is not possible for
there to be fewer than 52 paydays.

4. \$2216.20; descriptions may vary.

5. \$12/h; flat rate per arrangement per hour earns only \$10/h.

6. a) \$336.50; wage   **b)** \$598.00; wage
c) \$681.00; commission   **d)** \$1087.50; piecework
e) \$1307.50; graduated commission
f) \$391.20; commission   **g)** \$2739.20; commission

7. Explanations may vary.   **8.** \$390.30

9. Answers may vary. For an 8-h day, the gross pay is the
same. The Fish House pays the most if the employee works
less than 8-h day whereas the Tea House is better if one
works longer than 8-h days.

10. b) When sales exceed \$30 000 per week the straight
commission option is the best. If Jay cannot maintain
sales of \$30 000 per week, then the alternative will give
him a larger pay check.
c) Answers may vary.

11. $23.75/h

TUTORIAL 5.2
EXERCISES, page 233
Checking Your Skills

1. $35.00; $28.94

2. Answers may vary. The TD1 is an income tax form that details an employee's claim code and determines the amount of tax which will be deducted.

3. Different provinces have different provincial income tax rates.

4. a) Increases **b)** Increases **c)** Increases **d)** Decreases

5. a) $30.39 **b)** $28.83 **c)** $28.90
  d) $243.80 **e)** $285.85 **f)** $29.72

6. Explanations may vary. CPP and EI are not affected by contributions to an RPP or RRSP. Income tax deductions are calculated on taxable income. The greater the RRSP or RPP contribution is the smaller the taxable income and, thus, the smaller the income tax.

7. a) Jackie   **b)** Jackie
  c) Jackie   **d)** Yes, she earns more.

8. a) $848.92   **b)** $927.87

9. a) $845.64   **b)** $848.59
  c) Explanations may vary; additional deductions for CPP, EI, and income tax are taken from the $5 weekly pay raise.

10. a) Estimates may vary. $655
  b) Lower; her income is at the high end of the tax bracket so she may pay more.
  c) Yes; A $200 contribution will move Alina into a lower tax bracket. This will decrease her overall income tax by approximately $151 each week.

11. a) Estimates may vary. $1379.99
  b) Lower, because the taxable income is close to the high end of the tax bracket.

12. a) $412.50 **b)** Estimates may vary. $313.50 **c)** 76%

Extending Your Thinking

13. a)

Claim Code	Income Tax Deducted ($)	Percent of Taxable Income Deducted	Claim Code	Income Tax Deducted ($)	Percent of Taxable Income Deducted
1	483.08	28%	6	409.45	24%
2	475.55	27%	7	393.65	23%
3	459.00	26%	8	377.85	22%
4	442.45	25%	9	362.05	21%
5	425.90	25%	10	346.25	20%

  c) Decreases
  d) Equations may vary; $y = -15.8x + 504.3$

TUTORIAL 5.3
EXERCISES, page 239
Checking Your Skills

1. a) 907 mL **b)** 400 g **c)** 450 g **d)** 6 and 6

2. a) $49.99 for 12 cassettes **b)** No; explanations may vary.

3. a) Suggestions may vary. The Dirksens were away from home for March, and in April the weather was warm.
  b) $97.31, due to 4% increase
  c) Explanations may vary. You will know how much will be paid out each month.

4. a) $366.25
  b) No, explanations may vary. By the end of June, the total payments are $3355, but the family will have saved only $2197.50.

5. a) $2350.02 **b)** $221.70 **c)** $214.31
  d) Answers may vary. Miki knows he will have fewer monthly payments and can avoid missing any.

6. $187.69

7. a) No, they have only saved U.S. $252
  b) Can $386.11

8. Can $312.00

9. Yes, explanations may vary. The greater the value of the Canadian dollar, the cheaper the holiday in U.S. dollars.

10. Explanations may vary; an exchange rate of 71% one way is equivalent to an exchange rate of approximately 140.8% the other way.

11. £63.39

12. No, all property taxes will increase by the same percentage but not the same amounts.

Extending Your Thinking

13. a) $6.31   **b)** $84.16
  c) $231 431.80 **d)** $1 051 962.74

TUTORIAL 5.4
Investigation 1, page 245

2. Oct 1 – Maintenance Fee $9.75 and Oct 10 – Withdrawal $60.00

3. $382.05

Investigation 2, page 245

1. A float is needed to be able to give change. You need to know the amount of the float to be able to calculate the amount of cash taken in.

2. Deduct the float from the amount in the till.

3. Add the total value of the card and debt transactions to the previous result.

4. Subtract the total value of refunds from the previous result.

6. $200

7. Total cash is $553.55; Subtotal is $1209.63; Total take is $1197.24; The subtotal includes the float and refunds so it is not the value of the day's sales. The total value of the day's sales is subtotal − float = $1009.63.

8. $997.24   **9. and 10.** Answers may vary.

EXERCISES, page 247

Checking Your Skills

1. Items in Balance column: 405.76, 89.50, 794.04, 784.09, 196.85, 1009.41; final balance is $1009.41.

2. Balance $1171; Cheque 126 – Pete's Garage should be $68 not $58; Subtract Printed Cheques and Service Charge from transaction record; Subtract Cheque 128 – United Way from bank statement; Subtract Cheque 129 – Wayside Apartments from bank statement; Add pay cheque to bank statement.

3. $1529.61

4. No; final balance is $21.50; there is $1.50 extra, due possibly to a recording error.

5.

Month	Previous Balance	Payment Made	Purchases Charged	Balance Due	Credit Charges	New Balance
Feb	$314.65	$100.00	$193.75	$408.40	$5.72	$414.12
Mar	$414.12	$150.00	$59.60	$323.72	$4.53	$328.25
Apr	$328.25	$140.00	$421.83	$610.08	$8.54	$618.62
May	$618.62	$200.00	$39.65	$458.27	$6.42	$464.69
June	$464.69	$250.00	$58.11	$272.80	$3.82	$276.62
July	$276.62	$150.00	$77.21	$203.83	$2.85	$206.68
Aug	$206.68	$120.00	$163.09	$249.77	$3.50	$253.27

Extending Your Thinking

6. Spreadsheets may vary. Check the monthly printout with your bank statement.

TUTORIAL 5.5

Investigation 1, page 250

1. $4
2. $8, $20, $40
3. $2, $1, 33¢

4. Explanations may vary; divide the interest in one year by 365 and multiply by 40.

5. Interest = Amount invested × rate of interest × time invested in years

Practise Your Prior Skills, page 252

1. a) $340(1.3)^3$ b) $2y^2$

2. a) x^8 b) x^6 c) x^0

Investigation 2, page 252

1.
2.
5.

Year	Principal for Year ($)	Interest ($)	Amount at End of Year ($)
1	1000.00	50.00	1050.00
2	1050.00	52.50	1102.50
3	1102.50	55.13	1157.63
4	1157.63	57.88	1215.51
5	1215.51	60.78	1276.29
6	1276.29	63.81	1340.10

3. $50.00, $1050.00 4. $1050.00 7. 1.05

9.

Year	Amount at End of Year
1	$1000(1.05) = 1000(1.05)^1$
2	$1000(1.05)(1.05) = 1000(1.05)^2$
3	$1000(1.05)(1.05)(1.05) = 1000(1.05)^3$
4	$1000(1.05)(1.05)(1.05)(1.05) = 1000(1.05)^4$
5	$1000(1.05)(1.05)(1.05)(1.05)(1.05) = 1000(1.05)^5$
6	$1000(1.05)(1.05)(1.05)(1.05)(1.05)(1.05) = 1000(1.05)^6$

10. $1000(1.05)^9$

EXERCISES, page 255

Checking Your Skills

1.

Investment	Amount of Simple Interest ($)	Principal ($)	Annual Interest Rate (%)	Time (years)
a	101.25	500.00	6.75	3
b	42.53	945.11	4.5	1
c	102.38	4 500.00	3.25	0.7
d	1250.00	10 000.00	5.68	2.2

2.

Year	Amount ($)
1	$450(1.045) = 470.25$
2	$450(1.045)^2 = 491.41$
3	$450(1.045)^3 = 513.52$
4	$450(1.045)^4 = 536.63$
5	$450(1.045)^5 = 560.78$

3. a) $281.22 b) $166.81 c) $531.31

4. a) $393.72 b) $235.84 c) $35.70

5. $856.91 6. $146 932.81

7. c) Approximately 23 years at 5%; 12 years at 10%
   d) No, the amount increases by a greater factor each year; for example, after 15 years, the amount has doubled from 5% to 10%; after 25 years, the amount has tripled from 5% to 10%.

Extending Your Thinking

8. b) i) Approximately 7.2% ii) Approximately 5 years

TUTORIAL 5.6

Computer Lab, page 258

3. The equivalent number is 2. There are 2 semi-annual periods in one year.

4. There are 12 compounding periods when interest is compounded monthly.

5. The formula in D6 is = $D$5*(1 + ($D$2/4))^(A6*4).

6. The greater the number of compounding periods, the greater the interest.

7. a) $3181.05, $3198.22, $3207.04, $3213.01
   b) $795.26, $799.55, $801.76, $803.25
   When the principal is doubled, the amount is doubled. When the principal is halved, the amount is halved.

8. a) $1343.92, $1346.86, $1348.35, $1349.35
   b) $1877.14, $1895.84, $1905.56, $1912.18
   c) $2478.23, $2529.77, $2557.15, $2576.06
   When the annual rate is increased, the amount is increased. When the annual rate is decreased, the amount is decreased.

9. Both rates produce the same amount. 10. $444

EXERCISES, page 262

Checking Your Skills

1. $98.23

2. a) 7.12% b) Approximately 10.3 years
   c) Approximately 10.1 years

3. a) 19.2 years b) 18.8 years c) 18.5 years

4. a) i) $97.97   **b) ii)** $117.94

5. $6190.43   **6.** $1753.51

7. Answers may vary.
  a) 1075.00 **b)** 1077.63 **c)** 1077.88, if interest rate is 7.5%

Extending Your Thinking

8. a) $816.48; $816.61; $816.62   **b)** $812.36
  c) Answers may vary; most people invest for much longer time periods.

TUTORIAL 5.7
Computer Lab, page 264

3. $93.00   **4.** $2222.64   **5.** $215.64

8. $129.09   **10.** $266.73

11. Explanations may vary. You will earn more money at the higher percentage rate.

EXERCISES, page 269
Checking Your Skills

1. $1091.38   **2.** $188.29

3. 17.8%   **4.** $353.54; $784.96

5. a) $125.34, $4512.24   **b)** $70.28, $1265.04
  c) $112.78, $2706.72

6. a) $512.24   **b)** $65.04   **c)** $206.72

7. $180.00

8. Option b earns $26.58 more interest in 1 year.

Extending Your Thinking

9. Monthly payments: $520.86; $406.70; $338.52; total costs: $18750.96; $19521.60; $20311.20

TUTORIAL 5.8
Practise Your Prior Skills, page 274

2. About 17.5 kg

EXERCISES, page 275
Checking Your Skills

1. a) Approximately 26%, 21%, 3%, 29%, 9%, 2%, 10%
  b) Overspending: transportation; recreation and education; underspending: housing and utilities; savings; miscellaneous; within guidelines: food and clothing; health and personal

2. a) $8640 to $10 560   **b)** $6400 to $8320
  c) $3840 to $4480   **d)** $1920 to $3200

3. Budgets may vary.

4. Explanations may vary. The deficit is the difference between what you budget for and what you spend. The debt is the deficit that accumulates over time.

5. Budgets and graphs may vary.

6. Budgets and explanations may vary.

7. Budgets and explanations may vary.

Extending Your Thinking

8. Budgets may vary.

CONSOLIDATING YOUR SKILLS
What Should I Be Able To Do?, page 281

1. b) Answers may vary.   **c)** Answers may vary.

2. The first job paying $17/h

3. Estimates may vary. $476.85

4. $456.30   **5.** $1077.62   **6.** Can $1.51

7. a) $3336.19   **b)** $1434.40

8. Approximately 21.25 years   **9.** $6593

10. Approximately 7.18%

11. a) $398.89   **b)** $573.36

CHAPTER 6 CIRCLES
TUTORIAL 6.2
Practise Your Prior Skills, page 300

2. Diameters

Investigation 1, page 301

6. The midpoint   **13.** CE = ED

14. The distances will be equal; the midpoint

17. The line that passes through the centre of the circle, and is perpendicular to the chord, bisects the chord.

Investigation 2, page 302

7. The centre of the circle   **8.** The centre of the circle

11. The perpendicular bisector of a chord always passes through the centre of the circle.

Practise Your Prior Skills, page 303

1. a) 12.81   **b)** 12.69   **c)** 10.95

EXERCISES, page 307
Checking Your Skills

1. a) 4   **b)** 5   **c)** 8   **d)** 2.24
  e) 6   **f)** 8   **g)** 2.95   **h)** 9.26

2. 2.68 m   **3.** 35.77 km   **5.** 1.53 m

6. Answers may vary.   **7.** 7.5 cm

8. c) Answers may vary. It is more cost effective to have a smaller manhole opening but it may not be big enough to manoeuvre.

Extending Your Thinking

10. 1.62 : 1; they are the same

TUTORIAL 6.3

Investigation 1, page 313

11. $\angle BAC$ is double $\angle BDC$.

12. $\angle BAC$ will always be twice $\angle BDC$.

14. The measure of the inscribed angle is one-half of the central angle.

Investigation 2, page 315

9. $\angle ADB$ is a 90° angle

10. It will always be a right angle.

12. An angle inscribed in a semicircle is always 90°.

Investigation 3, page 316

7. The measures of $\angle BDC$ and $\angle BEC$ are the same.

8. They will be the same.

10. The measures of inscribed angles subtended by the same arc of a circle are equal.

EXERCISES, page 319
Checking Your Skills

1. a) 60° **b)** 90° **c)** 35°
   d) 64° **e)** 30° **f)** 220°

2. a) $x = 65°, y = 65°$ **b)** $x = 50°, y = 55°$
   c) $x = 25°, y = 35°$ **d)** $x = 90°, y = 38°$
   e) $x = 110°, y = 35°$ **f)** $x = 80°, y = 40°$

3. a) Explanations may vary. Some players have a shorter distance to get the puck in the goal and a better angle for their shot.
   b) In an arc or semicircle with the goal as the centre

4. Answers may vary. Place the square on a blank sheet of paper and mark the ends and the point on the top A, B, C respectively. AB is the diameter of the circle. Flip the square over and mark D, the point of the square on the other side of the circle. Draw lines between AB and CD so they intersect at the circle's origin.

5. The points form an arc of a circle. Explanations may vary.

6. c) Answers may vary.

Extending Your Thinking

7. $\angle ACB + \angle ADB = 180°$. Explanations may vary.

TUTORIAL 6.4

Investigation 1, page 324

10. $\angle ABD$ is always a right angle.

11. The angle will always be a right angle.

13. The angle between the radius drawn to a point of tangency and the tangent at the point is 90°.

Investigation 2, page 326

8. CE = ED **9.** They will be the same.

12. The lengths of the tangents to a circle from an external point are equal.

Investigation 3, page 328

11. $\angle EBF = \angle EDB$ **12.** They will be equal.

14. The angle between a tangent and a chord is equal to the inscribed angle on the opposite side of the chord.

Practise Your Prior Skills, page 333

1. a) 55° **b)** 132° **c)** 45° **d)** 52°

2. a) Yes **b)** Yes

EXERCISES, page 333
Checking Your Skills

1. a) $x = y = 14.1$ **b)** $x = 19.4, y = 19$
   c) $x = 12, y = 7$ **d)** $x = 18.3 = y$
   e) $x = 63°, y = 126°$ **f)** $x = y = 75°$

2. a) $x = 30°, y = 60°$ **b)** $x = 40°, y = 25°$

3. a) $x = 90°, y = 135°$ **b)** $x = 80°, y = 100°$
   c) $x = 50°, y = 130°$ **d)** $x = 110°, y = 70°$
   e) $x = y = 47.5°$ **f)** $x = 40°, y = 70°$

4. b) Answers may vary, for example a nautilus shell

5. 6606 km

6. 7.38 m. Add extra length for connecting the straps together

7. Explanations may vary.

Extending Your Thinking

8. 48.3 cm **9.** 43.2 inches

TUTORIAL 6.5

Investigation 1, page 338

1. a)

Number of Sides in a Polygon	Number of Triangles Formed	Sum of the Interior Angles of the Polygon (°)
3	1	180
4	2	2(180) = 360
5	3	3(180) = 540
6	4	4(180) = 720
7	5	5(180) = 900
8	6	6(180) = 1080
9	7	7(180) = 1260
10	8	8(180) = 1440
11	9	9(180) = 1620
12	10	10(180) = 1800

b) 15; 2700° **c)** $S = 180(n - 2)$

2. a) $S = 90(2)(n - 2)$ **b)** $S = 180n - 360$
   c) Answers may vary.

3. a) 360° **b)** 360° **c)** See 1a)
   d) They are the same. **e)** Yes; explanations may vary.

Investigation 2, page 340

6. They add up to 180°.

7. They will always be supplementary.

9. The opposite angles of a cyclic quadrilateral are supplementary.

Practise Your Prior Skills, page 342

1. a) 48° **b)** 135°

EXERCISES, page 343
Checking Your Skills

1. a) 720°   **b)** 1800°   **c)** 720°   **d)** 1080°

2. a) $x = 80°$, $y = 70°$ **b)** $x = 90°$, $y = 105°$
c) $x = 60°$, $y = 50°$ **d)** $x = 100°$, $y = 140°$

3. 130°

4. 4 4-sided polygons and 3 hexagons

5. 120°   **6.** $\dfrac{180(n-2)}{n}$

CONSOLIDATING YOUR SKILLS
What Should I Be Able To Do?, page 349

1. d) They are the equal.   **e)** They will always be equal.
g) Chords of a circle of equal length are equidistant from the centre of the circle.

2. a) 24   **b)** 4.9   **c)** 6.4

3. Answer may vary.

4. a) 3 feet   **b)** 8 feet

5. a) 6   **b)** 1.3   **c)** 5.7

6. a) $x = y = 90°$ **b)** $x = 120°$, $y = 60°$
c) $x = 25°$, $y = 50°$ **d)** $x = y = 51°$

7. a) $x = 125°$, $y = 85°$ **b)** $x = 50°$, $y = 70°$
c) $x = 80°$, $y = 100°$ **d)** $x = 40°$, $y = 80°$

8. 917.25 km   **9.** 10.6 cm

10. a) $180(n-2)$
b) Divide 180 by 2 and compensate by multiplying the brackets by 2.
c) 1260°

11. a) $x = 115°$, $y = 147.5°$ **b)** $x = 70°$, $y = 40°$

12. 12 cm

CHAPTER 7 MEASUREMENT
TUTORIAL 7.1
Practise Your Prior Skills, page 358

1. a) 19 : 25   **b)** 5 : 4   **c)** 3 : 1

2. 2.75 kg   **3.** $\dfrac{25}{32}$

4. 350 000 cm   **5.** 0.0134 m

Investigation 1, page 360

1. 17 500 cm by 5000 cm

2. 0.0004   **3.** 7 cm by 2 cm

5. 1 cm = 25 m, $\dfrac{1}{2500}$

6. a) Half   **b)** Double

Investigation 2, page 361

Answers may vary.

EXERCISES, page 363
Checking Your Skills

3. b) 9 cm

5. a) Enlargement   **b)** Answers may vary.

9. Answers may vary.
d) The straight line is less than or equal to the actual journey.

Extending Your Thinking

10. Answers may vary.

TUTORIAL 7.2
EXERCISES, page 370
Checking Your Skills

Answers may vary.

Extending Your Thinking

Answers may vary.

TUTORIAL 7.3
Investigation 1, page 374

1. to 7. Answers may vary.

8. The uncertainty of the sum is the sum of the uncertainties of the individual measurements.

9. The uncertainty of the difference is the sum of the uncertainties of the individual measurements.

10. The uncertainty of a sum or difference of measurements is the sum of the uncertainties of the individual measurements.

Investigation 2, page 375

1. 1. to 7. Answers may vary.

8. The uncertainty of the sum is the sum of the uncertainties of the individual measurements.

9. The uncertainty of the difference the sum of the uncertainties of the individual measurements.

10. The uncertainty of a sum or difference of measurements is the sum of the uncertainties of the individual measurements.

2. Yes

3. The uncertainty of a sum or difference of measurements is the sum of the uncertainties of the individual measurements.

4. (4.427 ± 0.0055) m, (3.813 ± 0.0055) m

EXERCISES, page 378
Checking Your Skills

1. a) ± 0.05 cm   **b)** ± 0.5 mL   **c)** ± 0.005 mm
d) ± 0.05 inches   **e)** ± 0.05 pounds   **f)** $\pm 0.05°$C

2. a) 37.40 ± 0.01 mm, 15.06 ± 0.01 mm
  b) 920 ± 1 m, 114 ± 1 m   **c)** 22 ± 1 km/h, 0 ± 1 km/h
  d) 8.54 ± 0.05 g, 2.06 ± 0.05 g
  e) 20.62 ± 0.05 s, 6.18 ± 0.05 s
  f) $\$400\ 000 \pm 20\ 000$, $\$170\ 000 \pm 20\ 000$

3. a) 10.5 cm, 13.5 cm   **b)** 46 mm, 50 mm
  c) 38 m, 42 m

4. (90 ± 15) mm

5. a) 42 cm   **b)** 59.2 cm   **c)** 28 inches

6. a) 11.3 ± 0.05 cm, 5.9 ± 0.05 cm
  b) 16.7 ± 0.15 cm, 0.15 cm

7. 760 mL, 740 mL

Extending Your Thinking

8. 36 030 m; error estimate 156 m

TUTORIAL 7.4
Practise Your Prior Skills, page 382

1. a) B   **b)** C

2. 2.875   **3.** 0.05%   **4.** 80%

EXERCISES, page 385
Checking Your Skills

1. a) 4.5%   **b)** 6.25%   **c)** 0.81%   **d)** 0.06%

2. a) 0.20%   **b)** 0.62%   **c)** 0.05%
  d) 0.05%   **e)** 0.24%   **f)** 1.25%

3. Mass   **4.** 4723.2 cm³, 4876.8 cm³

5. 27.4785 g, 27.4775 g, 27.478 g ± 0.002%

6. Answers may vary.   **7.** Answers may vary.

Extending Your Thinking

8. The metric ruler

TUTORIAL 7.5
Investigation, page 388

Answers may vary.

EXERCISES, page 391
Checking Your Skills

1. a) 74 000 cm², 69 000 cm²   **b)** 3.5%

2. a) ± 25 mL   **b)** 16.7%
  c) 425 mL, 375 mL   **d)** 6.25%

3. 64.1 cm², 1.3%

4. Answers may vary. For example:
  a) 0.028%   **b)** 1014.486 mm² ± 0.175%   **c)** 0.175%

5. a) 3.5 cm   **b)** 39 cm²   **c)** 1.4%

6. a) 10.5 cm, 10.4 cm   **b)** 10.45 ± 0.48%
  c) $\frac{1}{3}$

7. a) 7.5 g/cm³, 6.1 g/cm³, 10%

b) New caliper $(6.77 \pm 7$%) is more effective than a new balance $(6.77 \pm 7.5$%).

8. Estimates may vary.
  a) 32 000 stones, 0.6%   **b)** $\$60\ 800 \pm 11.1$%

Extending Your Thinking

9. $\$6833.36 \pm 1228.95$

TUTORIAL 7.6
EXERCISES, page 398
Checking Your Skills

1. a) 3.80 mm, 3.70 mm   **b)** 0.0082 inches, 0.0078 inches

2. a) (8.2 ± 0.3) g   **b)** (3.05 ± 0.05) cubic feet

3. Yes   **4.** c, d

5. A: 10.52, 10.48 and B: 8.24, 8.16

6. 0.08 mm

Extending Your Thinking

7. 7.74 mm, 7.40 mm   **8.** 0.27 ± 0.02 cm³, 4000

CONSOLIDATING YOUR SKILLS
What Should I Be Able To Do?, page 403

1. a) 0.53%, 3.33%, 1.11%, 1.43%, 3.33%
  c) 1.9 cm, 0.3 cm, 0.9 cm, 0.7 cm, 0.3 cm
  f) 2.35 cm², 0.204 cm³

2. a) 1 : 2 000 000   **b)** 66 km, 526 km, 694 km

5. a) 0.005 mm, 0.05 mm, 0.05 cm, 0.5 cm
  b) 37.2 mm ± 0.013%, 37.4 mm ± 0.134%, 3.7 cm ± 1.35%, 4 cm ± 12.5%

6. a) Answers may vary; 1.5 cm   **b)** 1.5 ± 0.05 cm
  c) 0.75 cm, 0.65 cm

7. Answers may vary.   **8.** 32.1 ± 0.3 mg

9. 2 mm, 1.9 mm   **10.** 1 h 32 min to 2 h

Index

loans, 264-265, 266
  total cost, 266
logistic model for population growth, 104-105, 109-110
loss, 24-25

M

map scale, 359-360, 362
maximizing:
  profits, 200-201
  revenue, 86-87, 204-206
maximizing revenue, 204-206
maximum or minimum values:
  graphing maximum height of projectile, 75-76, 77, 89
  in linear programming problem, 201, 202, 204, 206, 212
  occurrence at vertex, 89, 106
Measure menu in *The Geometer's Sketchpad*, 296-298
  area and perimeter, 297-298
  constructing a polygon interior, 298
  measuring circles, 296
  measuring length, 297
measurement error, 373, 377
measurement standards, 372
measurement uncertainties. *see* uncertainty of a measurement
measurements, adding and subtracting, 374-377
  different precision, 375
  same precision, 374-375
measurements, multiplying and dividing, 387-390
measuring instrument, 373, 390
midpoint:
  of a chord, 302-303
  of a circle, 315
mill rate, 237, 238, 280
minimizing costs, 202-204
minimum profit, 201
minimum value. *see* maximum or minimum values
misleading graph, 31-34, 35, 36, 52-53
monthly expenditures and budget guidelines, 273
monthly payments, exercises in calculating, 269, 270

mortgages, 258
motion detection, 115-117
multiple-bar graph, 37
multiple-line graph, 11-13
multiplication:
  by a constant, 144, 145, 151
  factor, 65, 68, 69
  of measurements, 387, 390

N

net earnings, 228
  calculating, 229-231
  estimating, 231-232
net profit, 12
no solution, 143
non-cyclic quadrilateral, 339
non-linear equations, 99, 106
  solving, 95, 98-99, 106
non-linear graphs, 95
non-linear system, 95
  of inequalities, 194-195
number of payments, with compound interest, 253, 254

O

Object information in *The Geometer's Sketchpad*, 294, 295
objective function, 201, 203, 204, 205, 212
one solution, 143
optimization problems, 170, 198-199, 200-206, 209, 210
  chapter problem (trail mix), 168, 198-199, 210
  steps for solving, 202
orthographic diagram, 366-369, 400, 406-407
overtime, 223

P

parabola, 77, 87, 106
pay periods, 223
payments per year, for compound interest, 254
payroll deductions, 228-233
  tables, 229, 230, 289
percentage error, 382-385, 397, 402

PHOTO CREDITS AND ACKNOWLEDGMENTS

The publisher wishes to thank the following sources for photographs, illustrations, articles, and other materials used in this book. Care has been taken to determine and locate ownership of copyright material used in the text. We will gladly receive information enabling us to rectify any errors or omissions in credits.

PHOTOS

Cover A. Maywald/First Light; **p. iv** Ken Fisher/Tony Stone Images; **p.v** Dave Starrett; **p. vi** Grov Mortimore; **p. vii** (top right) Artbase Inc.; **p. vii** (bottom) Dave Starrett; **p. viii** (bottom) Detlef Schnepel; **p. viii** (center left) Artbase Inc.; **p. ix** (top left) Dave Starrett; **p. ix** (center) Tom Raymond/Tony Stone Images; **p. 1** (top right) Dave Starrett; **p. 1** (bottom) Artbase Inc.; **p. 2-3** Dave Starrett; **p. 6-8** Ken Fisher/Tony Stone Images; **p. 9** B. Harrington III/First Light; **p. 12** Penny Tweedle/Tony Stone Images; **p.14** Julia Waterlow; Eye Ubiquitous/CORBIS; **p. 16** Artbase Inc.; **p. 20** Dave Starrett; **p. 22** Allsport Photography, USA/ Tony Duffy; **p. 23** Robert Pickett/CORBIS; **p. 24** Dick Hemingway; **p. 26** Al Harvey/The Slide Farm; **p. 27-28** Artbase Inc.; **p. 31** Hulton-Deutsch Collection/CORBIS; **p. 33** Howard Grey/Tony Stone Images; **p. 41** J. Miele/First Light; **p. 42** D. Baswick/First Light; **p. 43** Artbase Inc.; **p. 48** Environment Canada; **p. 52-53** Dave Starrett; **p. 59-60** Artbase Inc.; **p. 61** (center left) Dave Starrett; **p. 61** (top right) Artbase Inc.; **p. 62** (top left) Dave Starrett; **p. 62** (center) Alain Cornu/Publiphoto; **p. 63** (bottom) Artbase Inc.; **p. 63** (top right) Bettmann/CORBIS; **p. 64** The Purcell Team/CORBIS; **p. 66** Dave Starrett; **p. 67** Artbase Inc.; **p. 69** L.S. Stepanowicz/Bruce Coleman Inc.; **p. 71** CNRI/Publiphoto; **p. 75** Ian Crysler; **p. 76** Dave Starrett; **p. 81** Peter Guttman/CORBIS; **p. 82** (top left) Dave Starrett; **p. 82** (center left) Artbase Inc.; **p. 83-84** Artbase Inc.; **p. 86** Jerry Cooke/CORBIS; **p. 88** Amy Sancetta/AP Wide World Photos Inc./Canapress; **p. 91** (center) Al Harvey/The Slide Farm; **p. 91** (top right) C. Harris/First Light; **p. 92** Grov Mortimore; **p. 93** First Light; **p. 94** Artbase Inc.; **p. 97** Alfred Pasieka/Science Photo Library/Publiphoto; **p. 103** Artbase Inc.; **p. 104** (top left) Dave Starrett; **p. 104** (center) Artbase Inc.; **p. 107** Artbase Inc.; **p. 111** (top left) Dave Starrett; **p. 111** (top right) VANDYSTADT/Allsport USA; **p. 112** Dave Starrett; **p. 113** (background) Sanders/The Stock Market/First Light; **p. 113** (bottom right) Dave Starrett; **p. 114** Artbase Inc.; **p. 115-116** Dave Starrett; **p. 117** Artbase Inc.; **p. 118** Dave Starrett; **p. 121** Koji Aoki/Allsport USA; **p. 123** Alan Marsh/First Light; **p. 125** Peter Turnley/ CORBIS; **p. 126-130** Artbase Inc.; **p. 131** Dave Starrett; **p. 132** Artbase Inc.; **p. 135** Artbase Inc.; **p. 137** The Purcell Team/CORBIS; **p. 138** Artbase Inc.; **p. 140** Dave Starrett; **p. 141** VANDYSTADT/Allsport USA ; **p. 145-147** Dave Starrett; **p. 149** Artbase Inc. ; **p. 153** E.B. Graphics/Tony Stone Images; **p. 154** George Lepp/CORBIS; **p. 155-157** Artbase Inc.; **p. 158** Dave Starrett; **p. 159** VANDYSTADT/Allsport USA; **p. 163** First Light ; **p. 166** Dave Starrett; **p. 167-168** Detlef Schnepel; **p. 169** (center right) Detlef Schnepel; **p. 169** (bottom left) Artbase Inc.; **p. 169** (top left) Detlef Schnepel; **p. 171** Dave Starrett; **p. 173-176** Detlef Schnepel; **p. 180** Artbase Inc.; **p. 182-202** Detlef Schnepel; **p. 204** Terry Vine/Tony Stone Images; **p. 207** Artbase Inc.; **p. 208** Detlef Schnepel; **p. 211** (top left) Detlef Schnepel; **p. 211** (top right) Brian Bailey/Tony Stone Images; **p. 211** (bottom) Detlef Schnepel; **p. 214-215** Artbase Inc.; **p. 218** Detlef Schnepel; **p. 219** (top left) Artbase Inc.; **p. 219** (top right) Dave Starrett; **p. 220** (top left) Dave Starrett; **p. 220** (center right) Artbase Inc.; **p. 221** (center left) Dave Starrett; **p. 221** (top right) Artbase Inc.; **p. 223** Ian Crysler; **p. 224** Dick Hemingway; **p. 228** Dave Starrett; **p. 232** J. Henley/First Light; **p. 234** B. Carriere/ Publiphoto; **p. 236** (left) Artbase Inc.; **p. 236** (right) W. Cody/Westlight/First Light; **p. 238-241** Artbase Inc.; **p. 242** Dave Starrett; **p. 243** (bottom left) Ian Crysler; **p. 243** (center right) R. Watts/First Light; **p. 244** Chuck Savage/First Light; **p. 249** Jon Feingersh/First Light; **p. 250-254** Dave Starrett; **p. 258** Artbase Inc.; **p. 260** Dave Starrett; **p. 264** C. Savage/First Light; **p. 267** Dave Starrett; **p. 270** Pat Lanzafield/ Bruce Coleman Inc.; **p. 273-274** Artbase Inc.; **p. 278-279** Dave Starrett; **p. 279** (bottom left) A. Kulla/The Stock Market/First Light; **p. 279** (bottom center) Dave Starrett; **p. 282** Artbase Inc.; **p. 284-285** Dave Starrett; **p. 291** (top right) Detlef Schnepel; **p. 291** (center left) Artbase Inc.; **p. 292** (top left) Detlef Schnepel; **p. 292** (center left) Lee Valley Tools Ltd.; **p. 292** (center) Judy Mathieson; **p. 292** (center right) Artbase Inc.; **p. 293** (top) Detlef Schnepel; **p. 293** (bottom) Artbase Inc.; **p. 296** Detlef Schnepel; **p. 299** Dave Starrett; **p. 308** Keith Garrett/NGS Image Collection; **p. 311** Artbase Inc.; **p. 312** Dave Starrett; **p. 320** Dave Starrett; **p. 322** (top left) Detlef Schnepel; **p. 322** (center right) Artbase Inc.; **p. 323** Detlef Schnepel; **p. 324** R. Lewcock; **p. 331** Artbase Inc.; **p. 336** Dave Starrett; **p. 338** James Blair/NGS Image Collection; **p. 346-347** Detlef Schnepel; **p. 352-354** Dave Starrett; **p. 355** Artbase Inc.; **p. 356** Dave Starrett; **p. 357** (center) Everett Collection; **p. 357** (top right) Dave Starrett; **p. 357** (bottom right) Everett Collection; **p. 358** Dave Starrett; **p. 361** Dave Starrett; **p. 372** Artbase Inc.; **p. 373-374** Dave Starrett; **p. 376** S. Homer; **p. 772** Malayan Tapri, Metro Toronto Zoo/First Light; **p. 379** Dave Starrett; **p. 380** (top left) Dave Starrett; **p. 380** (top left) Dave Starrett; **p. 380** Lydia Pawelak/The National Ballet of Canada; **p. 381** (center) Dave Starrett; **p. 381** (top right) Lydia Pawelak/The National Ballet of Canada; **p. 384** Artbase Inc.; **p. 386** Dave Starrett; **p. 387** Michael S. Yamashita/ CORBIS; **p. 390-392** Dave Starrett; **p. 394** Tony Stone Images; **p. 396** Tom Raymond/Tony Stone Images; **p. 399** (top right) Ron Watts/First Light; **p. 399** (bottom right) Artbase Inc.; **p. 400-401** Dave Starrett; **p. 403-405** Artbase Inc.; **p. 412-422** Detlef Schnepel; **p. 164-165** (top) Dave Starrett; **p. 216-217** Detlef Schnepel

ILLUSTRATIONS

David Bathurst; 227, 308 (bottom), 335, 336
Mike Herman; 4, 5, 32, 74, 122, 124, 155, 179, 189, 196, 266, 283
Margo Davies Leclair/Visual Sense; 162, 209
Dave McKay; 321
Jun Park; 300, 359, 363, 395
Jane Whitney; 36 (top), 45, 49, 50, 51, 57, 128, 309, 331, 344, 351, 364, 404 (top left)
Rose Zgodzinski; 151, 239, 252, 269, 393